D1554895

THE MINES

OF

COLORADO

THE MINES

OF

COLORADO

OVANDO J[AMES] HOLLISTER

PRESS

New York · 1974

Published by Promontory Press, New York, N.Y. 10016

Library of Congress Catalog Card No.: 73-92642
ISBN: 0-88394-021-3

Printed in the United States of America

Library of Congress Cataloging in Publication Data

Hollister, Ovando James, 1834-1892.
   The mines of Colorado.

   Reprint of the 1867 ed.
   1. Mines and mineral resources--Colorado.
I. Title. II. Series.
TN24.C6H7 1973   338.2'0978

THE MINES

OF

COLORADO;

BY

OVANDO J. HOLLISTER,

(LATE EDITOR AND PORPRIETOR COLORADO MINING JOURNAL.)

———————

SPRINGFIELD, MASS.:

SAMUEL BOWLES & COMPANY.

1867.

SAMUEL BOWLES AND COMPANY,
Electrotypers and Printers.

PREFACE.

THE approaching completion of two lines of railway between the Mississippi Valley and the Rocky Mountains, will mark an era in the history of the nearer of the mining Territories — Colorado. It will infuse new life into mining, by giving safe, quick, and reliable communication, reducing freights and risks, thus cheapening supplies and furnishing a most necessary competition in the labor market, under which the production of the precious metals will be largely increased and the value and importance of property of all kinds proportionally enhanced. This cannot fail to arrest the attention of capitalists who are interested in Colorado gold and silver stocks, or are thinking of becoming so. It will be of yet more benefit to that large class whose capital is their muscle, because it will make accessible to them a new and large tract of virgin land, which, though far West, is still on the World's great highway, and therefore in no sense of the word in the backwoods. This region has a pleasant and healthy climate, and while its soil is unsurpassed in strength by that of the prairie States, it has a superior market in the adjoining mines. It most eloquently invites settlement and improvement. It will also give the Summer tourist a choice between the West and the East. It is not hazarding much to say that the Rocky Mountains offer the most delightful Summer resort of the New if not of the Old World. The climate is cool and bracing, the air deliciously pure and soft, the scenery both grand and beautiful, the forests full of game and the streams of trout, with hot mineral springs of high medicinal value boiling up at the root of every shade tree in the sequestered parks. The annexation of the Rocky Mountains to the Union by railways will open a new world to science, a new field of adventure to money and muscle, a new and pleasant place of Summer resort to people of leisure.

To meet the growing want of definite information concerning that interesting country, this book is put forth. It treats of the discovery of gold and settlement of the country, its geography, chorography, geology, mineralogy, and agriculture, its early efforts at self-government, and the progress and present condition of mining industry, including descriptive list of mining companies, principal improved mines, mills, machinery, and methods of treating ore—in short, it undertakes to give, as concisely and precisely as possible, and without any pretension, all that is known on the subject.   o. j. h.

CONTENTS.

CHAPTER I.

CHAPTER II.

CHAPTER III.

CHAPTER IV.

PAGE.

CHAPTER V.

CHAPTER VI.

CHAPTER VII.

CHAPTER VIII.

CHAPTER IX.

CHAPTER X.

CHAPTER XI.

THE MINES OF COLORADO.

CHAPTER I.

Glance at Pike's Peak prior to the Discovery of Gold—Discovery
of Gold on Ralston Creek in 1852, and on Dry Creek in 1858—
Effect of the News in the States—Crossing the Plains—Indians
—First View of the Mountains—Prospecting, Hunting—Placer
Camp—Auraria—Arapahoe County—Election of Delegate to
Congress and Representative to Kansas Legislature—Denver
Town Company.

IT is unnecessary here to inquire into the causes
of the immemorial movement westward of the human race from its cradle in Asia. It may be observed, however, as marking an era in the world's
history, that the planet is at last girdled; that the
extraordinary mineral discoveries of Western North
America have startled even the Orientals from their
accustomed lethargy; and they are moving from
China eastward, or rather westward, on the other
side of the globe, to meet the historic column on
this side, in the gold and silver fields of the Rocky
Mountains. Thus we have a double westward
movement, each wing starting originally from Asia,
and pursuing the same direction, only on opposite

sides of the earth, to the same destination. There
are those who think this double-action immigration
pressure will essentially modify the future of the
mining regions of North America. Buddhism and
Polygamy will be brought into contact with Chris-
tianity and Monogamy; but it would seem to be
the senility of age contending with the strength
and vigor of youth. There can be no doubt as to
which will triumph.

If we could examine the old Spanish archives in
Mexico and Spain, we might perhaps find detailed
accounts of explorations in the region of the Rocky
Mountains now comprising Colorado; but if so,
none of them is known or published to the world
at large, thanks, we suppose, to the Japanese policy
which formerly actuated the Colonial Governors and
Captains-General of Spain in America. About
twenty years ago a work was published which contained a full and authentic account of an expedition
in the years 1540–1542, by order of the Viceroy
Mendoca, and under the conduct of Vasquez Coronado. It consisted of three hundred and fifty Spaniards and eight hundred Indians. Starting from
Culiacan, the capital of Sinaloa, they reached the
sources of the Gila, passed across the mountains
to the Rio del Norte, wintered twice in the Territory of New Mexico, explored it from north to south,
and afterwards, taking a northeast course, crossed
the mountains, reached the buffalo plains, which they
traversed a considerable distance eastwardly and
as far north as the 40th parallel. Finding no gold
they returned to Mexico. The Spaniards did not

re-enter the country till the year 1581, and the conquest of New Mexico was not completed till about the year 1595. There is nothing of interest concerning this country in the published account of Coronado's long, fatiguing, resultless expedition. Had his party found the rich treasures of the Colorado Rocky Mountains, how different would have been the history of North America. But it seems that was not to be.

In our day the discoverer and first chronicler of these regions was the energetic and indefatigable Captain Zebulon M. Pike, after whom the "principal peak," as he calls it in his quaint and curious "Account," * was named. Colonel S. H. Long was

---

* "An Account of Expedition to the Sources of the Mississippi, and through the western part of Louisiana, &c., in the years 1805, 1806, and 1807 : Philadelphia, 1810."—Pike first saw the mountains from the Arkansas, November 15, 1806 ; November 24th to 28th he explored the north fork (Fontaine qui Bouit,) of the Arkansas, without discovering the soda springs, however, and ascended a chain south of the peak from which "the summit of the grand peak, which was entirely bare of vegetation and covered with snow, appeared at a distance of fifteen or sixteen miles from us, and as high again as we had ascended." Pike measured the altitude of his peak by triangulation "on the base of a mile," and counting the prairie 8000 feet above the level of the sea, made it 18,581 feet. He exaggerated in both instances. Subsequently he wandered about among the mountains with his few followers for two months in search of the sources of Red River, visiting the head waters of the South Platte, the Arkansas, and at last the Rio Grande, where he was taken prisoner by the Spaniards of New Mexico. In the Appendix to his "Account" Pike relates an incident curious enough in view of what has since transpired. He says he met in Santa Fe one James Pursley, from Bairdstown, Ky., "the first American who ever penetrated the immense wilds of western Louisiana," and who, after many adventures with the Indians, as whose captive he got

the second explorer of the country. The surgeon,
botanist, and historian of Long's expedition was
Dr. E. James, the first white man, so far as we
know, whose foot ever trod the summit of Pike's
Peak. He also measured its altitude by triangulation, and counting a point twenty-five miles below
the springs on the Fountain, as it is now called,
3000 feet above sea level, made it 11,507.5 feet.
His mistake was in estimating or calculating the
elevation of his base. This was in 1820. In 1843
Fremont paid a hasty visit to the soda springs at
the base of the peak. He was delighted with the
beauty of the little mountain-walled cove containing the springs, remarked that the water resembled
in taste the famous Selter Springs in the Grand
Duchy of Nassau, and was almost of the same
character though still more agreeable in taste than
that of the Beer Springs on Bear River of the Great
Salt Lake, and left us the following analysis of an
incrustation made by the water on a piece of wood:

Carbonate of lime,	92.25
Carbonate of magnesia,	1.21
Sulphate of lime, ⎫	
Chloride of calcium, ⎬	.23
Chloride of magnesia, ⎭	
Silica,	1.50
Vegetable matter,	.20
Moisture and loss,	4.61
	100.00

into the Pike's Peak region, came to Santa Fe. "He assured me,"
says Pike, "that he found gold on the head of La Platte, and had
carried some of the virgin mineral in his shot-pouch for months,
and that the Spaniards had frequently solicited him to go and show
a detachment of cavalry the place, but that, conceiving it to be our
territory, he had refused." Good boy.

The temperature of the water ranged through the day in one spring from 58° to 60.5°, and in the other from 61° to 69°. Next year Fremont returned from California via the Great Salt Lake, Bear River, the North, Middle, and South Parks. He found the Middle Park alive with buffalo and other game, and made the hight of the Ute Pass, between Breckenridge and Montgomery, 11,200 feet. "Here," says Fremont, "the river (Blue) spreads itself into small branches and springs, heading nearly in the summit of the ridge which is very narrow.* Immediately below us was a valley through which ran a stream (Platte,) and a short distance opposite rose snowy mountains (Lincoln,) whose summits were formed into peaks of naked rock." The South Park was at that moment the scene of a hard-fought battle between hostile bands of Utes and Arapahoes, and Fremont was obliged to fortify all his camps. On again arriving at Pike's Peak he measured it and made it 14,300 feet above sea-level, which agrees very well with the measurement of Dr. Parry made in 1862.

It was about this time or a little earlier that one Rufus B. Sage passed over the same route in the dead of December with a small party of trappers. He says the snow averaged a depth of twelve or

* The Blue and Platte both rise five or six miles west of the Pass, flowing east, parallel, about 1000 feet lower than its summit, and *at* the Pass, where the Blue sharply bends north and the Platte south-southeast, only from 7000 to 8000 feet apart. This has been eliminated by careful surveys of the vicinity, which, since Fremont's passage through or over it, has become an important mining center.

fourteen inches, but that the valleys and sunny hill-
sides were generally bare. He seems to have been
content to let the eternal mountains point skyward
in solemn grandeur while his party humbly clung to
the willow-lined streams that threaded the fertile
valleys, and so in a few days they were led out of
the woods and found themselves at the inevitable
springs like all the rest; where, says our friend
Sage, "the ground was free from snow and afforded
occasional spots of green grass." Sage also remarked the existence of a settlement of whites and
half-breeds, numbering fifteen or twenty families,
about thirty miles above the mouth of the Fountain
on the Arkansas, evidently the present site of
Canon City. There was also a trading post called
the Pueblo on the site of the present town of that
name, occupied at that time by ten or twelve Americans living with or married to Mexican women, and
carrying on a thriving trade with the Indians. The
latter were somewhat troublesome, were indeed the
only drawbacks to settlement in the vicinity.

The existence of gold and other minerals in the
Sierra Madre mountains, now comprising Colorado,
was already suspected. There was a story among
the mountaineers and traders, that a few years previous an old French hunter named Duchet had
picked up in one of the principal forks of Horse
Creek, a piece of rock containing native gold; that
he carried it in his hunting pouch until he got tired
of it, and suspecting not its value but only regarding it as an hour's novelty, threw it away. Subsequently, at Santa Fe, the emptyings of his pouch,

being in part particles of gold, attracted attention. But the old hunter could not again find the place.

Sage camped on the present site of Golden City during the winters of 1843 and 1844 successively, whence on some of his hunting excursions he penetrated the mountains to a considerable distance; but he records nothing in his published account of particular interest, more than his confirmed belief that it was a mineral region. For instance, crossing from Cherry Creek to the Fountain, he remarks: "The country hereabout for an extent of upwards of one thousand square miles, is much subject to storms of rain, hail, snow, and wind. I can account for it in no way but by supposing it to have some connection with the vast quantities of minerals lying embedded in its hills and valleys." Somewhat of a Sage by nature as well as in name. But the country in which he had long been traveling abounds in sage.

But we can scarcely pretend to give what was known of Colorado prior to the discovery of paying gold mines within her present limits, because our space will not permit. We have therefore only glanced at that period while hastening to the vastly more interesting time when the discovery and pursuit of gold invested her stupendous mountains with a more absorbing interest than even that with which science inspires her votaries.

It was the commercial collapse of 1857 that set many adventurous spirits in the then West peering into the obscurity beyond them for a new field of enterprise. A party of Cherokee Indians, traveling

overland to California in 1852, via the Arkansas
River and along the eastern base of the Sierra Madre to the North Platte at Fort Laramie, by some
means found gold in the banks of Ralston Creek, a
small affluent of the Vasquez Fork of the South
Platte, emptying into it near its mouth; and each
year thereafter parties of Cherokees had gone out
and prospected the streams in the vicinity of what
is now Denver City. At last they were successful;
they obtained a few dollars' worth of the glittering
dust, which they carried home late in 1857, exhibiting it freely as they passed through Nebraska and
Kansas.

The report of a new land of gold in the West
spread like an epidemic through the country drained
by the Missouri River, and soon traveled far beyond. These Indians appear to have gone home
and told their story on the confines of the Gulf of
Mexico, for Georgians were among the first to seek
the new gold country.

On the 9th of February, 1858, W. G. Russell,
with a party of nine men, left the state of Georgia
with a view of prospecting the eastern slope of the
Sierra Madre along the heads of the South Platte,
from Pike's Peak to the Black Hills. They arrived
on the head of Cherry Creek about the 1st of June.
They prospected Cherry Creek, the Platte and its
affluents as far north as Cache-a-la-Poudre, without
finding anything satisfactory. They returned to the
Platte, and about five miles up a small dry creek
which puts into the Platte seven miles south of the
mouth of Cherry Creek, a fine "prospect" one

evening rewarded their labors and enlivened their hopes. They dug large holes in the wet sand, put their "rockers" down in them, and dipping in water with cups washed out in a few days several hundred dollars' worth of gold. As soon as they got to work, some of the party returned to Kansas with the news. Pike's Peak was the nearest notable natural object, and so the new gold field—the Dorado of many feverish dreams—took its name from that.

In the last days of that Summer several small parties were organized, and left Lawrence, Plattsmouth, Omaha, Florence, Bellevue, Council Bluffs, and other of the Missouri River towns for Pike's Peak.* One party from Plattsmouth, numbering forty-five men, with fifteen wagons, was threateningly approached near what is now Fort McPherson (Cottonwood,) by about four hundred Cheyennes and Sioux. The train mounted an advanced guard of five, and having a guard of equal number on each flank, and one in the rear, ten footmen in single file on the Indian side of the train, and the fifteen teamsters all having arms in the fore ends of their wagons, they moved firmly along. The Indians came up on the flank one hundred strong in fine style, and halted. The chief and four of his braves made a circuit, and came down square in

---

*A Dutchman in Council Bluffs was observed gathering up a large lot of meal-bags. He was asked what he was going to do with them. "Fill them with gold at Pike's Peak," he replied. O! he could never do that, they said. "Yes I will," returned he, "if I have to stay there till Fall " It is matter of congratulation that people have become well cured of such charming infatuation.

1*

front. When within about twenty paces they were suddenly covered by the five rifles, and they halted, trailed their arms, made peaceful gestures, and demanded a parley. They wanted pay for traveling through their country. They were told that their Great Father had already paid them for this privilege. Seeing that nothing could be got by blustering, and being averse to fighting, they resorted to begging. A plug of tobacco was given them, and they sneaked off, Indian fashion.

Well might one of these pioneers,* in a new crusade on the Aborigines, write as follows in his diary, upon passing through one of their decayed villages :

"As I sit, in the early morning, and gaze on the ruins of this savage but once mighty people, their council-fires mere smouldering embers, a strange race overwhelming them in countless thousands, and pushing them away from the land where lie buried their fathers, I cannot but feel sad on account of their misfortunes ; and I think how well it may be that, in ages to come, the proud race which is now occupying *their* pleasant places shall in like manner be crushed out by a still stronger race."

That was before the renewal on the Plains of the desperate conflict which began on the Atlantic, and has been fought hand-to-hand between the American and the savage, the latter always pushed back, clear across the Continent. These men were so enlightened as to feel deeply the hard and inevitable fate of the Indians, and to recognize and accept

---

* William M. Slaughter, now Mayor of Central City.

their own destiny in the matter. The above-quoted sentences show the first, and the following the second:

"Several small encampments of Indians are in sight, but we have taken precautions against a surprise, and in case they attack many an Indian will bite the dust before it is over, for we are pretty well prepared, and mean to go through, Indian or no Indian."

Thus was the last dreadful struggle between the white and red man boldly braved by this handful of pioneers, for what? For the *chance* of finding an habitable land further west. That struggle we have just fairly begun, and no one doubts that it must go on to the extinction of the savages, involving great sufferings on our part, of course. Grant beat the rebellion with hard knocks, and perhaps gave man for man; having more men he was enabled to wear it out. It is not a bad illustration of our conflict with the savages. Both were inevitable, and both must end in the same way. The Government and the rebellion were incompatible on the same ground; so are our people and the savages. That was a life and death struggle, ended by the death of the rebellion: this is a life and death struggle, to be ended by the death of the savage— and the sooner it can be finished the better.

At the time of which we are speaking—September, 1858—there was little of that semblance of Tartaric civilization on the Plains which now characterizes them. Forts Riley and Santa Fe, Forts Kearney and Laramie, Salt Lake City and Camp

Floyd, were about the only inhabited points. The
first hunters for gold at Pike's Peak had no smooth,
hard road, with occasional stations occupied by the
white man, to follow; no accompanying endless
train of white-topped emigrant wagons and fleets
loaded with merchandise. The Salt Lake mail
passed them regularly until they struck the California crossing of the Platte.* They met a small party
from Cherry Creek once in a while, all of them
with goose-quills or little vials of gold dust, which
some of them called "the elephant," and were carrying home to show their friends, hoping thereby
to save them a pilgrimage to the Mountains to see
it; others were going to use "the elephant" to obtain reinforcements. They also met straggling parties from Salt Lake City or California, most always
packing a mule or two, and so much like Indians
that the latter never molested them. They might
have been overtaken by, or come up with, an Indian
trader's small train occasionally, or perhaps one of
Government supplies bound to Fort Laramie or
Camp Floyd; otherwise they were solitary and
alone.

After passing the California crossing they had no
road, but picked their way along in view of the
river as best they could. As they came within sight
of Long's Peak, lying like a smoky thunder-head in
the far and indefinite horizon, a hundred miles distant, we can imagine their exaltation of feeling.

---

* Eighty miles above the junction of the North and South Plattes;
a town called Julesburg, in the north-eastern corner of Colorado,
now marks the spot.

Pretty soon Pike's Peak could be seen compelling the clouds; and then the varied outline of the entire range of mountains between—one hundred miles in length, cutting boldly the evening sky, and doubtless exhaling the gold of the sunset, or perhaps mysteriously mingling with the cloud-lands—grew upon their vision, these men of the prairies, who had never seen a hill five hundred feet high! The grand old mountains, with their eternal and infinite solitude and solemnity strength and repose, were appealing to their hearts, as they always do to men, the moment they came in sight.

Mr. Bowles says of this view:

"All my many and various wanderings in the European Switzerland, three summers ago, spread before my eye no panorama of mountain beauty surpassing, nay, none equaling, that which burst upon my sight at sunrise upon the Plains, when fifty miles away from Denver; and which rises up before me now as I sit writing by the window in this city. From far south to far north, stretching around in huge semi-circle, rise the everlasting hills, one after another, tortuous, presenting every variety of form and surface, every shade of cover and color, up and on until we reach the broad, snow-covered Range that marks the highest summits, and tells where Atlantic and Pacific meet and divide for their long journey to their far distant shores. To the north rises the king of the range, Long's Peak,*

---

* The latest observations and calculations of the elevation of Long's and Pike's Peaks put that of the former approximately, at 14,056 feet; that of the latter at 14,216.

whose top is 14,600 feet high; to the south, giving source to the Arkansas and Colorado, looms up its brother, Pike's Peak, to the hight of 13,400 feet. These are the salient features of the belt before us; but the intervening and succeeding summits are scarcely less commanding, and not much lower in hight."

And Bayard Taylor, viewing them from another point, gives his impressions as follows:

"The view of the Rocky Mountains from the divide near Kiowa Creek is considered one of the finest in Colorado. From the breezy ridge, between scattered groups of pine, you look upon one hundred and fifty miles of the Snowy Range, from the Sangre de Christo to the spurs away toward Laramie. In variety and harmony of form, in effect against the dark-blue sky, in breadth and grandeur, I know no external picture of the Alps which can be placed beside it. If you could take away the valley of the Rhone, and unite the Alps of Savoy with the Bernese Overland, you might obtain a tolerable idea of this view of the Rocky Mountains. Pike's Peak would then represent the Jungfrau; a nameless snowy giant in front of you, Monte Rosa; and Long's Peak, Mont Blanc. The altitudes very nearly correspond, and there is a certain similarity in the forms. The average hight of the Rocky Mountains, however, surpasses that of the Alps."

And again:

"Nowhere distorted or grotesque in outline, never monotonous, lovely in color and atmospheric effect, I may recall some mountain chains which equal but none which surpass them. From this point (Denver) there appears to be three tolerably distinct ranges. The first rises from two to three thousand feet above the level of the Plains; it is cloven asunder by the kanyons* of the streams, streaked with dark lines of pine, which feather its summits, and sunny with steep slopes of pasture. Some distance behind it appears a second range of nearly double the hight, more irregular in its masses, and of a dark, velvety, violet hue. Beyond, leaning against the sky, are the snowy peaks, nearly all of which are from thirteen thousand to fifteen thousand feet above the sea. These three chains, with their varying but never discordant undulations, are as inspiring to the imagination as they are enchanting to the eye. They hint of concealed grandeurs in all the glens and parks among them, and yet hold you back with a doubt whether they can be more beautiful near at hand than when beheld at this distance."

Game began to abound. The gazelle-like antelope trotted gracefully up to the trail to see the invaders of their country. They soon learned by sad experience to be more cautious. A being had come among them to whose capacious maw everything was food—to whose numerous necessities everything must become subservient. He was to mar the beautiful, natural meadows with winding wagon-roads, muddy the clear streams, cut away the forests, disembowel the hills, and cover their sides

* Canon, a Spanish word implying a narrow, tunnel-like passage between high and precipitate banks. It is pronounced KANYON, and as it has been adopted by us, might as well be spelled so.

with unsightly rubble, tear out the gulches, exter-
minate the game, the fish, and the wild lord of the
soil together, and taint the very atmosphere with
impurity. The carrion-fly, the house-fly, the chin-
cha, the mosquito, and other similar civilized pests,
went to the Rocky Mountains only with the white
man; but the rapidity and ease with which they
became acclimated show that the country and climate excessively agree with them.

As the pioneers approached nearer the Mountains they began to prospect the numerous streams
cutting their eastern slope and putting into the
Platte, which for fifty or sixty miles after its escape
from, runs nearly parallel with them, and from
twenty to forty miles distant. Sometimes they
found the "color" with a good deal of black sand,
sometimes not.

On the 23d of October, the train which we have
been accompanying crossed the mouth of Cherry
Creek, "dry, and about one hundred yards wide,
banks twenty inches high," and came upon Jones'
and Smith's wigwams and the tents of D. C. Oakes
and Dr. Russell and party. Jack Jones was just
starting a corral-ranch house, the walls of which
were formed by rows of logs set on end in a
trench close together. Such houses used to be
quite common ; but few or none now remain.
Three miles further up the Platte on the western
bank were gold diggings worked by Mexicans and
called for them, "Mexican Diggings." For a few
days parties were constantly arriving and prospecting and hunting were carried on with vigor.

There does not seem to have been much success in the former line, only the Dry Creek before mentioned yielding an encouraging prospect. But the latter paid better. Antelope, deer, elk, bear and sheep, were plentiful, and it was not unusual for the mountain lion to present his countenance in camp, once going so far as to peer into a tent where a man had died of fever. In the dusk they were at first taken for the large gray wolf of the prairie ; but soon one of them was shot, when they were found to be a species of panther, standing two feet high and with a body four feet long—a new and formidable kind of wild fowl. But who ever knew the Western pioneer to quail before anything with his trusty rifle ?

The camp at the mouth of Dry Creek was called " Placer Camp," the first named place in the vicinity. The divide between the Platte and Arkansas was then covered with snow, but the very first pioneers did not fail to remark the unique and wonderful sandstone formations of the streams leading off that divide at the base of the main mountains. On the 31st of October ten inches of snow fell about the mouth of Platte Kanyon. Next day the adventurers were confined to their camps, and true to their instincts began to talk politics and town-sites. By the 4th of November a town-plat had been surveyed on the west side of the Platte opposite the mouth of Cherry Creek by William Foster, and christened "Auraria" by Dr. Russell whose party had come from a town of that name in Georgia. This region was then within the bounds of Kansas, and a county was defined and called "Arapahoe," after the neighboring tribe of Indians. An election was held on the 6th of November, there being about two hundred inhabitants in the new place, "six hundred miles from nowhere," as they designated it. H. J. Graham was elected without opposition, Delegate to Congress, and instructed to get the Pike's Peak gold mines set apart from Kansas as a new Territory. A. J. Smith was elected Representative from Arapahoe County to the Kansas Legislature. Of this proceeding, which now seems wonderful as an illustration of the organizing, assimilating character which our countrymen bear in common with the old Romans, William M. Slaughter, who we have before had occasion to quote, made the following philosophical entry in his diary :

"Just to think that within two weeks of the arrival of a few dozen Americans in a wilderness, they set to work to elect a Delegate to the United States Congress, and ask to be set apart as a new Territory! But we are of a fast race and in a fast age and must prod along."

On the 8th the Delegate from the new political camp started for Washington, loaded with letters from his constituents to their friends and to the powers that were. On the same day W. A. Mc-Fadden was elected President of the Auraria Town Company, Dr. L. J. Russell Secretary, and building commenced rapidly, every settler being allowed to possess as many lots as he would build on.

Arrivals from the States continued. A party,

entering or climbing the Foot-hills to hunt and prospect, scared up a flock of two hundred and fifty mountain sheep, which they followed a long way in vain. We find the following naive entry in their diary : " Game plenty here, but no gold "—a fix in which many a similar party has since found itself.

The mountain sheep is larger in size than the domestic animal of that name, and beside the head and horns, there is not much similarity. Its habits are much like those of the deer, its flesh equal in flavor to that of the buffalo and savoring somewhat of mutton, too, generally in good condition, tender and sweet. Both the male and female have horns, the latter about six inches in length, small, pointed and somewhat flat ; the former growing to the enormous size of two to three feet in length and six or eight inches in diameter at the butt. In short the male mountain sheep runs to horns. In color they vary from a dingy white to a dark brown, or even black. A strip of pure white extends from ham to ham, including the tail, which is short and tipped with black. Instead of wool they wear hair, shedding it annually. They "ba-ah," "ba-ah," like a domestic sheep, and the same odor is common to both. They are extremely hard to capture, even while young, and it is next to impossible to make them live away from their native hills. Hence the mountain sheep is not seen even in the largest zoological collections. They are not so often met with now as when Colorado was first settled.

One can imagine that the Plains at that time were a pretty panorama for a spectator, say on Bradford Hill. Here is a sketch of it, from our favorite diary:

"All the region, from Long's Peak around by the Cache-a-la-Poudre, Beaver and Bijou Creeks to the summit of the divide between the Platte and Arkansas, and back past where I stand 'to the place of beginning,' lies spread out at my feet like an unrolled map. West is a vast sea of dark-green mountains, sweeping away and upward into the clouds, tipped in the distance with the whitest of snow, now more or less agitated by the storm-spirit. These be the everlasting watch-towers of the Continent. But the first is the lovely part of the picture. There, spread out like a carpet, glowing in the rich splendor of the autumn sunlight, lies the brown, swelling plain, cut in various directions by wood-fringed streams—a magnificent sight! Columns of blue smoke rise calmly, and float leisurely away from Auraria City, from Placer Camp, and intermediate camps along the river. The American has come to this hitherto unknown region, and the sound of the rifle and the axe, the lowing of stock and falling of timber around the smoke columns, are sounding the death-knell of the wild beast and the wilder man of the soil—are proclaiming the fact that their restless and encroaching enemy has set himself boldly down in their midst, to scatter them like chaff, and to possess and improve the talent they have so long had buried in the ground."

During the early Winter a town called St. Charles was laid out on the east bank of the Platte, opposite Auraria, by a party from Lawrence, most of which returned home. The interests of St. Charles were left in the hands of a man who sold out to the "Denver Town Company;" hence, through the natural process of aggregation, DENVER as it now is.

CHAPTER II.

BEFORE proceeding further in our account of the discovery of gold in Colorado, it may be well to devote some space to a general description of the great physical features of the country. Of a new place we first want to know *where* it is, then *what* it is. Our description, in connection with the map which accompanies this volume, will at least serve to render succeeding chapters more intelligible.

Colorado, then, is almost square in form, is mounted upon the Sierra Madre precisely as one mounts a horse, and covers an area of 106,475 square miles; territory enough to make thirteen States as large as Massachusetts—as much territory as is comprised in the States of Massachusetts, New York, Pennsylvania, and New Jersey combined. It exactly occupies the space between the 37th and 41st degrees of north latitude, and between the 25th and 32d meridians of longitude west from Washington. Its northern boundary just fences up the mouth of the North Park, allowing the North Platte to escape

underneath, however; its southern boundary per-
forms the same office for the park of San Luis,
whence escapes in like manner the Rio Bravo del
Norte. The main bulk of the Sierra Madre lies
between the 28th and 30th meridians, leaving about
an equal area within the eastern and western limits
of the Territory on either side; and it extends from
the northern to the southern boundary of the Territory, elevated and expanded laterally to the full
of its gigantic proportions.

The following grand divisions of Colorado have
insensibly come to be recognized, and named by
the people : The Snowy Range, or The Range,
with its subdivision, the System of the Parks ; the
Foot-hills, with its subdivision, the Great Mineral
Belt ; the Valley, comprising the agricultural section, from the base of the Mountains eastward ;
and Over the Range, including all west of the
snowy crest of the continental divide. The latter
division is of little consequence, since the Basin of
the upper Blue, about twenty-five miles in diameter, is all of it that has yet been found of use. It
embraces the Middle Park, Bear, Grand, and Gunnison rivers, and innumerable broken mountain chains.
The bottoms of these rivers furnish hundreds of
square miles of excellent pasturage, but it is doubtful if anything but vegetables and the hardier cere-
als will mature on them, so cold and short are their
seasons. The Middle Park will receive worthier
mention in a subsequent portion of this work.
The peculiarities of the South Park, so far as they
vary from those of the Foot-hills, will be fully no-

ticed under the head of Park County. The North
Park is not inhabited. It is well-timbered and
watered, and abounds in game, but the existence
of valuable mineral deposits there, while strongly
suspected, can hardly be said to have been thoroughly demonstrated. The San Luis Park is larger
than all the others together, enjoys a warmer climate, and supports a population of perhaps ten
thousand Mexicans, who confine themselves to pro-
curing subsistence from the soil. The Honorable
William Gilpin owns something more than a million acres of land here, in two separate tracts, under
Spanish grants, which have been confirmed by the
Senate of the United States. A year or two since
he explored these estates quite thoroughly for mines,
and satisfied himself at least of their existence the
same as in other portions of the Mountains. The
Valley, being altogether agricultural and pastoral,
will be treated at length under the head of Agriculture. It is in the Foot-hills and the Snowy
Range the mines occur, and hence it comes within
our purpose to notice their characteristics somewhat in detail, here. We shall use the vernacular
of the people of the Territory in speaking of these
natural physical divisions.

Travelers on the Plains expatiate eloquently on
the gigantic mountain mass that crowns the great
plateau midway between St. Louis and San Francisco, "capped with eternal snow and gleaming in
the sunshine with untold beauty and splendor;"
but the truth is, the snow line is not reached in the
Colorado mountains at all, though masses of snow

lie in ravines, under beetling cliffs, and on the northern exposures of the higher altitudes perpetually. It is a peculiarity of the Range that the deep snows fall late—usually not till after New Years'—the fall becoming deeper indeed way into April and even May ;* and this moist snow it is that clings to the Mountains from base to summit and gives them that all but awful beauty which has so often struck travelers with amazement, as late as June. During that month their spotless snowy mantles begin to show holes. These feed on the fabric round the edges, until, by the first of August, very little or none of it is left. In tropical and sub-tropical climates the snow line is only reached at 5,000 to 6,000 feet above the timber line ; in the Alps, the difference between them is but 2,600 feet ; and it is not likely that it would be less than 3,000 to 4,000 feet in the Rocky Mountains. Well, the timber line in the latter is well marked along the slopes of the higher and more massy chains, and its average elevation above the sea is given by Dr. Parry at 11,800 feet, nearly corresponding with the same limit in the great mountain ranges of the globe nearer the equator. Thus the Schlagintweits give the limit of the trees on the Himalaya (lat. 31°) at 11,800 feet ; on the Andes within the tropics it is said by Humboldt to be between 11,000 and 12,000 feet ; on the San Francisco Mountain, in south-western New Mexico, Capt. Whipple found

---

* At Breckenridge, on the Blue, between 9,000 and 10,000 feet above the sea, there fell from September 7, 1859, to May 2, 1860, one hundred and fifty inches of snow.

2

pine timber about 12,500 feet above the sea ; and
only in Mexico have we been able to find it recorded
as growing higher—12,800.   On mountains of the
same and even lower latitudes the line of arbores-
cence is not near so high as in Colorado.   Thus on
the Peak of Teneriffe (lat. 28°) it reaches only to
7,300 feet ; on Mt. Etna (lat. 38°) to 6,600 feet, and
on the Alps of Switzerland (lat. 46°) it averages
6,500.   The cause of this remarkable apparent de-
viation from physical laws is questionless to be
found in the great *extent* of this elevated inland
plateau, the most expansive on the globe.   It is
1,600 miles wide in the latitude of Colorado, and
there it also heaves its giant masses to the highest
altitude.   Its length is co-extensive with that of
North America, and its average elevation not much
less than 5,000 feet.   It is far from the cold, moist
breath of the Atlantic Ocean.   Its elevated western
border condenses and catches the moisture from
the Pacific air currents, leaving them dry and warm.
The consequence is, the mean temperature of the
whole region is far above that of smaller mountain
ranges or isolated peaks of the same altitude and
under the same latitude.   As everywhere else north
of the tropics, coniferous trees form the extreme
limit of arborescent vegetation in Colorado, though
aspens and birches grow almost as high in favorable, moist localities.

The Snowy Range, divested of its primary spurs
and of its great wings—the Foot-hills—is not far
from twenty miles in width.   This includes a uniform system of spurs or wings thrown out on each

side between the water courses as if for support, and sloping down to timber in the course of eight or ten miles, something like, "to compare great things with small," the rafters from the ridge-pole of a house. The Range itself, the immediate crest of the Continent of North America, is somewhat broken in outline, often serrated like the teeth of a saw, whence the name, *Sierra*, scmetimes exhibiting the bare, native granite of the earth's crust in terrible masses, terrible from their gigantic desolateness and uncouth shapes, "which shape have none;" but in good part it is smoothly-rounded and grassy, accessible and passable in any direction during July, August, and September, from two to five miles broad, stretching itself like a huge, gorged anaconda, five hundred miles from north-west to south-east, enveloping the great parks in its folds and hiding myriads of small ones, suspending alpine lakes with lilies all their own on its rugged sides, often breathing like leviathan of the deep, and shaking storms from its angry mane.

Between 11,000 and 12,000 feet above the sea, the larger timber growth gives place to the *Pinus aristata Engel.*, having deformed trunks hidden by withered branches, and sending off leafy tufts close to the ground, as if life were dependent upon sheltering their roots from exposure. Soon, open patches, with a vegetation purely alpine, begin to appear. Suddenly, on climbing some little knoll, between snow banks, a profusion of alpine flowers bursts on the view. Among these Dr. Parry mentions *Primula angustifolia, Cymopterus alpinus,*

Eritrichium aretioides, Arenaria arctica, Silene acaulis, Aplopappus pygmæus, Primula Parryii, Sedum rhodanthum, Mertensia Sibirica, Sibbaldia procumbens, Saxifraga cernua, S. debilis, S. punctata, Caltha leptosepala, Androsace Chamajasme, Saxifraga Jamesii, Dryas octopetata, Mertensia paniculata, Chionophila (snow-lover) *Trifolium nanum,* and *T. dasyphyllum.* The tap-rooted *Claytonia,* and an Alpine *Thlaspi* give perfume and beauty to the highest summits. It may be more intelligible and satisfactory to the general reader to know that all these hard names stand simply for such plants as go to make up a mountain sheep pasture. When the snow is off, the sward of the highest peaks, whether composed of grasses, weeds, mosses or lichens, is of all things a flower-bed. Of the prospect from any point on the summit of the Range, it must be *seen.* No words can more or less than mock at it. One feels as though wings were starting from his shoulders, and his heart rises with something of the bodily sensation experienced upon wading slowly into a pond of cold water. The world you have left. It is far below you with its leaden clouds and fierce storms ; but heaven has come down to you, it envelops, penetrates, and purifies you. With the old Indian Chief, you say to the Sun, "My Father !" to the Earth, such earth as this, "My Mother !"

The following altitudes, from observations made on the ground by Dr. C. C. Parry and calculated by Prof. George Engelmann, are approximately correct at least, and will be found interesting as showing the distribution of the incipient population of Colorado and the hight of the most noted mountain passes:

1. WESTERN PLAINS.

Omaha (Library in State House,) - - - -	1,211
Julesburg, eight feet above river, - - -	3,703
Denver, - - - - - - -	5,317

2. BASE OF MOUNTAINS.

Franklin (St. Vrain's,) - - - - -	5,256
Boulder City, - - - - - -	5,536
Golden City, - - - - - -	5,882
Golden Gate, - - - - - -	6,226
Mt. Vernon, - - - - - -	6,479
Soda Springs (Pike's Peak,) - - -	6,515
Colorado City, 15 feet above water, - - -	6,342
Divide between Arkansas and Platte on road from Colorado City to Denver, - - - - -	7,554

3. EASTERN SLOPE OF MOUNTAINS, UPPER PLATEAU.

Central City, - - - - - -	8,300
Gold Hill, - - - - - - -	8,636
Osborn's Lake (Ward District,) - - -	8,821
Bergen's Ranch, - - - - - -	7,752
North branch of South Platte, Denver and Buckskin road,	8,028
Lake, where Denver road enters South Park, - -	10,041
Jefferson (South Park,) - - - - -	9,842
Tarryall, " - - - - -	9,932
Forty-six miles below Tarryall on the Platte, - -	8,151
Where the Tarryall road leaves or strikes Fontaine qui Bouit, - - - - - -	8,273
Three miles lower down, - - - - -	7,794
Junction north and south Clear Creeks, - -	7,086
Idaho (12 feet above South Clear Creek,) - -	7,800
Head of Virginia Kanyon, - - - -	9,690
Consolidated Ditch Office (Missouri City,) - -	9,073
Mouth of Fall River, - - - - -	7,930
Level of Clear Creek at Empire City, - - -	8,583
Base of Berthoud's Pass, - - - -	9,464
Georgetown, - - - - - -	8,452

4. PASSES.

Georgia Pass (South to Middle Park,) - - -	11,487
Berthoud's Pass (Clear Creek to head of Middle Park,)	11,349
Same (Gen. Case,) - - - - - -	11,371
Ute Pass (Fremont,) - - - - •	11,200

5. ALPINE SUMMITS.

Mt. Audubon (southeast of Long's Peak,) - -	13,402
Velie's Peak (north-northwest of Long's Peak,) -	13,456
Long's Peak (approximately,) - - - -	14,056
Mt. Guyot (west of Georgia Pass,) - - -	13,223
Pike's Peak, - - - - - -	14,216
Same (Fremont,) - - - - -	14,300
Gray's Peak (Argentine District,) - - -	14,251
Parry's Peak (northwest of Empire City, named by Gen. Case,) - - - - - -	13,133
Mt. Flora (a detached peak east of Parry's Peak,) - -	12,878

6. MIDDLE PARK.

Three-fourths of a mile from summit of Berthoud's Pass, western slope, - - - - -	10,696
Head of Middle Park, - - - -	8,690
Hot Springs of Grand River, 25 miles from head of Park,	7,725

7. TIMBER LINE.

North slope of Pike's Peak, - - - -	12,043
On the Range at Berthoud's Pass, - - - -	11,816
Eastern slope of ridge leading to Gray's Peak, -	11,643
Eastern slope of Mt. Engelmann, - - - -	11,578
Southern slope of Mt. Flora, - - - -	11,807
On Snowy Range, - - - - 11,700 to	11,800
Mt. Audubon, - - - - - -	11,300
Long's Peak, - - - - - -	10,800
Wind River M'ts., - - - - -	10,160

A peculiarity of the Range is its tortuous course. Rising gradually from the Laramie Plains in latitude 41° 30', north, and longitude 30° 30', west, (from Washington,) it assumes its average altitude—12,000 feet—upon crossing the 41st parallel, pours off north-eastward the waters of the North

Platte, and westward those of Green and Bear Rivers. It soon changes its course a trifle, striking east-southeast for about seventy miles, dividing the North and Middle Parks, and abutting squarely on the Plains in Long's Peak. Here it breaks sharply to the south-southwest, shedding from its eastern slope the numerous affluents of the South Platte, and from its western the Grand River Fork of the Rio Colorado. Pursuing this course perhaps thirty miles, it suddenly makes an ox-bow curve, forty or fifty miles in length, to the west, round the more immediate heads of Clear Creek. Thence it resumes its southerly course for twenty or thirty miles, starting eastward Bear Creek and the north fork of the South Platte, and westward the Snake and Swan Rivers, affluents of the Blue, the latter a tributary of the Grand about sixty miles in length, and emptying into that stream just before it escapes from the Middle Park. It is only on the Blue and its tributaries that mines have yet been worked west of the Range. We are now at the north-east corner of the South Park. Here the Range breaks suddenly to the west, presenting in a distance of twenty miles three wagon-road passes—the Georgia, the Breckenridge, and the Ute*—and culminating soon thereafter in Mt. Lincoln. This, in the words

---

* The hight above the sea of half a dozen practical passes through the Range in Colorado varies from 11,000 to 12,000 feet; and the average descent to the parks or elevated valleys of streams below is 2000 to 3000 feet, in a distance of eight to twelve miles. They rarely attain an elevation above the limit of trees, but usually show a near approach to it in a stunted growth of timber and the occurrence of various alpine plants.

of the Hon. Wm. Gilpin, "is a supremely grand focal
point of primary mountain chains, primary rivers,
and parks." It is in the same latitude as St. Louis
and San Francisco (39°), is about one thousand
miles from each and in the center between them.
Soon after the assassination of Abraham Lincoln,
the Hon. Wilbur F. Stone, then temporarily editor
of the *Denver Gazette*, wrote and published the following article :

"Movements have been set on foot in various
parts of the Union to erect suitable monuments to
the late President of the United States. Columns
of granite and obelisks of marble will soon be scattered over the land by the gratitude and munificence
of the American people, making their mute appeals
to the memory of the nation, throughout the generations to come, until these works of art shall
crumble to dust in the far-off time. While these
praiseworthy efforts are exciting the interest and
admiration of all true lovers of the good and great
dead, it may not be generally known that here in
Colorado we have a monument to the memory of
Abraham Lincoln, already erected by Nature's great
Architect, outstripping in grandeur, endurance, and
beauty, all the works of art the skill and wealth of
the world can conceive and adorn.

"At the elevated northwest corner of the South
Park, at the very head of the three great rivers —
the Platte, the Arkansas, and the Colorado — where
these mighty streams, flowing to the two oceans, begin their journey in the eternal snows of the dividing
Range—a corner stone of the three great counties

of Park, Lake and Summit, the two latter much
larger each than the State of Massachusetts — the
focus of the gold mines of the Territory, and over-
shadowing the picturesque little village of Montgomery as the pyramids overshadow the tents of
the Arab — stands Mount Lincoln, this mighty
monument of the Almighty's handiwork.

"One warm day in August, three summers ago,
the writer of this, in company with a gentleman
from Omaha, made an ascent of this peak, for the
purpose of taking its altitude. Starting early in the
morning, we slowly wound our way from the village
up through the dense pine forests until we reached
the limit of timber, where the pines dwindle into
dwarfs a foot in hight, twisted into fantastic con-
tortions by the storm blasts of winter. Then came
the carpeting of grasses and flowers, of a vegetation which terminated at the snow-line in moss and
lichens. Stopping every few minutes to rest the
lungs, tired of their expansion inhaling the rarified
air, and clambering over blocks of granite and
porphyry, fragments of quartz, lava and scoriæ,
and beds of ice and snow, all mingled in wild confusion, we reached the top, and about the middle
of the afternoon sat down upon the very apex of
this lord of the mountains. The sky was clear, the
temperature 50° Fahrenheit, and adjusting our instruments we took the measurement of altitude.
We made the hight to be over 15,000 feet above the
level of the sea. The summit is a conical peak,
which rests on the base of the mountain like
'Pelion on Ossa piled' — the apex terminating in

2*

about a square rod of level rocks and ice. In the centre of this area, stones have been piled up by prospectors climbing up at different times, until a monument-like pile has been formed, ten or twelve feet in diameter and about fifteen feet high, but which is altogether invisible from the foot of the mountain. A long slope reaches from the summit eastwardly to the valley of the Platte. The other sides are precipitous, and rent with yawning chasms hundreds of feet deep, into which the light of the sun never penetrates. At the end of an hour after our arrival, a storm approached from the west and swept over the mountain. In less than ten minutes from the time the clouds struck us, the mercury fell from fifty degrees to zero. Fierce blasts of wind roared and shrieked among the crags and snow darkened the air. In the midst of this, we commenced our slippery descent. We soon became charged with electricity so that the hair of our heads stood on end, sparks flew from the ends of our fingers and cracked at every step with a hissing sound that could be heard a distance of a hundred feet. Forked lightnings leaped from rock to rock and played about our heads, almost blinding the sight, but as our bodies were charged equally with the clouds and mountain, there was of course no danger. Black clouds rolled and tumbled over each other a mile below us like the uncouth gambols of terrible monsters in this upper ocean. Descending through the strata of clouds, we at last reached sunlight and entered the village at dark — the whole distance along the slope, from the valley

to the summit, being about ten miles.   Our report
was made to a meeting of the citizens of Montgomery, and in honor to the President under whose
administration Colorado had been organized and
settled, the peak was named 'Mount Lincoln.'

"Such is Mount Lincoln.   Few ever die having
beheld so magnificent a prospect as is seen from
its summit.   Colorado is spread out at your feet.
The South Park—sixty miles long and thirty wide—
with its undulating hills, green meadows, and a
thousand glittering lakes and brooks, dwindles to
a pleasure garden.   You look over Long's Peak,
north, almost into Dakota.   You look over the
plains of Utah, to the west, stretching towards the
golden shores of the Pacific.   You look over the
Spanish Parks, south, into New Mexico ; and turning to the east, your vision wanders over Pike's
Peak where the great Plains seem to rise up like an
emerald ocean.

"And such is Colorado's monument to our dead
but immortal President.   From its side, the great
rivers suck the nutriment which feeds both oceans,
and upon which ride the nation's navies and the
commerce of the world.   A thousand storms sweep
over it, but in vain to level it.   A thousand cataracts dash around its base, but from its summit
you hear not their murmurs.   A score of quartz
mills stamp their iron feet in thunders beneath its
shadow, but their sound dies half way up its sides.
Lightnings and thunders glance harmlessly from
its crest.   Tunnels may pierce its ribs, and the
mineral wealth of future centuries be poured out

into the lap of the world, but its foundations will remain unshaken. Its base is clothed with evergreens—sublime wreaths, such as never hung on the tombstones of emperors. Its top reaches so near the heavens as to attain the spotless purity of eternal white—bright emblem of immortality.

"Let, then, other States and other peoples raise their monuments of patriotism and of art to gild the fame of the great dead; but Colorado can point in all time to this proud monumental mountain, which rears itself as the gigantic spine of this continental vertebra—she can point it out hundreds of miles away, to the traveler as he goes from ocean to ocean on the future international railway, and exclaim with the old Latin poet Ovid: '*Exegi monumentum aere perennior, atque altior Pyramides*'— I have erected a monument more enduring than brass, and loftier than the Pyramids."

Appropriate, eloquent, and beautiful as that is, it is still unworthy of the subject. Here, as at St. Peter's or the Coliseum, is "matter for all feeling."

Later observations indicate the hight of Mt. Lincoln as nearer 17,000 than 15,000 feet. Nothing but a visit can give any adequate idea of the grandeur of Mt. Lincoln and the numerous scarcely lower peaks that are assembled, Titans in council, at the head of the South Park.

From Mt. Lincoln a spur, called after the little town on the Platte at its head, the "Montgomery Spur," shoots off directly southward about twenty-five miles, where it ends in the "Buffalo Peaks." Beyond this it is a low, serrated, wooded range, and

it soon curves eastward and finally northward,
meeting a similar range from the opposite direction in Pike's Peak, the two forming the complete
circular rim of the South Park, Mt. Lincoln at the
head, Pike's Peak, directly facing Lincoln east-
southeast and one hundred miles distant, at the
foot. It is as though the great spur, thrown off
from the Range at the north-east corner of the
Park, had opened for the first hundred miles of its
course, the two halves removing sixty or seventy
miles asunder to make room for the Park ; then,
becoming one again, but displaced forty or fifty
miles northward from Pike's Peak, had pursued its
descending course until it was lost in the bank of
the Mississippi River. A series of similar spurs
accompanies this mother of mountains throughout
its course, forming water-sheds between Hudson's
Bay and the Great Lakes, between the Missouri
and Yellowstone, and in regular succession the
Platte, Arkansas, Red, and Del Norte. On the
west they are more irregular, presenting us with
the Columbia and the Colorado, the latter having
several large tributaries — the Green, Grand, Gunnison, Puerco, and Gila — which show it more
especially.

The Range bears off westward from Mt. Lincoln
for twenty or thirty miles, in which distance it
sweeps round the head of the Arkansas. Thence
it strikes southward for perhaps seventy miles,
shedding off into the Arkansas on the east, Tennessee, Lake, Clear, Pine, Chalk, Cottonwood, and
South Arkansas Creeks, all of considerable size

and exposing by the immense furrows they have
cut into the heart of the mountain, innumerable
and rich gold-bearing quartz veins ; and into the
Gunnison Fork of the Rio Colorado on the west, a
succession of streams, not yet so well explored as
the others, but still known to open and make accessible an auriferous and argentiferous region of
bewildering extent.   In latitude 38° 30' a huge spur
branches off to the south-east, forming the eastern
rim of the Park of San Luis ; parting, first, the
waters of the Arkansas and Del Norte, and then,
as the Raton Chain, reaching far into Texas, the
divide between the Arkansas and Canadian Rivers.

Where this spur is thrown off, the Range begins
to bear a little west of south, and just below the
38th parallel it bends another ox-bow to the west,
two hundred miles in length and hardly twenty
across, round the head of the Del Norte.   Thence
it resumes its general course southward, soon passes
beyond the southern boundary of Colorado, becomes the Sierra Mimbres, and in about one thousand miles, plunges into the Mexican Andes, in
latitude 23° 30', in the Mexican State of Durango.

We have traced its huge folds an estimated distance of five hundred miles within the confines of
Colorado.   Its great, lateral spurs — those terminating in Pike's Peak and the Spanish Peaks and
Raton Mountains on the east, and the Elk and
Uncompagre Mountains on the west — make an
aggregate length of mountain range for Colorado
of ten or twelve hundred miles.

The Foot-hills are the advanced works of the

Range. They rise abruptly from the Plains to the hight of a thousand feet, which hight is generally increased by about two thousand feet in a width of fifty miles, where they lap on the Range. It is along this jointure of the Foot-hills and the Range that the great mineral belt of the Territory extends in a north-east and south-west direction from Long's Peak to the head of the Del Norte, having an average width of twenty miles. In the Foot-hills of St. Vrain's Creek, the Boulders, and Clear Creek, occur the larger moiety of the improved mines and mining towns. At the heads of the upper south fork of Clear Creek, a right-angle or fold of the Range is laid partly across this belt, leaving paying mines on about twenty-five miles of the upper Blue River. Otherwise it does not reach the Range until, crossing the root of the Montgomery Spur and the Arkansas River, it arrives on the heads of Lake and Clear Creeks, in the vicinity of the Twin Lakes and Red Mountains.

Let us note some of the more prominent characteristics of the Foot-hills before particularizing about the mines. We will take the liberty of supposing you to be a "pilgrim," just from the benighted East. As you approach the great barrier which forms the shore line you discover that it has a serious look. It is cloven from top to bottom by numerous escaping mountain streams, but you can see no chance of ingress. At last, when you get within less than ten rods of the wall, you distinguish the mouth of a deep cut opening shortly to the left instead of before you. You enter and cross a little stream fifty-eight* times in the course of eight miles. Sometimes you travel in the bed of it for rods together. Then you climb and descend a sharp ridge, and striking a small brook, follow it up four miles to the top of another ridge. Down, across, and up a third stream five or six miles to the top of ridge the third. Down a pretty steep hill four miles, across a dashing creek and up a gulch that rises four hundred feet in a mile. Such was the old road to Central City, Nevada and Missouri Cities being each a mile further up the forks of the gulch, with an ascent of eight or ten hundred feet. You can go west of Central City ten to fifteen miles before coming to the wings of the Range.

You might have followed up one of half a dozen creeks, and curiously noted how it gradually lost itself in many tributaries, and how the rocky walls and irregular slopes of its lower course had fallen back, and its kanyon become a smooth, sunny, grassy valley; itself overarched with willows, alders, and birches, its banks lovely with primroses and buttercups, violets and anemones, daisies and columbines, and many new and delicately-tinted flowers. But away from the brooks and moist places it cannot escape your notice that the aridity of the Plains has not deserted you. Stunted, snarled, and unsightly shrubbery strikes its roots in the rifted

---

* This may sound strange to those who roll over the road now in the handsome coaches of Wells, Fargo & Co. But on the 7th of June, 1860, the writer first toiled up Eight-mile Kanyon, and he happend to *count* the number of times the road crossed the run. It was fifty-eight.

rocks; thick tufted plants send tap-roots deep into the hard, gravelly soil in search of moisture; and the absence of deciduous-leaved trees gives to the woods a most cheerless aspect. The pines are neither thick nor thin on the ground, are rarely of large growth, but are symmetrical in outline and tastily grouped. But little animal life disturbs your meditations; the feathered tribes are few and far between, and their shrill cries make you wish they were fewer and further. No reptile glides noiselessly from under your foot; a tiny, striped-backed squirrel alone attracts your eye as he jerks himself across your path and with a "chitter" vanishes up a tree. Silence and solitude are the inheritance of these forest wilds, where even the loudest explosions rouse only a faint, short echo, and where the song of the winds is an eternal and subdued sigh.

Doubtless you will experience, too, the effects of a rarefied air. Upon moving about you will be "filled plumb full of short wind," as the Hoosiers say; persist in violent exercise and bleeding at the nose will result. You will observe an involuntary tendency to prolonged inspiration and forcible expansion of the chest, a seeking to make up for diminished density by increase of bulk. But be not alarmed; be careful; remember that good men are scarce; if your lungs are made of well-tanned leather they will soon learn by use to take in a larger bulk of air; your muscles will harden by exercise and give tone to the circulating vessels; while the purity, dryness, and most refreshing coolness of the atmosphere and that exhilaration which comes only of life in the woods or on the wave will make you feel like a new man — or woman. In a seven years' steady residence in Colorado the writer can scarcely recall a case of death by consumption, that fell scourge of the North and East. "During our protracted absence of fourteen months," says Fremont, at the close of his second exploring expedition, "in the course of which we had necessarily been exposed to great varieties of weather and of climate, no one case of sickness had ever occurred among us." Even persons predisposed to pulmonary complaints will experience benefit from the light air and pure water of the Foot-hills, if their lungs are yet strong enough to stand the extra exertion of the expanding process. But where the lungs are permanently disorganized, our advice would be such as we once heard a drunkard give himself—"hold up your head and die tough." Do not go to the Rocky Mountains in such case. The light air and extra exertion in breathing will but hasten the coming of the end. The prevalent diseases are fevers, rheumatism, and erysipelas, most of them due to improper food, exposure, privation, hardship or excess. But many a man has here found that relief from the nasty agues of the prairies which nothing else but death could give.

The climate "can't most always be told from where you sit." In June, July, and August, from one to three thunder showers, but very few of them violent, may be expected every day. Umbrellas are unknown, however. A stock of them was once taken to Central City, but no one wanted them, and they were finally thrown away. Everybody wears a rubber coat, on his shoulders, his arm, or the croup of his saddle. For the rest of the year it never rains. The early and late snows are the heaviest. About the middle of October a soft snow of twelve to thirty inches may be expected. These are the nicest snows of the whole world. They fall silently perhaps for sixty hours, spread the most spotless mantle over everything, decorate the pines with fantastic feathers beside which those of the ostrich pale. Suddenly the clouds vanish, and a heaven of perfect purity, blue as the ocean, appears. The sun rises in imperial splendor, and the high hills seem to hold up and offer to Heaven in sacrifice the purest gift their mother Earth can bring. As if she, too, had been partaker in the fall, and must in atonement bring sacrifice. And Heaven usually accepts this offering. In a day or two it will all have been licked up, save some trifling patches shaded by the sacrificial altars. This October snow ushers in the Indian Summer, which, during the first four Winters spent in the mines, lasted with few and short interruptions, until Spring. Those Winters are looked back to by old settlers as men look back upon the days of their youth. They were Italian, a little dash of snow and a cold snap once in two months or so, may be; but most of the time the softest air and brightest sun that ever wandered forth from the Elysian Fields. The last four Winters have not been unlike those of the same latitude in the East. That of 1863–4 was very severe. In the Foot-hills the tops of the

ridges are generally unpleasant during the Winter
months ; but the gulches, in which are the towns
and mining works, are like the great cities, unmind-
ful of the weather, unless, indeed, locomotion is
absolutely blocked, which occurs ten times in New
York where it does once in Central City.   During
the regular Winter the snows are completely worn
out, consumed, by the winds.   The southern slopes
of hills and ridges round Central City are never
covered with snow three days together.   It melts,
or is blown away.   In the Spring, from the middle
of April to the middle of May, two or three snows,
from twelve to twenty or thirty inches deep, may
be expected.*   These melt off at once, carrying the
old snows with them, starting vegetation and the
brooks, replenishing the springs, which are numerous and good, and putting the ground in fine condition to receive seeds of ·crops.   High winds prevail throughout the Winter.   They come from the
Range, and many old houses have to lean so hard
and so long against them that when they cease
blowing in the Spring they fall forward flat on the
ground.

On this elevated plateau, as high as 9,000 feet,

---

*The town of Nevada is a mile from Central City, nearly a thou-
sand feet higher, and between 9,000 and 10,000 feet above sea.
From September 4th, 1859, to April 5th, 1860, there fell at Nevada
sixty-nine inches of snow.   The mercury fell to fifteen degrees below
zero on the 13th of November, and to the same figure again about
the first of December, remaining there two days.   Thence to April
30th, it sank below but once—on December 31st, two degrees—and
averaged for the one hundred and forty-five days at seven o'clock
in the morning, 20 1-2° above zero.

fair crops of vegetables are made, two hundred
bushels per acre of potatoes or turnips being no
uncommon crop, the mountain tops also condensing
and sending down sufficient moisture to satisfy the
wants of the growing plants.   Attempts have been
made to raise the small grains, but so far they have
not succeeded.   Killing frosts may always be expected by the 5th of September, so that it must be
winter wheat if anything that would have time to
mature.   Last Summer the writer saw a piece of
barley, put in on the 9th of June and handsomely
headed out August 20th.   The whole region furnishes unequaled pasturage ; the well-worn paths
of the larger game cut the tops of portions of the
Range itself in all directions ; and there are thousands of little parks, swales, and creek bottoms
where hay can be made to advantage.

But mining is the great interest of the plateau.
Job tells us that "there is a vein for the silver, and
a place for the gold where they find it."   Doubtless
there should have been a comma after gold, but
there is not.   So that this Scripture is true.   The
place for gold is literally, "where they find it."   New
ideas are slowly gaining ground among book men,
as to *where* gold may reasonably be looked for.   By
science, it should only be found in metamorphosed
rocks, in the immediate neighborhood of eruptive
masses, and in surface deposits derived from them.
The fact is, it occurs where no igneous rocks come
to the surface—in sedimentary rocks but slightly if
at all metamorphosed.   The largest surface deposit
or *placer* of gold-bearing gravel in Colorado is on a

stream that nowhere cuts down through stratified rocks of comparatively recent formation to the eruptive granite or trap, nor can the strata from which the gold evidently came be said to be metamorphosed at all in the sense in which that word is used by geologists. It could not have come, either, simply from the abrasion of veins, because there is no group of veins in the vicinity large and numerous enough to have furnished a tithe of it. And then, after the surface detritus is carried away by the gold-digger's hydraulic, the solid bed-rock, a micaceous or schistose slate, is dug up, assayed, or brayed in a mortar and panned, and found to contain coarse gold to the tune of three or four ounces a ton.

But leaving this interesting question to the savans, let us hasten to say that in the early settlement of Colorado, the Foot-hills furnished many gulch, placer, and bar mines, that is, surface deposits containing gold which could be got out by washing. These placers were limited in extent compared with those of California, which fact is explained by Colorado's greater distance from the sea. She has about an inch of rain where California has a foot. Her mountains are approached by inclined planes six hundred miles long from which they rise only about six thousand feet, while the Snowy Andes of California rise almost from the sea-coast to a hight of twelve thousand to fifteen thousand. Where there is little water there will be slight wash, and where there is little wash there will be few surface gold mines. But plácer gold-mining is so ephemeral a business that it hardly deserves mention.

Quartz or vein mining, on the contrary, is among the most permanent pursuits of man.

By a vein, as a geological or mining term, in general, is understood an aggregation of mineral matter of indefinite length and breadth and comparatively slight thickness, differing in character from, and posterior in formation to, the rocks which enclose it.*

Wiessenbach, in a paper published in Cotta's "Contributions to the Knowledge of Mineral Veins," which is especially devoted to the subject of the metalliferous veins or lodes of Saxony, gives the following general classification: 1. Veins of sedimentary origin. 2. Veins of attrition. 3. Veins of infiltration, or stalactitic veins. 4. Plutonic veins. 5. Segregated veins. 6. Metalliferous veins, proper. The two latter classes are included in the class of regular, unstratified mineral deposits, and are the only ones of importance in the consideration of metalliferous veins.

Segregated veins are what their name implies. They are supposed to have been formed by the segregation of particles of similar nature from the gneissoid and schistose rocks in which they occur, while the mass was cooling down from a molten state. In other words, they are crystals on a large scale, and instead of occupying any pre-existing fissure in the country rock, make way and room for themselves by force of chemical affinity.

---

* We condense from Whitney's "Metallic Wealth of the United States," a rare and valuable work, our brief dissertation on the nature of veins, the geological occurrence of auriferous quartz, and the mineralogical occurrence of gold.

The auriferous quartz veins of most gold regions belong to this class of deposits. They consist of belts of quartzose matter, with sulphuret of iron, which near the surface is decomposed into a hydrated oxide, and contain gold disseminated through these substances, and sometimes in the adjoining rock in fine particles, or, occasionally, large lumps. These belts run with the strata and dip with them, and in other respects exhibit the phenomena of segregated rather than of fissure veins.

Practically, the most important feature of this class of deposits is that they cannot be depended on in depth as true veins, as they seem always to be richest near the surface, and frequently terminate altogether at no very considerable depth. Nor is the ore or metallic matter distributed through them with as much regularity as in the true veins, forming often a series of nests and pockets ranged in a general linear direction, and connected by mere threads of ore or barren vein-stone.*

---

* This opinion was published in 1854, before the auriferous quartz veins of Colorado had been discovered — before those of Australia and California had been much developed. In the latter country they have been wrought to a depth of 1,200 feet, and so far from being exhausted, are one hundred per cent. better in every respect than they were on the surface. We never were in Australia but have been told that the mines are already worked to a depth of 1,800 feet. What the opinion could have been based on unless upon the deep workings of Europe, which make against it quite as much as experience in California and Australia would seem to, we are at a loss to conjecture. We may be permitted to add that so far as we have gone down in Colorado, our experience is the same as that met with in California, and we are working at a depth of 500 feet.

Gash veins hold an intermediate position between segregated and true veins. Like the latter, they occupy pre-existing fissures, but they are of limited extent and not connected with any extensive movement of the rocky masses. They occur in sedimentary rocks but slightly metamorphosed, and owe their origin to unequal contraction of the strata by shrinkage. They may have been filled with mineral matter either by sedimentary deposit, or segregation, or both. They are still less reliable than the segregated veins, but sometimes their great number makes up for the want of continuous extent, and they are worked with profit.

A true vein is a fissure in the solid crust of the earth, of indefinite length and depth, which has been filled more or less perfectly with mineral substances ; or, in other words, an aggregation of mineral matter, accompanied by metalliferous ores, within a crevice or fissure which had its origin in some deep-seated cause, and may be presumed to extend for an indefinite distance downwards. True veins sometimes attain a length of several miles. They vary much in thickness, and nobody has ever yet seen the under edge of one. They are the principal repositories of the ores of the useful metals, and their exploitation is a matter of lasting importance, involving the employment of both skill and capital. They are rarely found singly, but rather in groups, often in a complicated net-work crowded into a narrow space. This is so true of Cornwall and Saxony that centuries have not fully developed even the more important facts concern-

3

ing them.   Usually but a small proportion of the
matter in the fissure is valuable ore.   The earthy
or non-metallic portion is called "gangue" or "vein-
stone," and is most commonly composed of quartz,
next of carbonate of lime in the form of calcareous
spar, lastly of fluorspar and heavy spar.   Different
districts have vein-stones as well as ores peculiar to
themselves, and the locality of an ore may often be
determined by examining a fragment of its gangue.
Sometimes pieces of the wall or country rock are
recognized in the vein-matter.   These are called
"horses."   The fissure itself is frequently of a complex character, forming parallel branches, and sending out ramifications from the main line of fracture,
until it seemingly becomes lost.   The branches that
leave the main lode are called "droppers;" and
when they concentrate and lead into it again, they
are called "feeders."   The walls of veins are often
smoothed and striated, as if there had been motion
of the lode against them accompanied by pressure;
these polished surfaces are called "slickensides."
The barren rock removed in excavating a vein is
called "deads," "attle," "rubble."   Fissures may be
of different geological ages, and where this is the
case, the phenomena attending them become doubly
complicated.   A system may be heaved out of
place, or given a new direction by a newer one, and
a younger system may heave both out of place,
change their direction, and mix things up generally.

Some of the quartz-lodes of Colorado have been
pronounced true veins by the best authority.   Prof.
Alfred Du Bois, for three years exploring and min-

ing in the South Park for a Philadelphia Company, says, in one of his reports: "The veins are all of good width—all will measure five feet or more, and some are very much wider, and well-defined, true, *fissure*, metalliferous veins." William H. Stevens, of Philadelphia, a man who commenced life twenty-five years ago in a Lake Superior mine, and who has studied the books and the rocks together on mining and kindred subjects through all the intervening time, gives his opinion to the same effect. Our judgment would be worth little, because our observation has been confined to the veins of Colorado, none of which is yet developed beyond a depth of 500 feet. But we have had many opportunities of consulting mining, geological, and metallurgical experts from all parts of the world, and their uniform verdict is, that the best-known gold-veins of Colorado belong, not to the class of segregated, but to the class of true veins.

In point of fact it is true that our veins are of larger and more uniform size, and that they yield more and finer gold the deeper they are wrought. This is also the case with the gold quartz veins of California, which are similar to those of Colorado in many respects, and have been worked to a depth of twelve hundred feet. The veins of Colorado occur in groups, like those of Cornwall and Saxony, often presenting the most complicated network on the surface, which is not much untangled as they are worked. They exhibit phenomena which can only be explained by referring their origin to different geological epochs, show displacement, cross and intersect each other at all conceivable angles, but still preserve the general course of the main belt, which is also the true course of fissure metalliferous veins the world over—north-east and south-west. These groups are usually a mile or two in width and two or three in length, and there may be two or three quite distinct groups abreast of each other in what we have termed the Mineral Belt. Perhaps they have one huge trunk vein running lengthwise through the group, having numerous branches of various size like those of a tree, and cross-courses answering to roots. We say *perhaps*, because enough has not been done yet to justify even the baldest theory concerning their mode of occurrence. If they have not fully arrived at the leading facts with regard to the veins of Cornwall and Saxony in centuries of work, as we are told by high authority, how should we have done so in Colorado, which is less than ten years old, whose lode-mining proper is indeed not more than five years of age?

With regard to the filling of true veins there are various theories, the most popular one among miners being that they were filled by injection from below. This theory finds no countenance among scientific men, however, who find it impossible to reconcile it with the actual conditions presented by the veins and vein matter. Among the explanations they offer are the following:

1. That of sublimation, or the volatilization of metallic matter from the great center of chemical action beneath—the ignited interior of the earth.

In contact deposits, and some other irregular forms of occurrence, where the mass of a bed seems equally permeated throughout with metallic particles, as in the mercury mines of Almaden, no theory better accounts for such diffusion than that of sublimation. But it does not account for variation in the character of lodes upon passing from one kind of rock to another ; nor for the presence in them of substances not volatile in their nature ; nor for any of the complicated phenomena exhibited by veins in their intersections with each other. So that we are constrained to regard sublimation as of secondary importance as an agency in the formation of regular, metalliferous veins.

2. The theory proposed by Werner, which may be called aqueous deposition. It presupposes a chemical solution covering the regions in which the veins are found, from which solution, by chemical precipitation from above, downwards, the vein matter was accumulated in the fissures of the rocks below. But if any such fluid, holding metalliferous substances in solution, had actually covered the surface, why should it have deposited its contents in the fissures rather than on the adjacent surface? A little reflection will convince any one that this theory is nonsense.

3. Lateral secretion. The views which are at present most generally adopted, assume a somewhat complicated series of phenomena as concurring in the formation of mineral veins. It cannot be doubted that the process has been a complex one, requiring a long period of time for its develop-

ment.   No one simple cause can be considered sufficient to account for all the facts, but the main idea
is that of *lateral secretion*, or segregation of the
mineral and metalliferous particles from the adjoining rocks in a state of chemical solution, and their
deposition upon the sides of a previously-formed
fissure under the influence of electro-chemical
forces.   This is the only theory that will account
for the often-noticed fact of the change in character
of a lode in passing from one geological or mineralogical formation to another of a different character;
and it seems to be more in accordance with the
other phenomena of veins than any other yet proposed.   Such is Whitney's conclusion, and we are
sorry that the scope and design of our work excludes
the facts and reasoning he brings together to sustain it.   It is a subject of great interest to miners,
well worthy their closest study both in books and
in the veins themselves where they pass their lives.

The gold-bearing rocks, or rather the rocks in
which auriferous quartz veins occur, are marked on
geological charts as confined to the oldest sedimentary groups, the palæozoic and azoic.   While the
strata of these formations have been so metamorphosed by the action of fire and broken and tumbled up by Plutonic throes as to render it all but
impossible to distinguish between them, there is
ground for the belief that the great gold deposits
of the world originated exclusively in the palæozoic
or lower series of all.   They are termed metamorphosed rocks; are most commonly slaty, generally
talcose although occasionally chloritic and argilla-

ceous; through a long series of similar geological events they have the same leading mineralogical characteristics, the world over, whatever their original composition or structure; and it is only in them that auriferous quartz veins are found. The productiveness of this quartz, nearly always the gangue of gold, seems to be in proportion to the thoroughness of the change wrought in the character of the accompanying or country rocks by heat. Where they are but slightly altered from the condition in which they were deposited, they are found to contain only traces of gold. Where, on the contrary, they have been invaded by igneous masses from below, broken, tilted up on their edges, and rendered crystalline in structure by being heated to the fusing point and afterwards allowed to cool, there is reason to expect the presence of gold as it is found in workable lodes. Veins which occur in the eruptive rocks are seldom of much value.

In general the quartz veins may be presumed to have originated at the time of the metamorphic action on the strata themselves; and when there are igneous rocks in the immediate vicinity, the development of the metallic contents of the adjacent veins is usually ascribed to their presence; since it is so often found that the metalliferous deposits are intimately associated with eruptive masses. It does not follow, however, that these phenomena throughout the world were confined to any particular geological epoch. There may have been a repetition of similar conditions at periods very remote from each other. One of the most striking facts developed by Murchison in his great work on Russia is that the impregnation of the rocks of the Ural with gold took place as late as the drift epoch. In the Southern United States no great change appears to have taken place since the epoch of the new red sandstone; and the date of the gold-bearing veins may with probability be placed between that formation and the carboniferous. In Australia the elevation of the auriferous strata and their impregnation with gold seem to have been later than the epoch of the coal. In California it is probable that the auriferous masses are included in slates of palæozoic age, highly metamorphosed; but of the period of the igneous action which may be supposed to have been the cause of their impregnation with gold, little can be predicated with certainty. In the Cordilleras of South America the period of metalliferous emanations seems to have been after the deposition of the cretaceous strata; and disturbances of the rocks which may have been attended with phenomena of this character have evidently continued down to a very recent geological period, both there and in California.

It must be plain to the reader by this time that very little is *known* as to how or when the lower sedimentary rocks were metamorphosed, the vein fissures made, filled with quartz or other vein-stone; or how or when the quartz or the whole rock strata in which it occurs, as the case may be, was impregnated, as the savans have it, with gold. We at least are most positively ignorant of the whole matter and confess to very little desire of being impregnated with a knowledge of it.   In the blaze of universal ignorance on the subject the Colorado rocks are likely to fare as well as any other rocks, and meanwhile it is of more interest to us how and when we shall get the gold out than how and when it was put in.

Gold and platina form an exception in their mode of occurrence to all the other metals in common use.   While silver, tin, copper, lead, zinc, iron, are obtained almost exclusively in the form of *ores*, that is to say, in combination with a *mineralizer*, of which the most common one is sulphur, gold is found, all over the world, in the native state, its combination with tellurium, an exceedingly rare substance, being confined to one or two localities, and therefore of no particular economical importance.   What is termed *native gold*, is an *alloy*— not an atomic union — of gold and silver — the latter forming from one-half to less than one-hundredth of the mass — with traces of iron, copper, and other metals.   It is the form in which nearly all the gold in use in the world has been obtained. Gold and iron are almost as intimately associated as gold and silver.   There is hardly a specimen of sulphuret of iron (iron pyrites — called *ore* in the vernacular of Colorado) in which a trace of gold might not be found by sufficiently delicate manipulation.   When the iron pyrites has undergone decomposition and become converted into a hydrated oxide, from exposure to the atmosphere or other cause, the gold may often be separated with advantage ; but in the attempt to separate gold from

3*

*un*decomposed iron or copper pyrites, there is a considerable loss in amalgamating ; so much so as to almost uniformly prevent, up to the present time, its being profitably done.   The efforts perseveringly made by different parties in Colorado to overcome this difficulty will receive attention in a subsequent part of this book.

It is not from workings in the solid rock that the gold of commerce has been chiefly derived, however, or at least not from the workings of man. Nature herself has been in the field for countless ages, separating it from the rock, washing, concentrating, and accumulating it in the superficial detritus lying on the rock in place, and included by geologists in the drift and alluvial deposits.   All that man has had to do, is, by various simple, mechanical contrivances, to separate the precious metal — in the form of round, flattened, and (rarely) crystalline particles, varying in weight from mere nothing to thirteen hundred and nineteen ounces — from the dirt.   This is called "placer mining," and as we have remarked before, is the most ephemeral at the same time that it is the most fascinating pursuit in the world.   No doubt the ancients derived their gold from such deposits, but who can now tell where they were ?   So we are fast arriving at the exhaustion of them in a new world, and the far future will perhaps find it equally hard to point out their locality.

CHAPTER III.

VERY early in the year 1859 the citizens of Auraria, in Arapahoe County, Pike's Peak, began to
scatter out to hunt for gold.   After a pretty thorough
prospecting of all the neighboring streams, they
settled upon Clear Creek, or the Vasquez Fork of
the South Platte, as being the richest.   Diggings
were opened on that stream, three or four miles
from the edge of the Mountains, and a town soon
sprang up, called "Arapahoe."   At one time there
must have been fifty houses in this town ; to-day,
not one remains on the spot to mark its site.
Another town was soon commenced, a little higher
up the stream, just where it fairly escapes from the
Foot-hills.   This was called "Golden City," and in
the latter part of the year was built up very rapidly,
reaching, during the next Summer, the highest
point of prosperity it has yet attained.   On Ralston
Creek, a small tributary of Clear Creek, diggings
were opened and worked with considerable success.

The creek bars were a mass of boulders of all sizes, and it was soon observed that the gold always occurred in scales, like flattened shot. From this it was inferred that it and the boulders came from a long distance in the Mountains, and from the same place.

Gold had already been struck in the Mountains, too, at that time. It was about the end of January that B. F. Langley lighted upon some placer or bar-diggings in a gulch on South Boulder Creek, which was full of fallen timber. Hence the name "Deadwood Diggings." By the end of March, quite a number of men were engaged at Deadwood, and considerable gold was being taken out.

About the first of April, George Jackson, with a party of men from Chicago, struck gold at the mouth of a branch of South Clear Creek, near what is now Idaho, which branch they named "Chicago Creek," after their home. The diggings were called "Jackson Diggings."

And now we have arrived at *the* discovery which at once settled the fortunes of the Pike's Peak community in the minds of everybody in it capable of reasoning from facts. The discovery of the lode called after himself, by John H. Gregory, would seem to rank among those great events whereby the race at large have profited. That in a section of broken mountains, extending the whole length and one-third the width of the United States, a man, *en route* for a distant country, should have been diverted in the midst of his journey two hundred miles to the south, should have proceeded directly to the spot—a ravine two or three miles in length—and in it and on its bordering hills have struck the heart of as rich and extensive gold, silver, and copper mines as are known in the world, is indeed marvelous. But there was method in the madness that led to this magnificent result. Of John H. Gregory, little is known. He was from Gordon County, Georgia, and left home in 1857 for Frazier River, on the Pacific, some four thousand miles distant from where he started. He drove a Government team from Leavenworth to Fort Laramie in 1858, where, by a succession of accidents, he was detained until the Spring of 1859. Meanwhile he heard of the discoveries of gold on the South Platte, and started on a prospecting tour along the base of the Mountains, south, early in January. He found nothing satisfactory until he arrived at the Vasquez Fork of the South Platte, which he followed up alone, his plan being to prospect thoroughly wherever the Creek forked, and to follow the branch which gave most promise. In this way he toiled up the Kanyon, perhaps the first white man who had ever invaded its solitude, to the main forks of the Creek, fourteen miles above Golden City; then up the north branch to the gulch that bears his name, seven miles, beyond which he could obtain nothing of consequence. Here he left the Creek, and took up the gulch. Where the little ravine, immediately south-east of the Gregory Lode, comes in, he again prospected, and finding it the richest of the two, he turned aside into it; but as he approached its head the

"color" * grew less, and finally entirely failed.
Gregory now felt certain that he had found the
gold; but before he could satisfy himself a heavy
snow-storm occurred, during which he nearly per-
ished.   Upon its clearing up, he was obliged to
return to the Valley for provisions, and leave his
discovery unperfected.

After considerable effort he prevailed on Wilkes
Defrees, of South Bend, Indiana, to accompany him
back into the Mountains.   They reached the spot
in a tedious journey of three days over the hills
and ridges.   This little party is hardly less an object of interest than Magellan seeking with a will
of iron, with an intelligence in advance of his age,
and with faith "as a grain of mustard-seed," to
circumnavigate the globe; or than Columbus, after
eighteen years of painful effort, sailing from the
Roads of Saltez through unknown seas to discover
a new world.   His attention turned thither by fly-
ing reports, Gregory had sought the unbroken wilderness on the heads of the South Platte; alone
and penniless but with a ripe intelligence, the fruit
of years of experience, he had commenced operations, and now, through the assistance of a stranger,
is about to realize the bright dreams that have
haunted him for months.   We confess to a strong
sympathy with the enterprising and energetic pioneer, and shall share in his joy if he shall be successful.   He was confident he had found the identical spot where the gold lay; and, climbing the

---

*A word used by prospectors for gold, meaning, literally, *gold*, in
finer or coarser particles and in greater or less quantity.

hill about where the wash would naturally come from, he scraped away the grass and leaves, and filled his gold-pan with dirt. Upon panning it down, his wildest anticipations were more than realized. There was four dollars' worth of gold in it! He dropped the pan, and immediately summoned the gods of the Egyptians, Greeks, Indians, Persians, and even, it is said, of the Hebrews and Christians, to witness his astounding triumph. That night he did not close his eyes. Defrees dropped asleep about three o'clock in the morning, and left him talking; Defrees awoke at daybreak, and he was still talking. They washed out forty pans of dirt, and obtained forty dollars. Then they returned to the Valley to get their friends.

The discovery was made on what is now Claim No. Five, on the 6th of May, 1859. A heavy storm prevented anything being done for ten days. From the 16th to the 23d, Gregory worked five hands on the claim, and with a sluice got out $972. He soon after sold Nos. Five and Six to Henderson & Gridley for twenty-one thousand dollars, and commenced prospecting for other parties at two hundred dollars per day. It may not be out of place to add here that on the 8th of September following, Gregory left Denver for home with thirty thousand dollars' worth of dust.

Let us briefly trace the history of these two claims, since it is not widely different from that of all others. Gregory advanced Henderson & Gridley two hundred dollars with which to commence operations, and their first four days' labor, with a

sluice returned them six hundred and seven dollars.
During the summer they took out seventeen thousand dollars. They had a large pile of quartz and
sluice headings and tailings beside, which they
sold to Gregory & Reese, then running a rude
quartz-mill on North Clear Creek, for seven thousand dollars.

In 1860 the east half of Discovery Claim was
leased to an association called "The American
Mining Company." Forty feet from the surface
they struck on the "cap,"* and instead of sinking
a shaft through it, continued to work out the whole
length of the mine. The quartz and cap or wall-
rock together paid them tolerably well for a few
weeks. One day, upon cleaning up, their amalgam
was very large and heavy, and they thought they
had a "big thing." Retorting it, they discovered
that their gold had escaped, and that their mercury
or "quick" had united with anything else than gold.
What they had left it would be hard to tell, only it
was not gold. This was the first experience of
difficulty in amalgamating, caused by the presence
of antimony, arsenic, galena, iron, copper, bismuth,
sulphur, etc., in the gangue or vein-stone of the
gold. Heretofore they had been operating on decomposed pyrites, quartz, dirt, gossan ; now they
had sunk further than water and other atmospheric
elements had penetrated, the iron and copper
pyrites were *un*decomposed, and for some reason,

---

* Properly, a narrowing of the vein, and not a complete capping
over, or closing of it, as would seem to be implied. In Colorado,
"cap" has come to be almost perfectly synonymous with "obstacle."

not to this day satisfactorily explained, their mercury would only unite with a small proportion of the gold. The mine soon ceased to pay these men, consequently they failed to make their payments, and the original owners took the property back. It was then leased to another party on the same terms, and with the same result. The west half of No. Five and east half of No. Six were then sold to Walter Lull. He soon found that he had bought an elephant, and gladly transferred his bargain to Lyon & Pullman. This firm also failed to make it pay, and the matter was compromised by the original owners again taking possession of the west half of No. Five. All this time the mine was in cap, and was worked the entire length.

Gridley finally sold his interest to Henderson. In June, 1862, Henderson put on a force, which worked night and day, up to February, 1863, when the cap was "raised," or pierced; in other words, the vein opened out again. The cap was one hundred and thirty feet deep in one end of the mine, one hundred and eighty in the other. During these last seven or eight months the rock taken out a little more than paid expenses, yielding eight or ten dollars a ton. From February to August, 1863, when the work ceased to allow the erecting of a hoisting apparatus, sixty thousand dollars were taken out. A thirty-horse engine was set up, forty hands put on, and up to the close of 1863, twenty thousand dollars additional were taken out. Negotiations had then commenced for the sale of the property, in connection with other on the Gregory, to parties in the East, and in the succeeding Spring it passed into the hands of the Consolidated Gregory Company, for the cash price of one thousand dollars per lineal foot, and a heavy consideration in the stock of the Company. It laid idle for a year. In the beginning of 1865, the brothers Rule, experienced mine-captains, commenced cutting down and timbering a working-shaft, putting in a pump, and opening levels for stopes. Their work has been thoroughly done, and rock can now be economically produced from the mine in almost unlimited quantity.

The above, as we said before, is not a bad illustration of the general movement of the Colorado quartz-veins. Nor from their nature is it strange. At first we find them yielding enormously in a simple sluice. It was not unusual for four or five men to wash out from the Gregory, Bates, Bobtail, Mammoth, Hunter, and many other lodes, then newly discovered, one hundred and fifty dollars a day for weeks together. Single pans of dirt could be taken up carefully from any of a dozen lodes that would yield five dollars. Zeigler, Spain & Co., ran a sluice three weeks on the Gregory, and cleaned up 3,000 pennyweights,* their highest day's work yielding $495, their lowest $21. Sopris, Henderson & Co. took out $607 in four days, and on a subsequent day, $280. Shears & Co., two days, $853,—all taken from within three feet of the surface. Brown & Co., one and a half days, $260; John H. Gregory, five days, $942; Casto, Kendall & Co., one day, $225;

---

*A pennyweight of gold is worth about eighty cents, coin.

S. G. Jones & Co., two days, $450 ; Bates & Co., one and a half days, $135 ; Colman, King & Co., one-halt day, $75 ; Defrees & Co., twelve days, with one sluice, $2,080.   In one day Leper, Gridley & Co. obtained $1,009 from three sluices.   One sluice washed out in one day $510.   Foote & Simmons realized $300 in three days.   The Illinois Company obtained $175 in their first day's sluicing from the Brown Lode in Russell District.*   Walden & Co. took in one day, from a lode in the same district, $125.   Jacob Pogue took $500 from a lode in the same district in three days.   Three men took from the Kansas Lode, in two days, $500.   Kehler, Patton & Fletcher averaged with five hands on the Bates Lode $100 a day for two months.   Day & Crane, on the same lode, with seven or eight hands, sluiced for ten weeks, their smallest weekly run being $180, their largest, $357.   J. C. Ross & Co., with four hands, averaged $100 a day on the Fisk Lode for four months.   F. M. Cobb & Co., on the Bobtail Lode, with four men, averaged from $75 to $100 a day for two months.   Heffner, McLain & Cooper worked four men at a sluice on the Clay County Lode, averaging $100 a day for ten weeks. Shoog & Co. averaged $100 a day for three months, sluicing with five men on the Maryland Lode.

These facts are well authenticated, and are inserted here because they are actual proof of the great richness of the Colorado lodes.   Is it supposable, because such results can rarely if ever be achieved now, that the fault is in the veins?   It is

*Adjoining Gregory District on the south-west.

in accordance with experience in California that gold quartz veins increase in size, richness, and uniformity as they descend into the earth. They have already gone to a sufficient depth on many lodes, not only to prove so much, but to demonstrate that *their* auriferous veins at least do not belong to the class of segregated veins, but are true fissures. So far as we have gone down in Colorado, we have developed the same vein characteristics as in California. The idea is that the Colorado lodes are true fissures, therefore extending downward indefinitely, and growing better in every respect the deeper they are worked. The facts stated in the last paragraph give the best idea in the world of what they were on the surface. If we are correct in our premises, it follows that if, by any process that should be cheap and therefore practicable, we could perform the same chemical changes in these deep vein-stones which the action of the elements had effected in those near and on the surface, the above figures, showing the yield of the surface-quartz in the sluice, fall short of the constant result which might fairly be expected.

By the 1st of July, 1859, there were one hundred of these sluices running within a short distance of Gregory Point. A year later their owners were generally lost in cap and sulphurets, their gold nearly all running off in the water used on the plates, leaving them a worthless mixture, not much superior to cold lead-pipe.

Meanwhile other diggings had been discovered, and were employing hundreds of men. We have spoken of the early discovery of gold in Deadwood Gulch, on the South Boulder. They were considered about five-dollar diggings, and four or five months after their discovery employed three hundred men. Later in the season, the Boulder was flumed in several places, to allow the working out of its bed. The prospectors scattered out, and mining operations were quite extensively carried on in Twelve-Mile Diggings (head of North Clear Creek,) on Left-Hand Creek and smaller tributaries of the Boulders. Quartz-veins of exceeding richness were struck at Gold Hill, twelve miles west of Boulder City, and about the 1st of October a rude quartz-mill was started there. All the Boulder diggings paid from three to five dollars a hand per day.

Bar-mining was also prosecuted quite energetically on the Platte above Denver, on Clear Creek near Arapahoe and Golden City, and on Ralston Creek near its mouth. Various contrivances were used to bring water into the mines. Wheels were put into the creeks to raise it out on the banks, and ditches from three to ten miles long were dug. Towne & Patterson washed out on the Platte, with a rocker, in fifteen days, one hundred and seventeen dollars. The Georgia Company, having brought water in a ditch three miles to the same diggings, washed out fifty-four dollars in four days with a tom. But mining on the streams in the Valley was eclipsed by the successes in the Mountains before the end of the season, and it was abandoned, never, probably, to be resumed.

On South Clear Creek, exploration and mining

were prosecuted from Grass Valley Bar, about twenty miles above Golden City, to the forks of the south branch of the Creek, fifteen miles higher. On the 9th of May the following laws were adopted at a miners' meeting in the Jackson Diggings, three miles above Grass Valley Bar:

"1.   Each claim shall be fifty feet front by two hundred and fifty feet deep.

"2.   Every claim shall be marked and staked with at least two stakes, and shall be improved within ten days after taking.

"3.   The discoverers of new diggings shall be entitled to one extra claim each."

By the end of May these diggings contained three hundred men, who were supposed to be making from three to five dollars a day per hand, with very indifferent mining facilities.   Later, however, companies were organized for the purpose of fluming the creek and getting at its bed, thought to be very rich.   A great deal of expensive and hard labor was performed, to little purpose on the whole, it must be confessed.   At one time there were fifty sluices running on Spanish Bar, two miles above the Jackson Diggings, alone.   But the creek was very rapid, the valley narrow and rough, the bars were masses of boulders of all sizes, the gold very deep and below the bed of the creek, and the pits were constantly flooded with water.   The sluicing of lode-dirt at Gregory Diggings, with so little trouble and such rich results, doubtless diverted the miners somewhat from this hard contest with almost insurmountable obstacles.

About the middle of June a destructive fire broke out and raged in the woods above the Jackson Diggings, which burned three men. Their remains were subsequently found, but they were never identified. People have since been so shy of these woods-fires that destruction of life has not occurred by them.

Near the 1st of August, George Griffith struck a lode on the mountain overhanging the junction of the upper considerable forks of the south branch of South Clear Creek, from which he sluiced out one hundred dollars in two days. Other discoveries were made in the vicinity, but richer diggings elsewhere drew the miners away from this locality.

On Fall River, a considerable tributary of South Clear Creek, coming in from the north-west just above Spanish Bar, lodes were struck, ditches dug, slides for letting down the quartz from the hill-sides made, and much work of a preparatory nature for mining, done. Lodes were struck in the hills all along Clear Creek, prospects from which were very large, although these were generally taken from narrow crevices. In the Fall these mines were mostly deserted, their owners going to the Gregory Diggings, to Denver, or to the States.

In the first days of June, Green Russell had discovered and commenced operations in the gulch that bears his name, a tributary of North Clear Creek, a little south of, and parallel with, Gregory Gulch. A week's work with six men amounted to seventy-six ounces* of gold. Others had taken

* Worth $16 to $18, coin, according to its purity and fineness.

claims above and below him, and toward the end of September there were eight hundred and ninety-one men at work in the gulch, producing an average weekly amount of thirty-five thousand dollars. There were in Nevada Gulch, in Illinois Gulch, and on Missouri Flats, upper tributaries of Gregory and Russell Gulches, at the same time, two hundred and thirteen men, producing nine thousand dollars a week, on an average. Because water, both for the gulches and lodes, became scarce, two ditches of considerable magnitude were projected, to bring it from the head of Fall River. These eventually became "The Consolidated Ditch," ten or twelve miles long, taking in at its head three hundred inches of water, and delivering on Quartz-Hill one hundred and fifty inches, which was completed during the Fall, Winter and Spring. It cost one hundred thousand dollars, and for the soft gristle of the young community was a big undertaking and quite a triumph.

In July the prospectors had found their way into the South Park. Two or three small parties were set upon by the Indians, and murdered and mutilated in the most approved Indian style. J. L. Shank and J. L. Kennedy were the first victims. Soon thereafter the bodies of six killed and scalped white men, and one dead Indian, were found. They were never identified. It is hard to say what put a comparative stop to these atrocities, except it were more care against exposure in small parties on the part of the whites. They did not retaliate, and this, with an insignificant exception or two, was the last of Indian troubles up to the year 1864. It was in August that extravagant stories came of the richness of the new discoveries in the South Park, and also far in the mountains on the Cache-a-la-Poudre. The consequence was a stampede from Gregory in both directions. Of the latter, little has ever been heard, and the inference is, they amounted to nothing, or could not be made available at that time. In the Park, however, gulch and bar-mining were carried on with reasonable success on all the affluents of the Platte ; and finally rich lodes were discovered where these streams issued from the Montgomery Spur of the Snowy Range, and the towns of Montgomery, Buckskin, Musquito, Fairplay, Tarryall, Hamilton, and Jefferson, sprang into being. At Tarryall, in September, the Rocky Mountain Union Company took out in one week, with four hands, four hundred and twenty dollars. Bowers & Co. took out fifty-seven ounces in a week, with three hands. W. J. Holman took out six hundred and eighty-six dollars in a week with five hands.

Many immigrants, arriving in the latter part of the season, *via* the Arkansas River, proceeded straight by the northern or southern base of Pike's Peak into the South Park mines, through a succession of delightful parks, furnishing a natural and easy road. Hence arose Colorado and Canon Cities —the latter on the Arkansas, at the entrance to the Mountains, the former on the Fountain, forty miles north of the Arkansas, and in the immediate evening shadow of Pike's Peak. Here is a lovely

4

section, and with its farms in the valley of the Arkansas and its tributary streams—with its mines in the Mountains, in the South and Arkansas Parks, is a complete, self-sustaining little world of itself, just as is the Platte, with its farms and mines. About two hundred men wintered in the South Park.

During August and September, parties crossed into the Middle Park from Montgomery and Hamilton, and discovered both placer and quartz-mines yielding gold on the upper Blue and its tributaries. Here, hidden by the huge folds of the primary Range, occurs a basin or cove, twenty to thirty miles in extent, abundantly watered, timbered, and supplied with pasturage, rich in the precious and many of the baser metals. On many of its streams gulch mining is still successfully carried on during the warm season of the year. In all the gulch and bar-diggings, in the South Park, on South Clear Creek, on the Boulders and on North Clear Creek, including •Russell, Illinois and Nevada Gulches; on main Clear Creek below Golden City, on Ralston, and on the Platte above Denver, it was estimated that the miners at work were making from three to five dollars a day to the hand. Men were prospecting from the head of the Del Norte to the head of the Big Laramie, ranging west as far as the mouth of White River.

In the Gregory District, several rude quartz-mills and some arastras, worked by water or teams, were in operation, returning handsome profits. Water began to be scarce, however, and work ceased on many paying claims—probably not more on that account than because the owners were elated at their good luck, and wished to go home and show it, never dreaming that they could ever want again or would need to work more themselves. That was before the era of sulphurets had well set in, and men to whom money was a new sensation, and who were making a cool thousand a week with little trouble, may perhaps be pardoned for extravagance and improvidence.

The pattern after which the mining districts and miners' laws were fashioned, had been roughly out-lined and adopted at a miners' meeting in Gregory Diggings, June 8th, 1859. The Gregory Lode was discovered in May. For a few days the small party which went to the spot with Gregory on his second visit, had a monopoly of the discovering and work-ing of lodes. Many of the best ones in the Gregory Diggings were found and claimed before the end of May, 1859. The Gregory Lode was taken in claims of a hundred feet each, allowing Gregory, as the discoverer, two claims. All this was easy and nat-ural, since there were just about enough men in the party to own the whole lode, divided in that way. Subsequently, Dr. Casto was elected and acted as Secretary, some record being absolutely necessary; and he and Gregory penciled down a few rules for the claiming and holding of lodes on an accidental page of foolscap—not extant—and this arrangement answered every purpose for the time being.

But by the 1st of June, Gregory Gulch, from

North Clear Creek to the confluence of Eureka, Nevada, and Spring Gulches, was crowded with canvas tents, log shanties, and bough houses, as thick as they could stand, and there was a great deal more room then than now. William N. Byers had pitched his tent about on the corner of Main and Lawrence Streets, Central City, and had suggested the name for the city, to be there, which it now bears. The gulch below was swampy, and overgrown with alders and willows. It was estimated that there were five thousand people in the gulch.

The more recent arrivals began to murmur about the *first* comers—none of them had been here a month yet—monopolizing everything; and contended for a re-distribution of claims on the Gregory, Mammoth, Hunter, Bates, Bobtail, Gregory Second, &c., cutting them down to twenty-five feet each. In consequence of this feeling a great meeting convened at Gregory Point, numbering some three thousand men. The chances of the first comers seemed small in this state of affairs, but by boldness, vigor, and address, they not only managed to extricate themselves but to come out stronger than they went in. W. G. Russell had just returned from Georgia with one hundred and seventy men who would do as he said, and having been a pioneer of the previous year, he naturally joined the pioneers of this year. The first move made was to get control of the meeting by nominating one of their number, Wilkes Defrees, for chairman. The meeting elected him of course.

They then proposed a committee of twelve men, one each from different States, to draft a code of laws that should once for all settle affairs. The meeting approved this proposition too. The pioneers then dexterously scattered through the crowd and nominated each other to such committee, the meeting approving in every instance. As the committee retired the strangers began to suspect something, but they had not been in the mines long enough to know that it was no place to hesitate.

The committee brought in the following report, which was read and adopted by sections, without giving time for discussion :

1. *Resolved*, That this mining district shall be bounded as follows : Commencing at the mouth of the North Fork of Clear Creek, following the divide between said stream and Ralston Creek, running seven miles up the last named stream to a point known as " Miners' Camp ;" thence south-west to the divide between the North Fork of Clear Creek and the South Fork of the same to the place of beginning.

2. *Resolved*, That no miner shall hold more than one claim except by purchase or discovery ; and in any case of purchase, the same shall be attested by at least two disinterested witnesses, and shall be recorded by the Secretary, who shall receive in compensation a fee of one dollar.

3. *Resolved*, That no claim, which has or may be made, shall be good and valid unless it be staked off with the owner's name, giving the direction, length and breadth, also the date when said claim was made ; and when held by a company the name of each member shall appear plainly.

4. *Resolved*, That each miner shall be entitled to hold one mountain claim, one gulch claim, and one creek claim for the purpose of washing : the first to be one hundred feet long and fifty wide ; the second one hundred feet up and down the river or gulch, and extending from bank to bank.

5. *Resolved*, That mountain claims shall be worked within ten days from the time they are staked off, otherwise forfeited.

6. *Resolved*, That when members of a company, constituted of two or more, shall be at work on one claim of the company, the rest shall be considered as worked by putting a notice of the same on the claim.

7. *Resolved*, That each discovery claim shall be marked as such, and shall be safely held, whether worked or not.

8. *Resolved*, That in all cases, priority of claim, when honestly carried out, shall be respected.

9. *Resolved*, That when two parties wish to use water on the same stream or ravine for quartz-washing, it shall be equally divided between them.

10. *Resolved*, That when disputes shall arise between parties in regard to claims, the party aggrieved shall call upon the Secretary, who shall designate nine miners, being disinterested persons, from which number the parties shall alternately strike out one until the names of but three remain, who shall at once proceed to hear and try the case; and should any miner refuse to obey their decision, the Secretary shall call a meeting of the miners, and if their decision is the same. the party refusing to obey shall not be entitled to hold another claim in this district; and the party against whom the decision is given shall pay to the Secretary and referees the sum of fifteen dollars each for their services.

On the 9th of July, 1859, another mass meeting was held at Gregory Point, at which it was—

Resolved, That for the settlement of difficulties and the purpose of preventing disputes, the miners of this district hereby enact: That there shall be elected in this district, by ballot, a President, a Recorder of Claims, and a Sheriff, for the term of one year from this date. That the President, Secretary, and one assistant, to be chosen by the people, be tellers of said election, and that it take place immediately.

The election took place, and Richard Sopris was chosen President, C. A. Roberts, Recorder, and Charles Peck, Sheriff. A committee was appointed to codify the laws of the district, and on the 16th of July, 1859, that committee reported to the adjourned miners' meeting the following laws and regulations, recommending the retaining of the original code with these additions, to wit :

1. It shall be the duty of the Recorder to take charge of and safely keep all records heretofore made by the Secretary, and all records made necessary by law shall hereafter be made by him.

2. All claims may be recorded if the owners see fit, but no claim that is being worked shall be obliged to be recorded.

3. When any miner has a lode claim which it is impossible to work to advantage this season, either from want of water or machinery, he may hold the same until the first of June next, by filing a statement of the reasons with the Recorder.

4. All water claims not used shall be recorded within ten days of the claim date, or they shall be considered forfeited.

5. All bills of sale or conveyances of claims shall be witnessed by at least two disinterested witnesses and recorded.

6. The books of the Recorder shall be always open to the inspection of the public, and shall never be taken from the Recorder's hands ; but any person shall be entitled to copy any record at any reasonable time.

7. All laws relating to trials of disputed claims are hereby repealed.

8 When any person is aggrieved with regard to a claim, he shall file with any commissioned Justice of the Peace, or in his absence, with the President of the Miners' Association, a statement of his grounds of complaint, which shall also have the names of the parties complained of, and a prayer that they be summoned to appear and answer. Thereupon, the Justice (or President,) shall issue a summons to the adverse party to appear and answer within three days. If he fail to do so, the complaint shall be taken as true and execution issue. If he appear and answer, the Justice (or President) shall summon a *venire* of nine persons from which each party shall strike off one until there remain but three, who shall proceed to hear the evidence of the parties with or without counsel, and try their case. Any juror may be challenged for cause shown either by his own evidence or that of others. Should the party losing, feel aggrieved by the decision, he may appeal to a jury of twelve men, by paying cost already accrued, which jury shall be selected by the Justice (or President), and their decision shall be final.

9. The Sheriff shall have power to serve notices and executions, and he shall have power to summon parties, put parties in posses-

sion of property decided to be theirs by law, summon juries and do such service as a Sheriff in any other place may do, and shall be entitled to receive double the legal fees provided by the Statutes of Kansas.

10. The fee of the Recorder shall be one dollar for each claim recorded.

11. The Justice (or President) shall be entitled to five dollars for presiding at each trial and making out the papers.

12. The jury shall be entitled to one dollar each per day.

13. The defeated party in each suit shall be liable for all costs of the suit, and the Justice (or President) shall issue execution for the same, which shall be collected from any property the party so liable may have, excepting tools, bedding, clothing, and necessary provisions for three months.

14. In any case either party may call upon the other to give security for costs ; the suit shall be dismissed if plaintiff, or defeated if defendant [shall fail to give such security.]

15. Any person may take up by recording, forty feet front and one hundred deep, for a building lot, but shall not secure the same against being used for mining if found rich. Should any person work out the ground on which a house stands, he shall secure the house against damages.

16. Any person or company intending to erect a quartz mill, may select or locate two hundred and fifty feet square, which shall be recorded. He may also claim the right to cut a race from any river to bring water to the same, and shall hold the water, not interfering with any vested rights.

17. The pre-emption laws established by the citizens of this county shall be recognized in the mines but shall not conflict with miners' rights.

18. Gulch claims shall be one hundred feet up and down and fifty wide, following the meandering of the stream, and shall be worked within ten days if water can be obtained ; if water is wanting, they may be recorded and held until water can be obtained. Any time after the 1st of September any miner may record his gulch claim and hold it till the first of June.

19. When any miner holds both a gulch and lode claim, if one be worked, the other may be held without working by recording the same.

20. When water companies are engaged in bringing water into any portion of the mines, they shall have the right of way secured

to them and may pass over any claim, road, or other ditch ; but
shall so guard themselves in passing as not to injure the party over
whose ground they pass.

21. When any company is formed for the purpose of discovery,
[by tunneling,] the parties engaged may stake off, record, and place
notices on ground two hundred and fifty feet each way from the
tunnel and running as the tunnel is intended to run.   After that, all
new lodes discovered by the company in tunneling, belong to the
company to that extent ; claims already taken are to be respected,
but claims cannot be taken within the limits staked off, if work be
progressing on the tunnel.   If work on the tunnel be stopped for
one week at any time, the original claim shall be forfeited and shall
be again open to claimants.

The committee's report was unanimously adopted by the meeting July 16, 1859.

These resolutions show very well the inchoate
state of mine tenure and jurisprudence, or rather
equity, for the first year of the new mining community.

On the 11th of February, 1860, a meeting of the
citizens of Gregory District was held at Mountain
City, a committee was appointed to codify and
amend the laws of said district, and report to an
adjourned meeting to be held on the 18th of February, inst.   Such portions of that report as retain
any interest at the present day, will be found in
Chapter XV. of this work.

The Justices of the Peace mentioned in these
laws were elected, or commissioned by authority of
Kansas, or of the Territory of Jefferson, usually
the former.   Under the operation of these laws,
the rude tribunals of justice in them provided for,
developed into an institution, full in their machinery, and universally regarded with as much defer-
ence as any courts of justice are among men.   At

4*

first they were only occasionally convened ; but as business increased and grew important, judges of the miners' courts were added to the elective officers of the mining districts, and these judges held regular terms, at which cognizance was taken of open offences against the peace or the common law as well as of disputed title, trespass, or other infringements of miners' rights, or laws.

Many new mining districts were formed in 1859 and 1860 out of Gregory District, the country adjoining, and throughout the mountains wherever mines were discovered, all of which copied their laws and customs from those of the parent district, though often modifying them in important particulars. It is impossible to get complete copies of these laws now, some of them having been lost, together with the boundaries of the districts. Colorado should take steps to collect and publish, authoritatively, what remains of them, as upon them must depend the settlement of important questions of title in the future. The mining districts and miners' courts lost their importance when the Territory was organized into counties, superseding the districts, and provided with regular courts in place of the miners' courts. Not so with the laws, however. Our object is, and must be from the nature of our work, not to preserve as many as we can of these laws, but to give an idea of their nature, their origin, and development.

CHAPTER IV.

NOT the least interesting of the incidents of the
Summer, was the visit of Horace Greeley, Albert
D. Richardson, and Henry Villard, of the *New
York Tribune*, the *Boston Journal*, and *Cincinnati
Commercial*, respectively. They were handsomely
received on their arrival in Denver, although the
stylish barber Murat charged Horace five dollars
for a shave. They visited the Gregory Diggings
in the first days of June, and, strange as it may
seem, upon a few hours' verbal notice, between two
and three thousand people gathered, American
fashion, to hear them, or rather to *make* them, talk.
We find Mr. Greeley's remarks, condensed as follows, in the *Rocky Mountain News* of June 18th:

"The Hon. Horace Greeley, the first speaker,
was received with three cheers. He alluded to the
cheering indications he had seen during the day
(8th inst.,) in examining the mines and sluices.
He had always had a suspicion—from which he

was not yet entirely free—that these mines would not prove equal in richness to those of California; but in view of the great discoveries of the last five weeks, there was evidently a vast future before this region. It was by no means probable that all the gold of the eastern slope was confined to this little area of seven or eight miles. He advocated the formation of a new State (a 'State movement' was already under way,) and trusted that one might be made and brought into the Union, without going through the troublesome and undemocratic form of a Territorial organization. He spoke at length of the peculiar temptations to drinking, gaming, etc., to which the miners were exposed, urging a steadfast resistance and avoidance; exhorting his hearers to look to untiring industry instead of speculation for their gains; to maintain good order, to live as the loved they had left—the brothers, sisters, fathers, mothers, wives and children—would wish; that when they returned they might carry with them the reward of their labors. If a gambler, after being warned not to do so, should persist in coming among them, he advised putting him on a good mule, headed out of the Mountains, and asking him if he would not like to ride. He should in a few days go hence to Salt Lake and California, and it was one purpose of this trip to do what he could to hasten the construction of the Pacific Railroad, which ought to have been built long ago. He was rousingly cheered on retiring."

The meeting was also addressed by B. D. Williams, H. P. A. Smith, A. D. Richardson, and Dr.

Casto. It must have been quite a grief as well as surprise to the bears and lions which had heretofore reigned sole monarchs of these wilds. At the request of B. D. Williams, then agent for Jones & Russell's "Pike's Peak Express," which furnished the miners their letters from home at twenty-five cents each, Greeley, Richardson and Villard united in a published statement of the result of their examination of the mines, giving the sluice-yields of various companies then at work, as reported to them, and a general view of the principal features of the new mining region ; ending by earnestly warning the people in the States against another rush to the mines like that of the early Spring just passed.

It may be observed that the States were full of the wildest rumors concerning the Pike's Peak mines, favorable and unfavorable. There had been a tremendous rush to them, and as great a stampede back. The *Davenport Gazette* alluded as follows to the subject:

"The *Cherry Creek Rocky Mountain News* comes to us printed on brown wrapping paper. The editor has evidently lied his paper black in the face. This number teems with glorious news about new discoveries of gold, and says the town is half deserted. So we heard, but not from *that* cause. It is all humbug, and Byers is evidently bought and sold," etc., etc.

As a burlesque on the really rich discoveries in various parts of Colorado, such squibs as the following were written and published :

"It is said that a man takes a frame-work of heavy timber, built like a stone-boat, the bottom of which is composed of iron rasps. The frame-work is hoisted to the top of Pike's Peak, and a man gets on and slides down the mountain. As he goes down swiftly, the rasps on the bottom of the frame-work scrape off the gold in immense shavings, which curl up on to the machine ; and by the time the man gets to the bottom, a ton of gold, more or less, is following him. This is the common manner of gathering it."

Stories of starvation on the way out, and over west of the Range, of the burning of Auraria and Mountain Cities, and the hanging of the pioneers of Pike's Peak, were carried back to thousands of homes in the States, by the emigrants who out-numbered, as early as April 1st, the immigrants. The trouble was, mining proved to be hard work ; and if that was all there was of it, most of these unseasoned adventurers preferred doing it at home. So stories were told, published and circulated about claims and sluices and pans having been "salted"* on Greeley and party ; but several of the most re-liable men in Gregory District united in a pub-lished statement, showing that such could not have been the case, because of the very short notice the miners had of Greeley's arrival. Toward the latter part of Summer the stampede had not only ceased, but men were arriving in great numbers, proceed-

---

* That is, that gold dust had been emptied into the sluices or fired from a shot gun into the dirt he was expected to examine.

ing into the Mountains, and only returning for provisions.   Colorado has never recovered, however,
from the effects of the stampedes of 1859 and '60,
the latter worse than the former.

We should not fail to mention the establishment
at Gregory Point, August 6th, 1859, of a newspaper by Thomas Gibson, called *The Rocky Mountain Gold Reporter and Mountain City Herald.*"   It
was a four-column, four-page sheet, filled, of course,
with mining news. From the first number, now
before us, it appears that a convention of one hundred and sixty-seven delegates had met in Denver
to frame a constitution for the new State of Jefferson, that was to be.   This will receive a separate
notice by and by.   A union church had been organized, the communion service celebrated, preaching
on Sundays and prayer-meetings on Wednesday
evenings provided for, at the mouth of Gregory
Gulch, now Black Hawk.   Golden City had then
been surveyed a month, contained fifty houses,
nineteen hundred and thirty men, and seventy
women.   Golden Gate, two miles north of Golden
City, where the Denver and Gregory road entered
and still enters the Mountains, was also flourishing, and indulging great expectations.   Davenport
had been laid out at the mouth of Left-Hand, a
town as completely passed away as those of the
Abo Desert in New Mexico.   Twelve-Mile Diggings, Left-Hand Creek, Boulder Creek, Jackson
and Jefferson Diggings, Tarryall, and Blue River
mines were each receiving due attention ; while
under the windows of the *Reporter's* log office, a

hundred sluices were running out gold to the merry
tune of twenty dollars a day to the hand.   Men
could scarcely believe in their good fortune.   They
were as much surprised at the astonishing richness
of the lodes as they were to find the Rocky Mountains, that mysterious, romantic dream-land of their
school days, a country of as much beauty, all still
and solemn and ancient and grand, as any in the
world.   To glance abroad, a great war convulsed
the most famous of the historic peninsulas of the
South of Europe.   In the telegraphic columns occurred frequently the names of the Po and Mincio,
of Solferino and Malegnano, of the Emperors Francis Joseph and Louis Napoleon, of King Victor
Emanuel, of Hess, Neil, and Schlick.   Cherbourg
was alive and quivering with excitement, and one
hundred and seventy-five thousand Austrian troops
were *en route* for Italy.   A State was arising here
in the wilderness of nature ; a nation was creating
there in the wilderness caused by the wreck of two
civilizations, inextricably mingled.   With the twelve
inches of snow that appeared on the hills the morn
of the 29th September, and scared the miners in-
continently out of the Mountains, this little journalistic enterprise seemingly failed.   The next Spring
it was started again in Denver, however, where it
finally became the *Denver Commonwealth*, and, after
exercising a large influence on the early fortunes
of the country, was merged into the *Rocky Mountain News*, that paper having been not only sub-
merged, but washed away by the great Cherry
Creek flood of May, 1864.

Nor should the inception of the *Rocky Mountain News* pass unnoticed here, especially since its files are the chief source whence this portion of this work is derived. On the 21st of April, 1859, at seven o'clock, P. M., its press arrived in Auraria, now West Denver. It was set up, and in twenty-seven hours began printing the first side of the first newspaper ever issued in the Rocky Mountains. William N. Byers and Thomas Gibson were the editors and proprietors. From the first number, dated April 23d, 1859, the journal has always preserved a creditable appearance, has ever been the able, intelligent and dauntless champion of the interests of the Territory against all opposers. From the six-column sheet first issued, it has grown, notwithstanding serious accidents by flood and field, to an eight-column, as handsomely got up and ably conducted as any journal in the West. All old settlers must rejoice in this, and younger ones ought not to begrudge it, for its success has been hardly won.

We have before referred to the attempt in 1858 to get the Pike's Peak Region set off from Kansas as a separate Territory. A sketch of it, and of successive efforts at organizing local government, is due not only to the wonderful genius of our people, but to a proper understanding of the general status of affairs prior to the regular Territorial organization by Act of Congress. On the 6th of November, 1858, H. J. Graham was elected without opposition, and by about thirty-five votes, to proceed to Washington and endeavor to have the

Gold Region set off from Kansas as a separate Territory. He repaired to the Federal Capital and exerted himself throughout the session to accomplish the wish of his constituents, but without success. Honor was his only reward, for he served at his own expense.

On the 11th of April, 1859, at a public meeting in Auraria, it was

" *Resolved*, That the different precincts be requested to appoint delegates to meet in convention on the 15th of April, inst., to take into consideration the propriety of organizing a new State or Territory."

The Pike's Peak country had been preliminarily organized the preceding Winter into a county of Kansas Territory, called Arapahoe, county officers elected, a Probate Court established, and, we suppose, voting precincts blocked out. Twenty-three precincts are mentioned in the proceedings of this meeting as already existing. A central committee was appointed, among whose duties was the designation of such additional precincts as the rapidly filling country should require.

After concluding that their discussions should have but one object—" the formation of a new and independent State of the Union"—and recommending a general election of delegates on the second Monday in May, to meet in convention on the first Monday in June, to execute their purpose, the meeting adjourned.

Fifty delegates, representing thirteen precincts, met on the first Monday in June. After organizing, eight committees were appointed to draft a constitution, to be submitted to a fuller convention called

for the first Monday in August. A further committee was appointed to form new voting precincts,
and the convention adjourned, to meet in August.

In the August convention forty-six precints were
represented by one hundred and sixty-seven delegates. There was a considerable effort to postpone
action for a time, but it was unavailing. A constitution was prepared, and its submission to the
people provided for on the first Monday in September. In case the people should reject the constitution, it was resolved by the convention that, on the
first Monday in October, a Delegate should be elected from the Territory, which they decided to call
" Jefferson," to proceed to Congress and again endeavor to have the Gold Region set off from Kansas. The constitution and the movement to form
a State were rejected by the people, two thousand
and seven, to six hundred and forty-nine—considered a very light vote.

The election of a Delegate to Congress was next
on the tapis. Eight candidates appeared in the
field, of whom B. D. Williams received a plurality
of votes. There was terrible ballot-box stuffing,
and there were not wanting parties who contested
the validity of the return of the Board of Canvassers.

Meanwhile, a scheme for a Provisional Territorial
Government had been concocted. A mass meeting
was held in Auraria on the 24th cf September, and
an address prepared requesting the people, on the
day they voted for Delegate to Congress, the first
Monday in October, to elect delegates to meet on
the succeeding Monday for the purpose of form-

ing this new, independent government. On the day of election, the county of Arapahoe, Kansas Territory, had its ticket in the field, its organization and the Miners' Laws having furnished all the government enjoyed so far. Right after the election the *Rocky Mountain News* talked as follows :

"Here we go, a regular triple-headed government machine. South of 40 (parallel) we hang on the skirts of Kansas; north of 40, on those of Nebraska. Straddling the line, we have just elected a Delegate to Congress from the Territory of Jefferson ; and ere long we shall have in full blast a Provisional Government of Rocky Mountain growth and manufacture."

Eighty-six delegates appeared at the appointed time. They made and adopted a new constitution, which had the unusual merit of brevity, and which they called "The Organic Act of the Territory of Jefferson;" apportioned the Territory into Legislative districts; nominated a full State ticket, including a Marshal, and provided for an election on the fourth Monday of October, inst.

Candidates for Legislative honors were not wanting. The Provisional Government was adopted, and the regularly nominated ticket elected with one unimportant exception, the vote being about eighteen hundred to three hundred. The Legislative Assembly convened on the 7th of November ; received Governor R. W. Steele's Message, which was a creditable document ; enacted many general and special laws, among the latter a charter for the City of Denver, under which an election was held

December 19th ; organized nine counties, for which
the Governor appointed Probate Judges until the
regular county election, first Monday in January,
1860 ; levied a poll-tax of one dollar *per capita* to
defray expenses ; and appointed committees to report to an adjourned session, 23d of January, full
civil and criminal codes.

While this was doing, the regular Kansas Territorial election had not been suffered to lapse in
Arapahoe. A full set of county officers and Members of the Kansas Legislature had been elected.
Opposition immediately arose to the Provisional
Government. A remonstrance against the proposed tax was signed by six or seven hundred
miners, and sent down from the Mountains. On
the 3d of January an election was held in Mountain
County (the name of Gregory District under the
Provisional Government *regime*) as to whether there
should be a county organization or not. The vote
stood, ninety-five for, to three hundred and ninety-
five against. In Arapahoe the county election under the Provisional Government occurred at the
appointed time. A Denver city government was
also organized under the charter and put in operation, and thenceforth Kansas and the Provisional
Government held divided sway in the Valley, while
the Miners' Clubs and Courts and the Provisional
Government did the same in the Mountains. That
is to say, such as felt friendly to one patronized it
with their business, and so of the other. Sometimes changes of venue were taken from one to the
other, and between them litigants were well fleeced

at least.   The Legislative Assembly of Jefferson
met pursuant to adjournment, in January, held a
long session, and enacted or adopted full civil and
criminal codes, which were published in the newspapers, but were never enforced to any alarming
extent.

Yet a fair degree of order and decorum obtained in the somewhat heterogeneous society of
the country.   Only one or two cases of violence are
recorded as having occurred anywhere in the mines
up to the regular organization of government in
1861, more than two years after the discovery of
the Gregory Lode.   The people were sober and in-
dustrious as a rule, and there were never any very
remarkable criminal cases brought before the Miners' Courts.   In Denver it was not so quiet, although the worst days of that town would not begin
to justify the hideous and altogether fictitious picture given of it by William Hepworth Dixon, A. D.
1866, to justify his absurd theory that boorishness
is peculiarly a Western product.   Up to the end of
March, 1860, three homicides and two duels had
occurred in Denver one of the latter resulting in
the death of Dr. J. S. Stone, the challenging party.*
Of the homicides, one had escaped, one been tried
before Probate Judge Smith, found guilty, sen-

---

* Dr. J. S. Stone was Member of the Provisional Legislature from
Gregory District, where he was also Judge of the Miners' Court.
Hon. L. W. Bliss, his antagonist, was Secretary, and at the time,
acting Governor of the Territory.   At a public dinner in Denver
the Governor made some offensive personal allusion to the Doctor
in proposing a toast.   An incident which tells as much of the state
of society at the time as any other that occurs to us.

tenced and hanged, and the other tried before Justice Hieatt and acquitted. Subsequently, ruffians, gamblers, and thieves overran the town, and no man's life or property was safe. One party set up baseless claims to a portion of the town-site, attempting to defend their action by force of arms. Another called themselves "bummers," and the best that can be said of them is, that they were bummers. They made a business of petty thieving, and also attempted to defend themselves by force of arms. The Postmaster assaulted a citizen with intent to kill, and successfully resisted arrest for it on the part of the city authorities. There was a man, or fiend, named Charley Harrison, who boasted that he had a jury in Hell, sent there by his own hand. He was the king of the desperadoes. One day he deliberately shot to death a negro, we suppose, for being a negro. For denouncing this, the editor of the *Rocky Mountain News*, William N. Byers, was forcibly taken from his office by Harrison's pals and conveyed to their den on Larimer Street—the Criterion Saloon—where they were going to murder him. But Harrison, experiencing a sudden shock of magnanimity or fear, probably the latter, spirited him away through a back door. The fiest-fiends had smelt blood, however, and were determined to taste it. So they lay in wait round the *News* office to assassinate Byers. Finally, one of them, named Steele, mounted a horse, and riding up in front of the office, fired two shots into it in hopes of hitting their victim. Two shots came from the office in response, one of which caught Steele under the arm and passed through his person. He did not fall from his horse, but, a crowd having collected, rode for dear life toward the open country. He was followed by men as well mounted and as determined as himself. Half a mile or so from the office a charge of buckshot brought him to the ground and he died. Steele's confederates fled, and only one of them, Wood, was taken. He was tried by a People's Court, and given his life if he would at once leave the country, which he did. It may interest the gentle reader somewhat to know, that on the breaking out of the civil war, these thugs ardently embraced the Southern cause. Returning from Richmond in the Spring of 1863 with Confederate commissions in their clothes, they were captured by a band of wild Indians in the Osage country, and their heads cut off. They died. It is to be hoped that Harrison is having a good time down below with his jury.

During the Summer of 1860 there were about a dozen murders and homicides committed in Denver. One man, named Gordon, seems to have taken Harrison for his exemplar. No second-class ruffianism would do for him. On Wednesday evening he shot down a barkeeper named O'Neil. O'Neil afterwards recovered. On Friday evening he shot twice at another man, missing him. The same evening he fell upon a barkeeper, named Gantz, knocked him down, and holding him down by the hair, succeeded in shooting him through the head, after ineffectually snapping his pistol four times. Gantz died. Gordon ran away. Sheriff Middaugh followed him into the Cherokee country, more than five hundred miles, caught him, and in spite of the most frantic efforts of a mad Leavenworth mob to release him, whether for the purpose of hanging or letting him escape we have forgotten, brought him back to Denver. He was tried by a People's Court, found guilty, sentenced and hanged. This case was remarkable in many respects. The unparalleled wantonness of the crimes committed ; the every way admirable carriage of the tribunal of the people and its officers in the pursuit, capture, detention, and trial of the murderer ; the extraordinary sympathy which finally sprang up for him, and which alternately entreated reprieve and threatened rescue ; and the firmness with which the stern decree of death was executed, fixed the attention of the young community, heedless as it was disposed to be. The citizens saw the grandeur of the human Nemesis, or perhaps rather of the instinct of self-preservation, and experienced a security in well doing unfelt before. The ruffians comprehended that their day had passed—that they must move on to some more remote outwork of civilization to enjoy longer their late impunity.

Besides the victims of justice already noticed, improvised People's Courts, usually presided over by a Probate Judge or a Justice of the Peace, tried and acquitted four homicides, and tried and hanged three murderers between the end of March and the end of September, 1860. Their officers also settled with one squad of horse thieves, as told by our friend Wharton of the *Rocky Mountain News*, in

5

his late "History of the City of Denver." A party in pursuit of Gordon came upon three of these miscreants, one of whom made his escape. A second was drowned in attempting to swim the Platte River ; the third was captured, given twenty-five lashes, and twenty-four hours in which to leave the country. He left. To resume: It was not until well along in the next year that the organization of Colorado Territory was perfected under an Organic Act of Congress.

This body, occupied with the "Impending Crisis," the "John Brown Raid," the admission of Kansas, and the making of a new President, although favorably disposed toward the new community, did nothing until the very close of the session,—26th of February, when the Organic Act was passed,—but take the preliminary steps to treating with the Indians for the gold lands. Through the efforts of Williams, more post offices were established by the Department. The Representatives to the Kansas Legislature protested against the gold region being regarded as a part of Kansas, but took care to get through three or four special acts for charters. The laws of the Provisional Government had been published, but there was no effort to enforce them. And so we leave this interesting subject for the present, remarking that if the people did not have a good government, it was not for want of effort in that direction.

Up to May, 1859, the miners had depended on the post offices at Forts Laramie and Kearney for their mails. An occasional express was sent to

Laramie, but the delay was wearing—how terribly so, none can know but those who have felt it. The heart of the wanderer in the West goes ever back to the home of his childhood. Thence the winds bear him the perfume of the days that are no more —all the fond memories of young life. It is he who prizes letters from home. Often the want of them is the sole cause of his falling into bad habits. It leaves him sick at heart, and inclines him to reck-lessness. The charges on letters, weeks old, were fifty cents each ; newspapers were *non est comeati-bus.*

On the 7th of May, two coaches of the "Leaven-worth and Pike's Peak Express," arrived in Den-ver, in nineteen days from the States. The line first ran *via* Fort Riley and the divide between Soloman and Republican Forks, to the Republican between the one hundred and first and one hundred and second meridians. Thence up that stream to near its source, thence across Beaver, Bijou and Kiowa Creeks, through the pineries, to Cherry Creek. A construction train accompanied these coaches, stations were established at intervals of twenty-five miles, and stock put on for a daily line. As run, the road was six hundred and eighty-seven miles long by odometer measurement. The Com-pany had fifty-two new Concord coaches, and made the first track on the route most of the way, under the supervision of B. D. Williams. A money, package, and letter express was added to the pas-senger business.

Soon after, the Company, of which John S. Jones

and William H, Russell were the chief men, purchased the stock, route, and contract of the Salt
Lake & California Mail Company, and removed
their stations, stock and force to the Platte River,
carrying the overland mail to South Platte crossing, and thence branching to Denver and Fort
Laramie.   Their charge on letters was twenty-five
cents each, papers in proportion.   The Postmaster
at Leavenworth was directed to deliver all mail
matter for Pike's Peak to the Express Company, so
long as they would carry it free of expense to the
Government.   There was a regularly constituted
post office at Auraria, but the Postmaster was
obliged to contract with the Express Company to
carry the mails tri-weekly to Fort Kearney at the
same rates the Company already charged—twenty-
five cents a letter and ten a paper—in addition to
the United States postage.

By the end of the year several postmasters had
been appointed, but no post routes established.
The Leavenworth & Pike's Peak Express Company had secured a charter from the Kansas Legislature, and adopted a new name—" Central Overland California & Pike's Peak Express Company."
In this were William H. Russell, John S. Jones,
William B. Waddell, Luther R. Smoot, Alexander
Majors, J. B. Simpson and others.   In connection
with their regular mail, passenger and express business, they started a pony express, carrying letters
for one dollar each, from Leavenworth, Kansas, to
Placerville, California, in ten days !   The first pony
arrived in St. Joseph from San Francisco on the

13th of April, 1860, in ten days. This wonderful enterprise made the Company very popular throughout the West. The Butterfield Mail Route through Arizona, all the rage a year before, passed out of date. The entire attention of the country was concentrated on the central route. This, with the gold discoveries at Pike's Peak and the silver at Washoe, at length forced upon Congress the great advantage of carrying the mails between the Atlantic and Pacific States overland rather than by water. A movement was immediately made toward establishing three overland mail routes across the Continent. But the nation has since had its energies absorbed in a different and less pleasing task than discovering and developing its unknown resources, and to-day there is but one mail route. It is due to justice to say that it is managed to perfection, and transmits the mails by two thousand miles of staging more regularly than they were transmitted a few years ago between New York and Washington or Boston

As before stated, a foot of snow whitened the hills and gulches infested by the miners on the morn of the 29th September. The climate of the region was then unknown ; there was but a slight stock of provisions in the country and especially in the Mountains, and it is no wonder, seeing such a fall of snow so early in the Autumn, that the miners stampeded, afraid of being snowed in and starved out. Probably not more than fifteen hundred men wintered in all the mines in 1859. These found the mildness of the weather an agreeable

surprise. The first snow melted and ran off in a
few days, and was followed by as lovely an Indian
Summer as ever was enjoyed anywhere. This may
almost be said to have lasted throughout the Winter, since there were but three or four falls of snow
accompanied by severe cold, and these spells were
comparatively short. A few men stuck to their
toms, and especially their hand-rockers, burrowing
immediately on some rich pay streak, in the gulches,
all Winter. In the three months ending January
31st, one man took out twenty-four hundred dollars
in Nevada Gulch with a rocker.

A "gold rocker" is a sort of cradle, with a coarse
iron screen for the first bottom. The operator sets
it beside a spring, brings to it his pay dirt, puts it
on the screen and pours on water from a cup with
one hand, rocking the cradle with the other. A
"tom" is the same principle enlarged. The dirt is
shoveled from the pit on the iron screen, and the
water conveyed to it in a stream. Two or three
sluice-boxes, with rifles for quicksilver, are attached.
A "sluice" is a square wooden box, open at the
top, of any desirable size or length—though the
longer the better—through which a heavy stream
of water runs constantly. A dozen or twenty or
fifty men shovel the dirt into it, or loosen it so that
the water will carry it in. There are quicksilver
rifles in the sluice to catch the gold. A man keeps
it clear of stones with a sluice-fork. Sometimes,
where the bed-rock is favorable, a trench is cut in
it, answering to sluice-boxes. The water is so led
as to carry into it all the dirt in the gulch ; and

when that is done the sluice is cleaned up. The quick and gold are apt to escape in the rock crevices, and this sort of a sluice is by no means commended. The rocker was chiefly used in the Winter, because of the scarcity and freezing of water in the gulches.

As early as the middle of July, Lehmer, Laughton & Peck started a Spanish "arastra" for grinding quartz near the mouth of Gregory Gulch. An arastra is a circular trough, generally ten or twelve feet in diameter, made of stone, in which other and heavier stones, called "mullers," are dragged round continuously, thus grinding up the quartz. They are generally run by water, and do not do their work so badly. The above-named firm started the first one ever run in Colorado, thus pioneering a business of which very remote times are not likely to see the end.

On the 17th of September, Prosser, Conklin & Co. got up steam in a steam quartz-mill the first time in Colorado. Shortly their mill, which was small, was in successful operation

By October 1st, there were five arastras running on North Clear Creek, two small wooden stamp-mills also, all by water, and four arastras building. These were realizing about two hundred dollars each per week, working on the headings of the sluices—that is, such quartz as was too coarse to pass through the screens used. The latter were pierced with about half-inch holes.

On October 7th, Coleman, LeFevre & Co's steam mill started, but soon broke down. By the 4th of

November it had been repaired, again started, and in the first seven days' run on Gunnell quartz, produced 1,442 pennyweights of gold. At this time they were fifty-six feet down on the Gunnell, the decomposed pyrites or gossan of the surface was giving place to a more solid material, but it paid at the rate of sixty dollars a ton, and grew richer the deeper they went. At seventy-six feet from the surface, they realized from fifteen tons, seventeen hundred dollars.

A rude quartz-mill had been in operation for several months at Gold Hill—between Left-Hand and North Boulder Creeks—and a large water-mill was building in the Autumn. The owners of lodes were busy getting out dirt and quartz for the expected mills in the Spring. The Cotton, Fisk, Bobtail, Clay County, Gunnell, Maryland, Casto, Kansas, Burroughs and other lodes had out and piled up some three or four hundred tons each, the success of the Coleman & Le Fevre mill with Gunnell rock greatly encouraging the miners.

Tunnels were started—nine in Nevada alone running under the Kansas and Burroughs Lodes, and two elsewhere. These were pushed with energy till toward Spring; many of them being driven from fifty to one hundred and more feet. Having been somewhat injudiciously located—that is, too near the surface, and any other location was impracticable from want of capital to drive long, deep tunnels—they were not of much if any practical use, and were generally abandoned toward Spring for the gulches and the surface of the lodes.

Very fair roads had been made into the Mountains — one *via* Golden Gate, one *via* Bradford. They were not so perfect as now, but were a vast improvement upon the first hill-road, over which in places twenty yoke of oxen were required to *climb*, without dragging anything worth mentioning, perhaps a wagon containing a sack of flour. A road from Denver to the South Park, *via* Mt. Vernon and Bergen's Ranch, had been projected and was vigorously pushed through the Winter. So also was the St. Vrain, Golden City and Colorado Wagon Road, which avoided Denver entirely. A fair wagon road ran from Canon City into the South Park, also one from Colorado City. There were trails from the South Park to the Middle Park, and one from Gregory. On the 4th of March, 1860, Kehler & Montgomery's express coach arrived in the mines from Denver, the first ever run on the line.

5*

CHAPTER V.

NEVER did Spring open on a more hopeful people
than the inhabitants of the Territory of Jefferson
in 1860. The richness and great extent of the new
gold fields were considered proven. The pioneers
had penetrated the previous season from Taylor's
Park, away south of the Arkansas and a hundred
miles in the Mountains, to the Cache-a-la-Poudre,
north-west of Long's Peak, and the Black Hills.
Between was a bewildering scope of country,
scratched indeed, but not prospected thoroughly;
and in view of the unparalleled richness of the
lodes and gulches in the Gregory District, the most
sanguine expectations were not unreasonable.
Under the greatest disadvantages, mining had been
prosecuted there with the most gratifying success.
Now they were to have the benefit of experience;
of machinery, saw-mills, cheap provisions, implements and supplies; of established laws and regulations; of roads and means of transportation; of

postal facilities; of a great influx of people, many of them women, many of them bringing more or less capital, and coming at least prepared for the emergencies of the season. The agricultural capacities of the country had been found much greater than was at first expected, and the settlers were better prepared to make use of them. The Winter had been chiefly spent in prospecting and many rich discoveries had thence resulted.

It was not long after the opening of the year before the old miners began to seek the Mountains. By the first of May immigrants were arriving from the States at the rate of a hundred a day. It was estimated that up to that time eleven thousand wagons had passed Plum Creek, bound for Pike's Peak. The Platte Route may be said to have contained, for a full month, but a single train, extending from the Mountains to the Missouri River. A great many came up the Arkansas, and went directly into the South Park. The Gregory District was the especial destination of most of the new comers, however. It is hardly necessary to say that the general aspect of affairs appeared gloomy and forbidding to them. All the known claims were of course occupied ; and there was such an almost universal willingness to sell at good figures as to justly raise suspicion. There was little else to do but work by the day in the poorly secured lodes, or the deep, wet gulches, and wages were not much higher than in the States in proportion to the nature of the labor, and the expense of living. It does not seem very strange, either, that the old settlers—

who had been in the mines a year!—were somewhat cold toward the immigrants. They felt that
they had earned what they had got, and that there
was chance enough for others to do likewise. Surely, they said, all these strangers cannot expect
employment here on our ground ; let them branch
out and find mines for themselves, or if not, go
back. So the dwellers in wagons, in tents, in
booths, prospected—which is a discouraging business except to the prospector by nature, who must
have the faith of a martyr—made continual pur-
chases of claims which they knew not how to work,
gold washing being a nice business, and were obliged to throw up; cut saw-logs or cord-wood, or
engaged in such other work incidental to mining, as
the case admitted ; or finally, laid round and consumed the grub they had brought with them. The
whole district was full of tents and camp-wagons;
it was overrun with people. An amusing story is
told of a party that had concluded the Pike's Peak
mines did not amount to much, and were about to
return to the States. They had heard that the lode
dirt in the Maryland would wash out four dollars to
the pan. They went there as a last resort before
leaving, and asked permission to try it for themselves. They were let down into the shaft, and
shown where to fill a pan of dirt, which they did.
They closely watched its washing, and were, we
suppose, *painfully* surprised to have all their conclusions upset by finding $8.68 in the pan. They
thought they would look round a little more before
they left.

A heavy snow storm about the first of May was also well calculated to dampen the spirits of the new men. The Consolidated Ditch had not been finished, and water was scarce. Buildings, it is true, were springing up as if by magic, and operations were extending ; "big things" there were, too, in old and new discoveries ;—one man in Russell Gulch rocked out ninety pennyweights in a day ;—but wages were quite low ; it seemed there were no more big things to strike ; it was hard to get letters from home ; and is it wonderful they felt discouraged ? Still they poured in. Sowers & Co. started a line of coaches between Denver and the Mountains. In June the Western Stage Company put on a line ; the two could not begin to accommodate the travel. The Russells came in from Georgia *via* the Smoky Hill Route, on which they made a favorable report. Gregory came in with a party and a quartz-mill, which he erected in a few days, ran awhile, taking out two hundred dollars a day, and sold for six times its cost. John H. Gregory not only knew how to find mines, but it appears he knew how to sell out at the right moment.

The discovery of California Gulch, very rich and five or six miles long, and of a half dozen other less considerable gulches on the Arkansas, Blue and Swan Rivers, drew attention from the Gregory Mines ; and of the unexplored fields the Middle Park and the Arkansas Park absorbed thousands ; but by the first of June men might be seen facing homeward with a dejected air, as if under conviction for sin, or convinced that gold mining was very hard work. Still, the incoming tide was vastly the strongest. For perhaps two months not less than five thousand a week came in, and as they generally brought grub enough to live on for a few months, they wandered around, joined every stampede—of which there were many—in short, didn't think of returning to the States till Fall. Ere that time quartz-mills had sprung up like mushrooms in every gulch in the Gregory District, and a vast deal of labor was called for to keep them running—for run they would, pay or no pay, to keep up appearances.

The year before had witnessed the starting of two or three steam and several water quartz-mills ; these were good seed sown in rich soil, as the crop of this year was destined to show. In June a new steam mill of six stamps was got into operation in Nevada, the first day's run producing five hundred dollars. Another started up in Lake Gulch, and a steam saw-mill in Eureka Gulch. An eight-stamper was located at the foot of the Bates Lode, and a twelve-stamper just below the Burroughs. The first trials in some of these mills met with difficulty in the adulteration of the quicksilver. By the end of June, it was said one hundred and sixty quartz-mills had left the Missouri River for Pike's Peak ; but this was doubtless an exaggeration. As high as six arrived in one day, however. On the 1st of July there were sixty mills in the Gregory District, and some thirty arastras. The latter were generally more successful than the former. A writer of the time says :

"Somehow the mills as a general thing do not save the gold ; why, it is hard to tell. There must be some difficulty beyond the mills—doubtless the want of experience in the men who run them. Crushing quartz is a new business to them ; and as it is a very nice one, requiring skill, and as all of us as yet lack this skill, we fail in almost every attempt, just as any one does in a new vocation, about which he knows nothing. Some of the mills have tried quartz from the Bates, and pronounced it worthless, while the arastras get two hundred dollars a cord from the same stuff."

And again :

"There is not attention enough given to mining. Every one seems to think there is an easier way to make money than by digging, so that all other enterprises than mining are being overcrowded. I think they will find out to their sorrow that the gold has to be dug out of the ground before it can get into their pockets."

Thus it will be seen that the difficulty of saving the gold from Colorado rock is not of recent origin, but was encountered at the beginning, though there were then more instances of success than latterly. The inclination to neglect mining, and trade, speculate, do anything but mine, is also an evil as old as the country, and doubtless destined to outlast it.

Loveland, Link & Co's six-stamp mill in Nevada started about the first of July, and its first run of eight hours on Burroughs quartz produced $321.55. Another run of twelve hours on Missouri quartz produced $400.   In Eureka, the Enterprise Company, with ten stamps, in ten days took from 150 tons of Burroughs quartz $4,400.   The St. Louis mill, eight stamps, took $178.75 from Fisk quartz in twenty-four hours ; another time they took from twenty tons of the same quartz, $375.   Wimple & Co., in Nevada, crushing for other parties at seven dollars per ton, took out in five and a half days from Forks quartz, $3,930.   Cheney & Co., of Lake Gulch, cleaned up $1,250 from a five days' run on the Justice.   The Milwaukee Mill, eighteen stamps, running on Mammoth quartz, took out in four weeks, $5,250.   But these were exceptional cases. Of those in which the product only about paid expenses, we have no record.

After a while, the flush times caused by the erection of so many mills and a thousand other buildings besides, died out, and mill men began to take their bearings.   It was found that while a few of the best lodes would yield thirty to ninety dollars a ton, excepting these the great bulk of quartz could only be made to yield about the average cost of crushing—seven dollars.   Hence there were at once idle mills—a sort of intermittent disease with which Colorado is still troubled.   It was hoped that larger mills and purer quicksilver would supply the defect in the business.   But a little circumstance soon dissipated that fond hope.

The park of the South Boulder and Left-Hand had always been an interesting spot.   At Gold Hill there were as many mills running in proportion to the extent of the discovered mines as in

Gregory, and paying reasonably well.   During the Spring the Gold Dirt Lode had been struck, and very rich it was.   By the end of the year six quartz-mills were running from it.   One sluice took out, in seventeen days, $2,227.   Hurlbut & Co's six-stamp mill started October 1st, and up to January 5th, 1861, had taken out $11,526.94, and had been idle four weeks of the time   Between June and November two men realized from the lode, over and above all expenses, $35,000.   Hollister & Co. struck pyrites on the lode seventy feet from the surface.   Before that they had been working sixty hands, and their weekly yield of gold was from $1,500 to $2,000   Upon striking the pyrites, a run of eighteen hours gave but one dollar and forty cents.   They commenced experimenting.   A pan of " tailings " * was boiled in quicksilver.   The amalgam therefrom yielded $9.70.   The same material was exposed to the frost two nights, and boiled again in quicksilver, yielding this time $4.80.   The process was repeated with the following results : $3.67, $6.34, $2.73, $1.04, $1.06, $0.33, making a total of $29.67 from the pan of tailings.   Then it was seen that the stamp mills were very deficient ; and from that day to this the problem has been, how to separate the largest percentage of bullion from the rock.   While this has been a difficult, perplexing, expensive, and most discouraging labor, the fact of the exceeding richness of the gangue-rock has ever remained present with experimenters to encourage effort.

---

* Crushed ore as it comes from the mill.

All this year prospecting for lodes was vigorously carried on in Clear Creek County. On Spanish Bar a mill was started during the next January which got $300 from its first run of fifteen tons. There were Spanish Bar, Morris, Montana, Downieville and Union Districts on the main creek, and Iowa, Fall River, Lincoln, Cumberland and Upper Fall River, on that stream. In these, numerous lodes, some real, others not so real, were discovered and recorded, and a few of them considerably improved. Preparations were making in all of them for building mills, when Winter came, and none of them got into operation till the next Spring.

We have space but for a glance at the placer mining of the season. In the old Gregory District it was prosecuted in every gulch with the greatest vigor, though it is impossible to ascertain with what success. There were few claims that could not be bought at more or less reasonable figures; and to buy and sell seemed to be a more general object than to work. Russell, Gregory, Nevada, Eureka and Spring Gulches, also Illinois and Leavenworth, Missouri Flats and Quartz Hill, were lined and covered with men busy tearing up the ground. It is probable the average production amounted to very good wages, and that was about all. In the Boulder mines, as well as in those of Clear Creek County, placer mining had been chiefly abandoned ere the season was half gone, and all the energies of the people bestowed on quartz-vein discoveries and development. The South Park mines showed the same tendency in a less degree. On the head of the Arkansas, west of the South Park, early in the Summer was discovered a gulch well calculated to attract a stampede of the wildest description. It was called California Gulch, and was taken up for ten miles in length, and supported a population throughout the season of four or five thousand. For a mile below the discovery shaft it paid extraordinarily and regularly. Above and below it was spotted and streaked, and on the whole did not more than pay expenses. The discovery of McNulty Gulch, a few miles off, drew five hundred loose-footed men in a single day. In this there was a vast amount of stripping; it was quite spotted, but all things considered, turned out very well. There were a dozen gulches discovered and worked on the Arkansas, Blue, Swan and Snake Rivers. Five dollars a day to the hand would doubtless be a large estimate of the yield of all the gulch, bar and patch diggings worked during the season, or indeed ever in the country.

The design of our work compels us to hasten on over the succeeding three years. There was but a slight immigration in 1861, and the fore part of the season was very dull in the quartz mines. Still, everything steadily improved. New towns in all the mining districts sprang into being, and the old ones replaced log houses with stone or brick, or substantial frames, and extended their area. There has never been wanting to Colorado the cry of "hard times," nor has her improvement in every respect ever ceased for a moment. It should be borne in mind that dull times in a mining country

would be considered flush times anywhere else.   If
a thousand people are not coming and going every
day ; if towns of tents and booths and cabins do
not spring up in a night ; if mining does not pay
one hundred dollars a day to the hand, and if this
money is not in vigorous circulation, it is called
"hard times."   Such things go by comparison.   At
the time we are considering, a mill occasionally
made a successful run ; new lodes, such as the
Perigo, Phillips, or Orphan Boy, that were really
" big things," were found once in a while ; but the
mill men were all new to the business, and only a
few could make it pay.   For a few months quartz-
mining was regarded as almost a complete failure—
and this, although the mines were not yet " hogged
out," and although supplies, provisions, and labor
were very cheap.   The best St. Louis flour sold in
Denver for $4.50, and in Central City for $7.50.   It
was simply that they did not yet know how to treat
the rock.   They kept trying, however ; and by the
end of 1861 things had assumed a great deal better
look.   A majority of the mills contrived to run
steadily and make it pay.   New districts were
opened up.   Trail Run, Mammoth, Buckskin, Mosquito, Montgomery and other places furnished a
demand for mills that could not get paying quartz
in Gregory District.   A regiment of volunteers had
been raised for the war, and Salmon River had begun to draw away the adventurers who had no
luck ; so that idlers grew scarce and wages became
firm, with an upward tendency.   The Bobtail,
Gregory, Mammoth, Bates, Gunnell, Burroughs,

American Flag, Forks, Flack, Rhoderick Dhu, Horse-fall, German, Perigo, Clay County, Gold Dirt, Fisk, Cotton, Gregory Second, Gregory Extension, and a few other lodes whose names do not now occur to us, produced such rock as could be made to pay in the mills. From a little pocket struck on Quartz Hill and called " Lone Star," one hundred pounds of quartz were taken, pounded up in a hard mortar, and panned down, yielding $3,000. Thousands of dollars' worth of gold specimens came from the pocket, but it was finally emptied. From one hundred and thirty tons of rock out of the Horsefall Lode (Gold Hill), the Union Company got $5,341.50. Edgar De Peyster cleaned up, from ninety tons of Gold Dirt rock, $3,115.89. J. Q. A. Rollins took $3,000 from the same quantity of the same rock. The Laclede mill took $1,873.95 from twenty tons of Bobtail rock. Lee, Judd & Lee, got $1,299.20 from five tons of Bobtail rock, carefully selected and run. E. J. Sweet selected twenty feet of cupriferous rock from Field's claim on the Bobtail, and got by a stamp mill, more than $700 from it— at the rate of $600 to $700 a ton. This was done on a wager of $100, between Sweet and Field, as to what was the best quality of rock, each selecting twenty feet of the kind he considered the best. It was the biggest yield ever obtained in the Territory.

As an indication of the energy with which prospecting was everywhere pushed, we may state that during the year ending June 1st, 1861, the Recorder of Spanish Bar District recorded twelve thousand five hundred and thirty lode claims, three hundred and three bar, twenty-five gulch, and three hundred water-mill sites. On November, 4, 1861, Nevada was almost destroyed by fire—fifty houses and property in all worth sixty thousand dollars being burned ;—but it soon rose from its ashes more substantial and prosperous than before. During all the time we have gone over, enterprising men were studying out improvements, particularly in treating the rock,—the same as now. Novel crushing machinery was tried and abandoned ; there were plans for pulverizing the ore* by chemical baths, by the use of steam and fire ; and one man—Dr. Burdsall—experimented long and patiently with smelting, His furnace was destroyed in the Nevada fire ; and though he seemed to get encouraging results, and still struggled on after that for a time, yet the public soon heard no more of him. In another place we shall endeavor to group together such items of interest in connection with processes for treating ores, as the recorded history of the country presents. There were great improvements made, however, in the construction of the batteries and plates, the manner of feeding the stamps, the use of copper plating, and the preparation and purification of mercury.

All through the year 1862, there was no special complaint of difficulty in quartz mining or milling. At the end of that period many mills were doing

---

*Although there is no strictly *gold ore*, or at least very little, that of which we are treating having become a complication of gold, silver and copper, and frequently of some other metals and minerals, may properly enough be termed *ore*.

very well. Perhaps a few instances of yields would not be out of place. Lee, Judd & Lee, with forty-seven stamps, were averaging about $4,000 a week from Gregory and Bobtail ores. Sykes & Whitney took from 112 tons of American Flag, $2,092. Hayes & Kinkead took from thirty-five tons of Gregory, $1,980.20. The same firm took from sixty tons of Bates, $1,306.80, and from eighty-five tons of Gregory Extension, $3,256.60. Laflin & Smith, from Caledonia (Wide Awake), forty tons, $1,500; Sabin & Grover, from forty tons Flack, $1,348; Vore & Allen, from Tenth Legion (Empire), at the rate of $35 a ton, surface quartz; the Western Mill, from thirty-eight tons Illinois, $1,062.20; Holman & Co., from thirty-eight tons Tennel (Trail Run), $1,500, and from Freeland, forty tons, $1,032; Williams & Co., from seventy tons Orphan Boy (Mosquito), $4,512; D. D. White, from twenty-three tons of the same, $1,862. The Kansas, Gunnell, Topeka, Dyke, American Flag and Flack were from one hundred to one hundred and fifty feet deep, and were averaging about $20 a ton.*

In the commencement of this work we gave a sketch of the history of the discovery claim on the

---

* We are aware that these disjointed statements are not statistics in any legitimate sense of that term; they are given the same as the yields of sluices were before to show something the richness of the ore when and where it could be demonstrated. Colorado mining has not yet been reduced to an art. There is not a miner in it for instance who can give more than an *estimate* of the quartz he crushes in a year, of its yield and cost per ton. The numerous disadvantages under which the business has been carried on have this to answer for.

Gregory as an illustration of that of all the lodes.
Here is a similar sketch of a claim on the Bobtail
up to the beginning of 1863. The first pay was
decomposed quartz, struck six feet from the surface, and extending downward thirty-nine feet, the
crevice four feet wide, and averaging forty-one dollars per ton. Here a cap was struck, which proved
to be twenty-six feet thick, yielding an average of
twelve dollars per ton. Then the crevice was again
struck, three and a half feet in width, and extending seventy feet downward, yielding an average
per ton of thirty-eight dollars. A second cap was
here struck, which proved to be thirty-five feet
thick, and which averaged fifteen dollars per ton.
Then came a three-foot crevice for forty feet, yielding sixty dollars per ton. Up to date the operator
had been in the third cap for forty feet, the ore
paying forty-two dollars per ton. The claim was
No. Two, east, and we now have it sunk to a depth
of two hundred and sixty feet, it having produced
in all $204,000. It will be observed that it in-
creased in richness as it was sunk upon. The first
crevice yielded forty-one, and the first cap twelve
dollars per ton. The last crevice yielded sixty, and
the last cap forty-two. We have said that the gold
quartz veins of California are found richer and
wider as they are mined to greater depths. Is it
not safe to assert the same of the Colorado lodes,
in view of such facts as the above?

It was about the beginning of 1863 that Behr &
Keith arrived in Colorado, and commenced experimenting with ores, an account of which we reserve

to another time.   We do not find much change in
the business of quartz-mining during that year.
The lodes exhibited the same characteristics of
open and pinched crevice; of ore in which the gold
was comparatively coarse and free, and in which it
was so contaminated by the baser metals and poi-
sonous substances as to be impossible of amalgamation, or so fine as to nearly all run off in the water.
The mills were removed from Lake and Russell
Gulches and Missouri City, into Gregory and its
tributaries.   The towns concentrated and became
Nevada, Central, and Black Hawk.   All through
the Summer business of every description was
prosecuted with great energy.   But the mines were
growing deeper, and accumulating more water.
Owing to the careless manner in which they had
been worked, they were unsafe, and required improvements; and generally, from two hundred and
fifty to three hundred feet from the surface, a stratum of ore was struck, with which the mills could
do nothing to profit.   Still, there is no positive evidence that there existed a necessity for a general
transfer of the mines to capitalists.   It was not
until one or two sales of mining property had been
made in the East at large figures, that it was discovered that mining in Colorado could not be carried on without capital.   So far it had been done,
although about the end of 1862 an Eastern Company had brought in a fifty stamp mill, and located
it in Mammoth, (head of South Boulder.)   But a
year's operations of that Company should have
been sufficient to warn the miners against the ap-

6

proaching change. That it did not, was perhaps due to the fact of its out-of-the-way location. There is no necessity for a history in detail of the transfer of the quartz-mines of Colorado to Eastern men. It is sufficient to say that a mania for Colorado mining property was created in New York and Boston about the end of 1863, and fabulous prices,— in several cases a thousand dollars a foot, were given for improved mines. Surely that was temptation enough: we need look no further for the causes of the mania for selling out which responded in Colorado to the mania for buying, in the East. We must glance at the condition of placer-mining meanwhile.

During the years 1861 and '62, placer-mining in Colorado saw its palmiest days. It was gone about systematically and not feverishly, and with more experience, generally paid better than it had previously. From a calculation made on a great many returns from sluices and toms, we estimate the yield, not only in Gregory District, but in the South, Middle, and Arkansas Parks at five dollars a day to the hand. In 1863 the business gradually died away, because the gulches, most of them worked over three or four times, had become completely exhausted. In some few of them in Gregory District, and in more in Summit County, a great number of claims were bought up by associations, and with long ground sluices and large heads of water, made to pay. But gulch, bar, and placer-mining, as a business of any importance, had died out in Arapahoe in 1859, in Boulder and Clear Creek counties in 1860, in the Parks in 1861, and in Gilpin County in 1863.*

We have before spoken of the Provisional Government of Jefferson Territory, of the Sovereignty of Kansas, of the People's Courts, and of the Miners' Laws and Courts. There were still other attempts at organizing government, but they hardly deserve mention. Gov. Steele's Provisional Legislature met again late in the Fall of 1860, but no attention was paid to it, and on the 7th of December it adjourned without day. Honor might well have been the subject of its story for it never got any other pay.

On the 26th of February, 1861, a bill organizing the Territory of Colorado with its present boundaries was passed by Congress, and the following Federal officers appointed by the Government: Wm. Gilpin, Governor; Lewis L. Weld, Secretary; B. F. Hall, Chief-Justice; S. N. Pettis, and Charles Lee Armor, Associate-justices; Copeland Townsend, Marshal; Wm. L. Stoughton, Attorney-General, and F. M. Case, Surveyor-General. Gov. Gilpin arrived out on the 29th of May. He first visited the settlements in the Territory, and then had a census taken by the Marshal, according to the returns of which there was a population of 25,329; white males over age, 18,136; under age,

*In the Parks it now shows signs of reviving. It is to be put upon a different basis from what it has formerly been. Instead of working in 100-feet claims, great tracts of country are being secured by incorporated companies sufficient to justify considerable outlay for bed-rock flume and for steam machinery to handle the dirt. A full account of this will be given hereafter.

2,622; females, 4,484; negroes, 89. On the 10th of July he assigned the Judges, the Judicial Districts having been constituted before as well as they could be, and the Supreme Court immediately organized. Next day he declared by proclamation the Territory one Congressional District, divided it into nine Council and thirteen Representative Districts, and ordered the election of a Delegate to Congress and of a Legislative Assembly. This body convened on the 9th of September, was very respectable in point of ability, adopted full civil and criminal codes for the Territory, and enacted some wise mining legislation, which is given in Chapter XV. of this work. It fully and distinctly recognized the miners as the source of all authority with regard to the mines, re-enacted their laws, legalized their courts, confirmed their decisions, and provided for the transfer of cases from them to the regular courts, so that the transition of business from the old, imperfect organizations to the regular and complete one now in existence was easy, smooth, and natural. Hiram P. Bennett was elected Delegate to Congress.

On the 1st of May, 1860, the *Rocky Mountain Herald* commenced the issue of a *daily* edition, and three months later the *Rocky Mountain News* followed suit. The overland telegraph reached Fort Kearney toward the end of October, and Julesburg the next year, but was not built up in to Colorado until near the end of 1863. The Consolidated Ditch was finished and water let in on the 10th of July, 1860. About the same time the mint of Clark,

Gruber & Co., of Denver, began to coin money.
This was afterwards bought by the Government, in
pursuance of an act of Congress of 16th April, 1862,
providing for the establishment of a U. S. Branch
Mint at Denver.   In the early part of 1863, Gen.
Geo. W. Lane arrived in Denver, and entered on
his duties as Superintendent of the Mint. It has
never been allowed to coin, only to melt and assay,
and within a year, to purchase and give draft on
U. S. Treasury or sub-treasuries in the East, the
Government of course assuming the cost and risk
of transportation of its bullion across the Plains.   In
August, 1860, the first regular U. S. mail service
was extended to the Mountains.   This was also the
date of the enlistment of the First Colorado Volunteers, afterward transformed into the First Colorado
Cavalry, known in Colorado as the "Pet Lambs,"
of which Jno. P. Slough, now Chief-Justice of New
Mexico, was appointed Colonel.   There was some
irregularity about the raising and especially the
equipping and subsisting of this regiment, so that
they were not recognized and paid as United States
troops until eight months after their enlistment. It
is perhaps doubtful whether or no they would then
have been recognised had they not marched nearly
a thousand miles, and in one hard fought battle,
and two brisk skirmishes, broken and driven from
New Mexico all those lean and hungry Texans, who
called themselves with a delightful humor, "Baylor's
Babes"; who had left San Antonio for the Pike's
Peak gold region about three thousand strong, swallowed Fort Fillmore without winking, rather beaten

Canby at Val Verde, and had since that event been coming northward, covering the country as the frogs did Egypt, and wearing it out.   They had got twenty-five miles north of Santa Fe when they were met by the Pet Lambs.   The Babes and the Lambs each rebounded some five miles from the first shock, which was more like the shock of lightning than of battalions.   The reserves of both sides having come up the next day, the Babes and Lambs each went forth to mortal combat again.   The ground was not unlike the roof of a house ; the Babes reached the ridge-pole first, and by the weight of numbers and the advantage in position, during a seven hours' fight, forced the Lambs back, off the roof.   Night fell upon the scene and the Babes and the Lambs each sought their own corner.   The Lambs found theirs all right, but the Babes did not. It appeared that a part of the Lambs had been there during the fight and destroyed their commissary and transportation, totally.   There being no grub in New Mexico in general way, there certainly was none now since armies had been sustained by her during the Winter, so that the Babes had to go home to get something to eat.   The Lambs accompanied them to the door and wished them a safe journey.   And so ended the war of the Babes and the Lambs in the Rocky Mountains.   All this occurred in March and April, 1862, when Logan was storming Donelson, and Grant, or Sherman, or Buell, or somebody, was winning, or losing, or drawing the bloody game of Shiloh.   Gov. Gilpin always insists that his "Pet Lambs" broke the far left wing of the Rebellion—that they led off in the march of victory organized by the great War Minister.

It would seem that this regiment was most opportunely raised, and that it saved Colorado from Texan invasion. But there was great dissatisfaction with the way in which it had been done, both in Colorado and in Washington. So that between April and May, 1862, Gov. Gilpin was superseded by Dr. John Evans; Secretary Weld by Samuel H. Elbert; Attorney-General Dalliba, who had previously superseded Stoughton, by Samuel E. Browne; Marshal Townsend by A. C. Hunt; and not long afterward, Surveyor-General Case by John Pierce.

A second regiment of volunteers, of which James H. Ford was commissioned Colonel, was enlisted along in 1862, and ordered to Missouri. They were joined there, in May, 1863, by a third regiment raised in Colorado. The two were consolidated, mounted, led by Col. Ford, and to the end of the war, especially in the movements against Price on the occasion of his last invasion of Missouri, were conspicuous where danger was to be met and glory won.

The City of Denver was again incorporated in November, 1861, and this time it included Auraria and Highland, and the charter was made to stick. The town had always had a common school. A second one had been established early in 1861. The M. E. Church, South, and the Catholics had each a place of worship, built for that purpose, before the town was two years of age. The Methodists and the Episcopalians had each an organization, place of meeting, Sunday schools, and regular services. In course of time the M. E. Church, South, seemed to fade away and the Episcopalians bought their church building, enlarged and named it " St. John's in the Wilderness." The Methodists built a church edifice on the sandy banks of Cherry Creek. The rains descended and the floods came in 1864, and washed it away, doubtless that the Scripture might be fulfilled. Then they went up town and erected a noble structure, the handsomest in the City, and not on the sand. So that it stands to this day. A large, brick Seminary was built in 1863-4, which is now self-sustaining if not flourishing. The Mountains were not behind the Valley in establishing anew the religious and educational institutions of the civilization left behind but not abandoned. There were day and evening schools in every cluster of shanties, and all the leading Christian sects had organizations, places of worship, and regular services before the Territory of Colorado was created.

In the second Congressional election, September, 1862, there were three candidates in the field— Hiram P. Bennett, ex-Gov. Wm. Gilpin, and Col. J. M. Francisco. The first represented the Douglas Democracy, indifferent to the fate of the negro but true to the Union; the second was supported by the Abolitionists proper; and the last by the Breckenridge Democracy. Bennett was elected by a large plurality. Early in 1861 a treaty was effected with the Cheyennes and Arapahoes, some of the Chiefs, however, refusing to sign it, by which the United States acquired nearly all the land in the Territory. The Chiefs who refused to sign this treaty have always been sulky, and in 1864, went to war to drive the whites off their land. They need killing. In April, 1863, the heart of Denver was burnt out by a terrible fire, but by the end of the year it had risen from its ashes so much better than before that good citizens audibly wished the balance of the town might be burned over once. Their wish was and was not granted, for in the Spring of 1864, Cherry Creek, which is normally a wide bed of dry, hot sand, rose suddenly one evening about twenty feet, and washed a good portion of the town clear of all incumbrances, goods and chattels, houses and lands, legal fictions and lawsuits ; so that, as Gen. Bowen remarked in a pensive manner, "it flowed unvexed to the sea." Since that no buildings have been built in its bed or on its banks, and people cross it even with fear and trembling.

During the Winter of 1860 a great stampede occurred to the San Juan Mountains, in south-western Colorado. Immense masses of quartz and ore are said to exist there, but the country was almost inaccessible, was very high in altitude, and the gulches had no gold in them to speak of. The consequence was much suffering and some wisdom gained. Not a man was left in the San Juan mines six months after they were first heard of and rushed for. Silver discoveries made a great excitement

6*

also all through 1860.   But nothing was ever done besides the making of a few assays and the shedding of great quantities of ink in their behalf.   We have now approached the period of the great change in mining—when capitalists bought up the quartz mines and proceeded to try their hand.   We shall endeavor to give a clear view of the affair and the results in the succeeding chapter.

CHAPTER VI.

Condition of the Mines at the End of 1863—Transferred to Eastern Capitalists—The April, (1864) Panic in Stocks—Temptation to Speculation in Gold Mining—Why the Miners were generally embarrassed at the End of 1863—Why the Eastern Mining Companies have been comparatively unsuccessful.

DURING the Summer of 1863 a mine or mining interest had occasionally passed from the hands of a Coloradan into those of Eastern capitalists. It was not hard, because Eastern bankers had been in constant receipt of the gold produced by certain mines; and when from a variety of causes the owners of those mines had become considerably involved, they were glad to have their property taken off their hands, indebtedness and all, leaving them a small or large consideration clear. As to the capitalists, they expected, by having the use of money and by working on a large scale so as to economize labor in every branch of the business, to throw all the profits of former mining completely in the shade. The pioneers were generally men of no capital but their muscle and their courage. The mines worked easy on the surface ; windlasses and horse-whims answered for hoisting ; there was but a slight accumulation of water to be drawn off ; the gold was coarse and free in the quartz, from long exposure

to the elements ; fuel was cheap ; there were considerable placer mines, which made money plenty
and times easy, and everything therefore went on
swimmingly. But as the mines grew deeper and
filled with water, increasing the labor of hoisting and
compelling the use of steam for that purpose ; as
fuel and timber became scarce and dear, and the
ores more difficult of treatment—in short, as the
curtailing of facilities and the increase of expense
incident to the necessary expansion of the business
were beyond both the means and ability of mine
operators as a class, they become badly involved and
embarrassed.   Observe how natural and unavoidable was all this.

Well, bankers who had shipped the gold produced
by the mines, and who therefore knew their capacity,
advanced money on them, and eventually came to
own them. It was easy for them, through parties
in the East who were also aware of the extent and
richness of the veins from gold shipments, to organize stock companies for the purchase and working of them. The effect was to arrest mining
generally, and set everybody to establishing title, pro-
curing certificates of yield, and selling out.   A small
army corps of sharp fellows soon created quite an
excitement on the subject in the East, which was
the more easy that greenbacks were plentiful and
terribly depreciated ; and this raged five or six
months ere it flattened out, which it did suddenly
on the 18th of April, 1864.

In the bubble-burst, however, Colorado stocks
fared no worse than others ; and as soon as the panic

had subsided a little, the business was re-commenced both in Colorado and the East. All the mines not sold were bonded, in which condition, of course, they could not be worked. The men who had discovered and steadily developed the country became the most inveterate speculators in the world. This evil still hangs over mining industry like an eclipse, crippling it perhaps more than all else combined. It would seem from past experience that gold mining derives as much of its fascination from the chances it offers for successful speculation, as from its delightfully painful uncertainties of all descriptions, or its honest advantages as a legitimate business. So long as there is a market for mining property, it is incontestable that people will sell rather than work it. It is only when the market is glutted or dull from paucity of returns that any real, earnest effort to make the mines pay is ever thought of. It is pleaded in defence of those who first sold out the mines, and of those who are keeping up the same worthy practice, that quartz mining is impossible without capital. To a great extent it has been so in Colorado ; but the time is coming when, if mining will not pay without drawing assessments from the pockets of stockholders continually, it will be abandoned.

The reasons why capital has been required in Colorado are, that the expense of living and of mining, and the loss in value from the inadequate treatment of the refractory ores, were so great as to exhaust the profits of surface mining, instead of leaving them to be used in furnishing the more costly apparatus required for deeper mining. The great reason that the companies organized with ample capital in 1864, have made out so poorly, and now, ere they have had any dividends, are called on for more capital, is that the cost of living and of work advanced immediately upon the inauguration of their operations one hundred per cent., and nothing until very lately could in the least make it recede. But let us be a little more detailed in statement.

In California quartz mining has generally been conducted by individuals or partnerships instead of by incorporated companies. This is a great advantage to begin with, since people will be more careful in using their own than others' money. They first find out what had best be done, then do it themselves as economically as possible. When gold veins in California have been quartz to a great depth,—not sulphurets, as those of Colorado universally are a short distance from the surface,—they have been worked with the most gratifying success. All improvements have been made with what was taken from the mines, leaving still very large profits, and all the time enhancing the value of the property, because gold veins grow richer and larger as they go down into the ground. But it must be borne in mind that labor, mining supplies, and provisions have been as cheap in California as in the Atlantic States. Neither, in these cases, had they refractory ores to contend with, of which the stamp mill cannot be made to save more than one-half, one-fourth, or one-tenth the value.

Had Colorado been equally as favorably situated in these respects, she never would have carried her mines to an Eastern market,—never would have needed a dollar of foreign capital for their development; but on the contrary would have furnished the ways and means for their working, and paid regular and fat dividends besides, until they were sunk beyond the reach of profitable mining *from this side*. Colorado was not so situated, however. Located in the midst of the Continent, equi-distant from either ocean; five hundred to a thousand miles from civilization in any direction—from any source of supplies; her climate a novelty, making agriculture an entirely new business; afflicted with the pests which always destroy the first few crops of a new country; all she consumed, all her implements and supplies for farming and mining, have been subject to an average tariff of ten cents a pound. This proportionately enhanced the price of labor. At first the mines were worked with little or no expense, and with the richest results. The miners supposed it would always be so, and the money was spent or thrown away as a rule. This is a repetition, but we wish to clear up this point, so must trace the course of mining connectedly. The decomposed quartz of the surface was exhausted the first year, and for the next four the difficulties of caps, pinches, and sulphurets were encountered with varying success, only that the miners seemed to come out second best in the end. It was owing somewhat to inexperience and extravagance; more to the unusual expense of mining as compared with

the same in California or other countries ; most of
all to the refractory character of the ores, that at
the end of 1863 the miners found themselves pretty
generally tied up with a short string.   The mines
were sold in the East ; and now that we had capital,
why did we not succeed ?   Conceding, for the sake
of argument, that we did not, let us answer in all
sincerity.

The civil war in the States had drained the
springs of Western progress ; a nation of producers
had become a destroying and consuming army ; the
labor withdrawn from every field of production, and
the increased consumption incident to a continental
war, had greatly advanced the rates of raw material.
Added to this, and having the same tendency, was
the depreciation in the currency which naturally
followed the failure of the Government to provide
for any considerable portion of current expenses by
taxation.   The war had swallowed up the young
men, the horses, the stock, the transportation of the
great Plains—all that had before contributed to
people, develop and enrich the West.   Under such
auspices opened the season of 1863.   Things grew
worse.   That Summer was remarkable through the
West for an extensive and protracted drouth.   Nearly all the tributaries of the Upper Missouri ran out.
The Platte dried up.   Boats could not ascend the
Missouri above the mouth of the Kaw.   Stocks
grew light on the Missouri River.   The feed was
burnt up by the sun on the Plains, and stocks of
provisions and groceries, of clothing, hardware and
general merchandise, grew lighter in Colorado to-

ward Fall, especially as there was quite a drain to supply the new mines of Montana. About the 20th of October Winter set in—a worse season than all the previous Colorado Winters together. Stock froze by the hundred on the Plains. Supplies going forward were corraled up by the snow and cold, and many of them lost; more did not arrive out till the next year—indeed it is hardly too much to say that machinery, started early in 1864, is not yet done arriving. Prices in Colorado advanced accordingly. Hay and grain were steady for months at from fifteen to twenty cents a pound. Fuel advanced one hundred per cent. in price, and has there maintained itself ever since. The weather was so cold as to force the almost entire suspension of mining. It was during this Winter the developed mines of Colorado changed hands. It was thought—indeed it was *figured* out a hundred times—that by an extension of the business expense might be curtailed, and with improved apparatus and enlarged experience an increased yield secured. Nearly all the companies immediately invested in tremendous quartz machinery,—several of them purchasing stamp mills with all accompanying machinery equal to crushing from fifty to one hundred tons of ore per day—huge establishments with boilers weighing fifteen thousand pounds, 150-horse engines, and from fifty to one hundred stamps weighing eight hundred pounds each, besides any amount of cast-iron pans of various patterns, the whole extravagantly disproportioned to the mines they were intended for. The foun-

dries and machine shops in the States were generally making war *materiel* for the Government—
and this was the first delay. The few that went to
work in the mines were nonplussed in the Spring
by a heavy wet spell. Floods descended and carried away towns ; high water changed the channels
of streams, destroyed ranches and crops, and rendered the Plains impassable till late in the season.
Surface water united with the currents from below
in the mines and drove out the miners. Transportation was scarce and high, but it was going forward
at some rate when the Indians on the Plains declared war, destroyed trains, attacked coaches, and
cut off all communication for two months in the
very best of the season. Colorado had already furnished two full regiments of volunteers, and in the
heart of 1864 twelve hundred three months' men
were called out to chastise the Indians. This regiment was permitted to strike a single blow on the
eve of its disbandment, and the rebound from that
struck the Platte Route again in the succeeding
mid-Winter, desolating it for two hundred and fifty
miles, and again cutting off all communication for
two months. Freights kept rising, and so did provisions, supplies and wages. The result was that
by the time the mammoth mills and machinery had
arrived out and been set up, the treasuries of the
companies were completely drained ; and the long
abandonment of the mines having allowed the
walls to soften and fall in—they never having been
half supported in the early mining—there was no
resource at hand but the pockets of the stockhold-

ers. But few of them had exercised the commonest prudence or sagacity. They had not counted on time as an element of success, had not taken account of the actual or possible obstacles to even eventual success. Some of the companies had been organized on ridiculous bases, with watered capitals, on fragments of mines scattered over a township, under the excitement of false hopes, dishonestly raised ; others for speculation solely. Not content with sending men to Colorado to represent their interests who were in many cases most unfit for it, they insisted on managing mining by telegraph from New York and Boston. Many invested in new and novel machinery on the strength of some petty test made in the East.

But above and worse than all else among the causes of the comparative failure of the Colorado mining companies, was the fact that they started out on a wrong system. It is given up that the best stamp mills save only about one-fourth of the gold in the ores, wasting all the copper and silver, which together in many cases are worth nearly if not quite as much as the gold in value. Then was a stamp mill the worst investment that could have been made for the purpose sought. This was not so well known then as now. Calculations were based on the yields of the mills the preceding Summer, which were good. Neither could any one foresee the extraordinary rise in prices, the severe Winters, wet Springs, and Indian troubles which then occurred for the first time.

These are some of the reasons why the compa-

nies have not been able to realize dividends. Of
their actual condition a view will be given in another
place. With the close of the war, and the consequent return of the enterprise of the country to its
natural channels ; with peace on the Plains, good
crops, cheap freights, and general low prices, including wages ; and especially with an improved
treatment for the ores in connection with recent silver discoveries, a considerable degree of prosperity
and improvement may not unreasonably be looked
for in the immediate future. With the advent of
a railroad from the States, which will have been
finished to near Denver during the coming Summer, and the introduction of a metallurgical treatment that shall extract *all the value* from the ores,
the success of Colorado mining will doubtless surpass the utmost that even enthusiasts have dared
to hope.

But in stating why the companies of 1864 have
not realized dividends, we have really given the history of the past two years—1864–5—and indeed of
1866 to a great extent, and perhaps we may here
as appropriately as anywhere close this chapter.

CHAPTER VII.

Gilpin County—Present Condition of the Improved Lodes—Names of Mining Companies—Amount of Development—Condition of Mines and Mills—Machinery—Processes, &c.

Gilpin is the smallest as it is the richest county of Colorado. It embraces North Clear Creek and its tributary gulches,* Gregory, with its feeders, Eureka, Nevada, and Spring; Russell, with its branches, Lake, Willis, Elkhorn, Missouri Flats, Illinois, Leavenworth, Sawpit, Graham, Davenport; Chase, widening soon into Quartz Valley, again narrowing and called, Peck; and Missouri, the latter the only one of the group which is not of the group, coming, as it does, from the ridge that divides North Clear from South Boulder Creek, while the others come from the one that divides North from South Clear Creek. North Clear Creek is not far from twenty miles in length, and is formed by the natural intersection of half a dozen little brooks, which used to constitute what was called Twelve-Mile Diggings. It is a roaring torrent when the

---

* Gulch is the distinctive appellation among miners of those tributaries of the creeks which convey into them the melting snows, but for the greater part of the year, are dry. Where they are washed for gold, water has to be brought to them in canals for that purpose.

snows are melting and running out, and for about three months of each year, furnishes unlimited water-power; carrying in the Winter, however, no more than two hundred inches. Its course is south-eastward and it empties into South Clear Creek fourteen miles above Golden City, so that it and all that is connected with it, are well within the Foot-hills.

About half way from its mouth to its source, Gregory Gulch comes down to it from the west, flanked at slight distance by Russell on the south and Chase on the north. We say comes *down*, for in the course of two miles it falls more than a thousand feet. At its head is the town of Nevada; half way down, marking the confluence of Eureka and Spring Gulches, is Central City, the county seat and the metropolis of the mines; at its mouth, Black Hawk, noted for its quartz mills, crowds the assembled hills. These towns are all one in reality, being joined together by nearly continuously built-up main gulch streets. Central City and Black Hawk each sustain separate municipal governments, however. The population of the county is nearly ten thousand, and is mostly confined to Gregory and Nevada, Spring and Eureka Gulches—the first two the same gulch under different names.

The bordering and wedging hills were densely wooded when the mines were discovered, but the trees were small, and few now remain within five or six miles around. This, with the pock-marks made by prospectors on every hill-side, and the fierceness and thoroughness with which the gulches have been turned inside out, gives the country about Central anything but an inviting look. Water was early brought here from Fall River, a stream west of, parallel with, and rising higher in the Range than North Clear Creek, in what is called the Consolidated Ditch, which delivered on Quartz Hill, between Nevada and Russell Gulches, one hundred and fifty inches of water. This was to run the toms and sluices in the gulches. The mills have generally used steam power from the first. The rapid consumption of the wood within reach has already caused search for a substitute. There are two ways of meeting the wants of the future in this respect. Hydraulic may in great measure be substituted for steam power by the construction of a reservoir at the head of Fall River—which locality almost seems to have been made for such purpose so well adapted is it — and the requisite enlargement of the Consolidated Ditch. Upon full and careful examination of the ground, it has been estimated that the expenditure of $100,000 would bring enough water to the top of Quartz Hill, so that, by dividing it into three channels thence to Black Hawk, it would pass over all the principal lodes, giving 120 powers of 33 1-3 feet head and 300 cubic inches volume, equal to forty horses, and from Black Hawk to the mouth of North Clear Creek, thirty more of the same head and greater volume. This canal to be covered and a railway laid on it, so as to make the large tract of woodland between Central City and the Range tributary to the mines. The reservoir would be filled every

Spring while the snows are melting and there is an inmeasurable surplus of water, thus not robbing the lower Fall River country of its natural stream. Then, if mining should become a separate branch of business from the treatment of the ores, as it no doubt ought and will, these powers to be used for hoisting, crushing, and dressing, the ore to be taken to the coal-beds at the base of the Mountains for treatment, or the coal to be brought up, either of which would nearly dispense with the use of wood-fuel. But it would necessitate the construction of a railway from Black Hawk *via* Clear Creek Kanyon to Golden City. A careful survey has demonstrated the entire practicability of this project, the grade, with three tunnels—aggregate length, 3000 feet—averaging about 100 feet per mile for the distance, twenty-one miles. In view of the benefits that would result from their completion, these great enterprises are the most feasible of any we know of. The prospect is that the consumption of fuel will go on increasing until there will be no escape from one or the other or both of them.

It is within a radius of one and a half miles from Central City that all the lodes and improvements mentioned hereafter in this chapter, occur. Tumbled headlong into so small a compass are Bobtail, Bates, Gregory, Mammoth, Quartz, Casto, and Gold Hills, with their complicated net-work of rich veins, to say nothing of as many more with no special names. The outlying districts of the county, and there are some, must be consigned to a separate chapter. For precise information with regard to the boundaries, streams, towns, and topography of the county, the reader is referred to an accurate map on a large scale, delineated from careful surveys by Messrs. Morse & Hill of Central City. The examination of the mines of Gilpin County, a report of which follows, was made in August 1866, by the writer in person.

GREGORY LODE.

The Black Hawk Gold Mining Company have 500 feet on the Gregory, being No's 1, 2, 3, 16 and 17 west; 200 on the Foot & Simmons, 250 on the Gregory Extension, 76 on the Bobtail, and a great deal of less developed mining property. It is with that which is productive we have to do. They are working 1, 2 and 3 on the Gregory, running a level 380 feet from the surface. The first level is the bottom of the old mine, and is about 300 feet from the surface. Above that there is still much virgin ground. The lower level will soon be finished, exposing ground nearly 100 feet deep by 300 long, and in all probability two crevices, the entire length, from five to fifteen feet apart. These will doubtless come together at a greater depth. The Gregory main crevice varies in width from two to four feet; the other crevice is perhaps half as large. The working shaft is on No. 2, and is strongly timbered. A six-inch pump removes the water from the entire mine. On No. 1 there is also a shaft, now 330 feet deep, opening on the surface in a 20-stamp mill. The hoisting and pumping are done by a 150-horse

7

engine, which also furnishes motive power for the mill. The Foot & Simmons mine shows an average crevice a foot in width, is run by the Consolidated Gregory engine adjoining, and is in very good shape, worked by regular levels, the first two of which are exhausted ; the third, at a depth of 260 feet, now furnishing stoping ground. The main shaft is being carried down in time for the fourth level. Dump cars convey the ore to the shaft on tramways, there is little or no water in the mine, and it is worked very economically.* In the Bobtail mine, operations are suspended for want of a pump. The last work done was excavating a level 400 feet from the surface, and taking out the back. In the floor a crevice is exposed for 64 feet, three feet wide—nearly half of it pure ore. There is a large engine-house, with a 40-horse engine, on the Bobtail mine. On Gregory 16 and 17, there are shafts 60 and 90 feet deep respectively, both of them on good veins of ore. Nothing has been done on them for two or three years. On the Gregory Extension a shaft has been sunk 285 feet, and a level run near the bottom in either direction 40 or 50 feet. The crevice is yet rather pinched, the ore badly mixed with poor rock.† The mine furnishes just enough water to run the hoisting engine. A wooden railway and car convey the ore 300 yards to the mill in Black Hawk. The Com-

---

* It has since been abandoned for the present ; cause, the crevice is too narrow to make its working a paying business.

† Work has since been stopped on this mine and the hoisting engine sold.

pany have a large, frame, stamp-mill in the heart of
Black Hawk—sixty 880-lb. stamps.   The crushed
material runs over short stationary copper plates
on to shaking tables of the Keith pattern, whence
it passes into Cornish buddles for concentration.
The engine is 150-horse, and is supplied with water
from North Clear Creek, which passes between the
engine-house and mill.   A steam pump and sufficient hose provide reasonable guarantee against
accidents by fire.   This mill and that on the
Gregory have produced during the Summer not far
from $3,000 a week.   The Company have twenty
stamps not yet set up, and a large amount of mining supplies.   It is at present under the management, in Colorado, of W. L. Lee, one of the original
owners, still a very large stockholder, and an in-
comparable *business* man.

The Consolidated Gregory Gold Mining Company
have 500 feet on the Gregory Lode, adjoining that
of the Black Hawk Company on the west, being
Nos. 4, 5, 6, 7 and 8.   The main shaft is on the
west end of 5, is six by eleven feet in the clear,
very securely timbered with eight and ten inch
timbers, and is 315 feet deep.   The shaft contains
a nine-inch pump, which easily drains the mine.
There is a hoisting shaft on 7, 280 feet deep, and
between 5 and 7 a winze for ventilation.   There is
also a shaft on 4, the bottom of which is expected
to be intersected by level No. 2, the latter, under
the main shaft, 290 feet from the surface.   All these
shafts enter permanently into the plan of mining,
5 and 7 for working the mine, 4 and 6, winzes for

ventilating. Level No. 1 is 230 feet from the surface, and has ground above it only west of the shaft. It is now run 220 feet, and is to be pushed to the west end of the mine. The ground above this level, westward from the shaft, will average 50 feet in depth, and from two to three in width. Level No. 2 is 290 feet from the surface, and is now in about 55 feet west and 66 east, to be driven to the ends of the mine, the back stoped out, the main shaft always sunk in advance, levels run, and the process repeated every ten fathoms forever. Forty men are drifting and sinking shafts, and enough ore is being taken out to run a 60-stamp mill. Worked on the system inaugurated, there is practically no limit to the amount of ore that may be raised, and at the least possible expense. The mine was formerly owned by half a dozen men, who gouged it out as came handiest, and it has taken much time and labor to get it into working shape. The brothers Rule are the present managers—old mine Captains of long experience in England and Mexico. What they have done may well serve as a model for others. On the surface there is a shaft and engine-house over No. 5, 30 by 70 feet in dimensions, containing a 45-horse engine, and machinery for pumping and hoisting. A line of shafting 183 feet long runs the shaft on 7, which has a house over it 30 by 60. All the machinery is well put up, and answers its purpose. The Company, like nearly all other Colorado companies, purchased a 100-stamp mill in 1864, which was never brought further than the Missouri River. They are now looking to matting, as the treatment for their ores. The smelting works of James E. Lyon & Co. will be described elsewhere. They are now manufacturing most of the ore taken out by the Company.* James E. Lyon is Managing Director. M. B. Hayes has personal supervision in Colorado.

The Narragansett Gold Mining Company own 400 feet on the Gregory, adjoining that described above on the west, being Nos. 9, 10, 11 and 12. Two shafts, located about centrally on the mine, are sunk to a depth of 360 feet. Two hundred and eighty feet from the surface occurs level No. 1, driven nearly or quite the whole length of the mine, and disclosing a 20-inch ore crevice all the way; 80 feet lower, level No. 2 has been driven nearly or quite the whole length of the mine, also disclosing an average ore crevice as above. One hundred feet west of the main hoisting and pump shaft, a winze has been excavated between the levels for ventilation. Above the upper level most of the ground is considered worked out. A seven-inch pump drains the mine, which produces an immense quantity of water. A large stone mill is built on the property, into which the ore is hoisted from the main shaft. The mine furnishes the necessary water, the mill contains forty 880-lb. stamps and a few iron pans, and is driven by an 84-horse engine. The Company ceased operations in June, 1866, with the view of adopting a better treatment for their ores. Eben Smith has had the supervision of the

---

*They have since been consolidated with the Consolidated Gregory Company's other property.

affairs of the Company in Colorado; and supposing a stamp mill to be the best treatment for the ores, which it is not, there are no better works in the country.

The Rocky Mountain Gold Mining Company come next, and own 13 and 14. They have two shafts on 13, one more than 200 feet deep, usual size and well timbered, exposing an ore vein from eight to eighteen inches wide for the lower 75 feet, and having a 20-inch ore crevice in the bottom. Another shaft on 13, 66 feet west, has been sunk to 160 feet in depth, developing an ore vein in the bottom of ten inches; 160 feet from the surface a level, driven 35 feet west, lays bare an average ore vein of twelve inches. There is a whim-house on the surface 30 by 60, horse power used for hoisting; crevice barely struck on 14, seventy tons of ore out. The Company own a 20-stamp mill in Black Hawk, which has been closed since 1863. Nothing has been done on the mine since June, 1865, no agent having been in Colorado since that time.

No. 15 is owned by ———, and is not much improved. Nos. 16 and 17 belong to the Black Hawk Company, and have been noticed. They carry the vein from Gregory Gulch to within forty feet of Packard Gulch.

The Benton Gold Mining Company here take the vein, though under another name—that of "The Michigan Tunnel Property"—and run 600 feet, crossing the Mammoth Lode near the top of Mammoth Hill, and extending 100 feet beyond. This Company, under the management of Jonathan Cox, a mine captain of great experience, are sinking a shaft in Packard Gulch, about 40 feet from the east end of the mine—now down 60 feet, and so over-flown with water from cross-courses as to necessi-tate the putting in of a six-inch pump, with a large engine, 60-horse—to drive it, which is being done.* The shaft shows a vein of ore 14 inches wide, which yielded $108 a ton by actual test in Lyon's smelt-ing works. Here the lode, going west, seems to fork, or rather a spur puts out to the right, diverg-ing from the main vein 40 feet in 100 of lineal con-tinuation. There are two feet of ore in the floor of the adit on this vein all the way, but it has not yet proved rich, assaying about $30 a ton only. The adit on the main vein has been driven 220 feet west, intersecting there the main shaft, and con-tinuing 20 feet beyond. In the floor of this adit the regular ore vein appears, but there is none in the back. The main shaft is continued 37 feet below the adit, being 120 feet deep in all. It is twelve feet between walls, but shows as yet an ore vein of only six inches. The Company have ma-chinery for a mill of fifteen stamps and six pans at Atchison.

The Bissell Gold Mining Company are working a vein called Bissell, next west, and no doubt an ex-tension of the Gregory. They own 300 feet, and are down 40, with a three-foot crevice, ore just coming in. The Company also own 300 feet on the Haman Lode, Casto Hill; have a shaft 105 feet deep, the vein a mixture of ore, quartz, and

---

* It has since been completed, and works to perfection.

country rock, five feet wide ; also 300 feet on the Wolverine Lode, in Illinois Central District ; shaft 50 feet deep, twelve feet between walls, the crevice ore, quartz and country rock. They are operating only on the Bissell and Wolverine, and have no mill nor machinery. This is as far west as the Gregory vein is worked. Dr. Bissell, of Central, is agent for the Bissell Company.

The Briggs Gold Mining Company adjoin the Black Hawk Company on the east, are located in Gregory Gulch, and own and work 250 feet on the Gregory and the same on the Briggs, a parallel vein, from twelve to forty feet distant from the Gregory. Both crevices have been generally worked out to a depth of 150 feet. There are two shafts, the east one the usual size for pump, ladder, and bucket ways, sunk and admirably timbered 230 feet deep. There is a mine at each end of this, much deeper, and each supplied with a pump ; hence there is little trouble from water in the Briggs mine. The west shaft is sunk and curbed 120 feet deep. Both of them open in the mill, which is a large frame, filled in with brick, containing fifty 880-lb. stamps, two large buddles, two Dodge crackers, a 100-horse engine, tanks, drums, and other machinery. The material runs over thick copper plates and into Cornish buddles, is concentrated, and the rock thrown away, the mineral being placed aside for future use. Since the new mill started—February, 1866—the mine has been in the poorest stratum of ore ever known in it. There has been ore on the south crevice for 80 feet of the east end, and on the north crevice for a little distance in the west end. From the east shaft west, on the north crevice, there was also some pay 100 feet deeper than that on the west end. The last clean-up showed a decided improvement. The mine has always paid so well and uniformly that the necessity of sinking down and back-stoping has not been felt. This pinch in the crevice, together with the difficulty of fully supplying the large mill, will compel it. So far the new mill has only about paid expenses; but a good deal of poor stuff had to be used to keep it going. It took sometime to get the plates in order, and there have been construction expenses to meet. They are working forty hands, at an average weekly expense of about $1,200. The Briggs mine has been one of the most, if not the most successful of the Colorado quartz mines. During the first year of the present Company's existence, its published financial statement showed $100,000 profits. Mr. Reynolds of Central is the Colorado agent of the Company.

The Smith & Parmelee Gold Company join the Briggs on the east, have 300 feet on the north, or Gregory Extension crevice, (so called) and 800 on the south or Briggs crevice (so called). They have much other valuable mining property, but it is with this chiefly we have to do. On the surface the two crevices run nearly together at one end, and are 24 feet apart at the other ; as sunk upon, they diverge from each other. The north crevice is worked out perhaps 140 feet deep and 200 long, and has a shaft 160 feet deep. It has been

7*

nearly full of water for three years. The south crevice is worked out perhaps 200 feet long, in the west end 250 feet deep, in the east 310. The east shaft is now 360 feet deep, the west 305, both being sunk to a depth of 400 feet. The west shaft has a six-inch pump, and a cross-cut is being run from it to the north crevice 250 feet from the surface ; this is now in 42 feet, and is supposed to be nearly through. Both shafts in the south crevice being 400 feet deep, a level will be excavated connecting them, and a cross-cut will then be run through into the north crevice, and that undermined by driving a level the entire length of it if practicable, without a shaft for ventilation, when an immense body of ore will be exposed. The ore is hoisted out of the east shaft which is run by a line of shafting from the mill. The west shaft opens directly in the mill in front of the batteries. The average width of these crevices is 30 inches, which is of course an estimate—only exploitation can determine the width of any crevice definitely. The mill has twenty-five 500-lb. stamps driven by a 25-horse engine, and supplied with water by Gregory Run. The old stationary copper plates are used. During the seven months next prior to February 17th, 1866, the mill produced 3,611 ounces of gold, coin value $59,580. It was shut down to look up a better process for treatment, but the opening of the mine was continued. On the 1st of August enough stamps were started again to pay expenses. The first three weeks' clean up from ten stamps was 130 ounces. Subsequently the company were running four mills very successfully. D. D. Belden, is the agent in Colorado.

The New York Gold Mining Company join the Smith & Parmelee on the Gregory Extension, east; they have 250 feet in length, a shaft 208 feet in depth, developing in the bottom a handsome ore vein. The property is in dispute with the Smith & Parmelee Company, and nothing has been done on it since early in 1865. Next east are the 250 feet of the Black Hawk Company, then some territory owned by private parties, 250 feet belonging to the United States Gold Mining Company, and 400 feet belonging to the Manhattan and Gregory Companies. Thus we have given a sketch of the Gregory vein under different names for about 4,000 feet in length, and the Bissell Company are no doubt working the continuation of it west under still another name. Judged by its production, the Gregory stands at the head of all the Colorado lodes. The New York Company also have 150 feet on the Fisk, No. 5 and half of No. 6 east; a shaft perhaps 130 feet deep, with a considerable level and very large vein of ore; also a mill in Black Hawk of 35 stamps, steam and water power, a 1,400 foot flume and a 34 1-2-foot overshot wheel. The mill is leased to the Gunnell Company, the New York Company not being at work. J. B. Fitzpatrick, of Black Hawk, represents the Company in Colorado.

THE MAMMOTH LODE.

Commencing at the west end of development, on the east bank of Spring Gulch, Harley B. Morse, of Central City, owns 1,282 feet; has eight shafts, from fifteen to fifty feet deep each, disclosing a dirt and quartz crevice all the way.

Jerome Riggs & Company, of New York, own the next 200 feet, and have two shafts, one 130, and one 90 feet deep; have a good show, but being on the top of Mammoth Hill, must go deeper for the ore.

The National Gold Mining Company own the next 233 feet east; shaft 280 feet deep, two crevices, each six feet wide—key-rock or horse between, eight feet wide. The Company were organized in 1864, but never have done anything.

The Gold Rock Mining Company own the next 260 feet east; shaft on the east end of the mine, 100 feet deep, usual size, five by eleven in the clear; seven feet between walls, five-foot dirt and quartz crevice. They are now sinking ten feet a week. They have a mill on the lode 30 by 70, with Dodge crackers and Cornish rollers for crushing; also a 30-horse engine and machinery, not yet set up. They expect to dress and smelt the ores. The hoisting is now done with a windlass. They will get water for the mill from the Lake and Packard Gulch, both near by. The surface dirt used to yield $20 a ton. The Company also own 1,000 feet on the Pendleton Lode, in Russell Gulch, and have a shaft on it fifty feet deep, with a six-foot crevice of galena and iron pyrites. They are not working it now, but will soon do so. The next 600 feet on the Mammoth are owned by three or four different parties, and are not much improved; shafts twenty or thirty feet deep along, and the crevice generally struck.

The Mammoth Gold Mining Company own the next 300 feet, on which is a shaft 132 feet deep, six feet in width of ore in the bottom, copper and iron pyrites and sulphurets, which pays in the Keith furnace $50 to $60 a ton. The next and last 400 feet are owned by the Black Hawk Company and Riggs & Co., who have on it three shafts, 90, 100, and 183 feet deep respectively.

The Mammoth is thus seen to be opened for 3,275 feet on the surface, and it is thought not improbable that the Bobtail is a continuation of the same vein, displaced laterally about 100 feet. It discloses the largest crevice generally and the longest, indicating that it is the strongest vein in this locality, and it is appropriately named "Mammoth." It is not unlikely that it crosses Spring Gulch west, and as the Illinois Lode is finally lost in the cap of Quartz Hill.

THE BOBTAIL LODE.

The Bobtail Gold Mining Company own 433 1-3 feet running east from the little ravine which divides Gregory and Bobtail Hills. They have a shaft house on the west end of the mine 30 by 50, exclusive of a stone engine-room 18 by 30, containing a 50-horse engine and complete hoisting apparatus. A level has been run the whole length of the mine, 135 feet from the surface at the west end and 245 feet at the east. Above this, in the west end, is virgin ground, 100 by 160 feet, rather pinched vein, but it is believed will pay for taking out.   Sixty-six feet below, another level has been started from the east shaft each way, and run 20 feet west and 54 feet east, showing a good ore vein throughout.   An incline has been driven from the shaft-house to the east shaft, striking the latter 171 feet from the surface.   They expect to bring out the ore from the eastern portion of the mine through this incline. Two shafts are to be worked in connection with the incline, one 54 feet from the east end of the mine, 320 feet deep, and one in the center of the mine, 195 feet deep ; there is another shaft 170 feet deep, under the shaft-house, through which ore from the west end of the mine will be raised directly into the shaft-house.   The east shaft has been in cap for 100 feet, but the crevice is now opening out. The centre shaft has never yet been worked by the Company, and the bottom is full of water.   The west shaft has been in cap 40 feet, but is also opening out.   All the shafts are to be sunk, and the mine worked by levels and back-stoping.   The mine was formerly owned and gouged out by Tom, Dick and Harry, and the Company have been at work since November, 1864, getting it in shape.   Six or seven hundred tons of ore have been taken out, and run by custom mills, with not very satisfactory results, being refractory.   The Bobtail, Sterling, Black Hawk, Brastow and Sensenderfer Companies, and Mr. Field, together owning 767 feet on the Bobtail, are putting in a six-inch pump,* which is expected to

---

* After much bother this pump was got well going about New Years.

drain the whole lode. The Bobtail Company have been badly troubled with gulch and surface water, and have obviated the difficulty by a bed-rock tunnel in the gulch 130 feet long, conveying off the surface water before it can seep into the mine. The Company have no mill nor treating machinery. A. N. Rogers of Central, is superintendent. This Company have not shown the confidence and energy which the great value of their property would seem to warrant; they have either never had a sufficient capital, or else have been unwilling to use it liberally.

The Sterling Gold Mining Company own 66 2-3 feet on the Bobtail, next east of the property last above described. The mine is worked out to a depth of 365 feet, and has a 30-inch pay-vein its entire length; 700 tons of ore out for which they have been offered $70 a ton. They hoist with power from the Black Hawk Company's engine, on the territory next east of them. They have 100 feet each on the Fisk and Bates Lodes; a shaft house and shaft 185 feet deep on the first, well timbered and supplied with ladders to the bottom; a shaft thoroughly timbered on the last, 100 feet in depth. They have a steam 15-stamp mill in Chase Gulch in running order. E. C. Gould of Black Hawk is the agent. The Black Hawk Company own the 76 feet adjoining the Sterling east, and it has been noticed elsewhere.

The Brastow Mining Company own next east, 66 2-3 feet, having an old shaft 400 feet deep, not now used, and a new shaft 400 feet deep, five by ten

in the clear, and well timbered.   The mine is generally worked out to a depth of 400 feet.   The ore
vein in the bottom is 24 inches wide the whole
length, and the ore runs from $35 to $70 a ton,
under stamps.   Sixty-eight tons were lately sold to
go to Swansea, Wales, for $100 a ton.*   The Com-
pany expect to sell their best ores regularly to the
Swansea men.   They have a shaft-house 40 by 45,
with an L covering the old shaft.   The hoisting
power is got from the Black Hawk Company's
engine adjoining.   There are now 350 tons of ore
out.   In twelve weeks 420 tons were raised with
five drills, ten-hour day-shifts only.   The Company
also own 926 feet on the Clay County Lode, in
Lake Gulch, with one shaft 75 feet deep, and one
200, both in cap.   This lode paid as largely as any
in the country on the surface.   The Company also
have 260 feet on the Nottaway Lode, in Russell
Gulch, shaft 60 feet deep ; also a mill in Lake
Gulch, frame, calculated for thirty 750-lb. stamps
and twenty Dodge pans, with a 50-horse engine,
machinery not put up.   If Vivian & Sons do not
purchase the ores, they will put up a few stamps
and some dressing machinery and smelt.   H. B.
Brastow of Lake Gulch is agent, and part owner.

The Sensenderfer Gold Mining Company own the
128 feet next east of the Brastow Company on the
Bobtail.   Their mine is pretty much worked out to
a depth of 400 feet.   The crevice seems to divide

---

*Twenty tons have arrived and been treated in Swansea, the re-
sult being about $300 in value per ton, according to the best author-
ity at our service.

near the center of the mine ; one fork is called Branch, of which the Company have pre-empted 800 feet, and upon which they have drifted eighty. The ore vein throughout the mine averages 24 inches in width. There are two working shafts, with an engine, hoisting machinery, house, etc. Seventy tons of ore have been sold to James E. Lyon (of the smelting or matting works), for $85 a ton. The Company have a 20-stamp mill in the upper part of Black Hawk, with steam and water power, in good order, running and paying. The property has not been worked more than half the time, but has produced $100,000 in the last two or three years, John Sensenderfer of Black Hawk is agent and large owner. No pay has ever been struck east of this mine on the Bobtail, although the effort has not been wanting. The Clinton Gold Mining Company about a year ago sank a shaft 100 feet on No. 9 east, but it is thought they were not on the crevice. They became discouraged, and quit. H. B. Brastow is the Clinton Company's representative. The Bobtail is considered the richest of the Colorado gold lodes.

THE GUNNELL LODE.

The Gunnell Gold Mining Company, own 450 feet on the Gunnell Lode, including No. 1 east of Discovery and running thence, west. The main shaft, 163 feet from the east end of the mine, is 438 feet deep and sinking, and underlies to the south about 100 feet in that distance ; is well timbered, and contains a six-inch pump, now worked successfully for fifteen months. East of this shaft the ground is chiefly worked out to a depth of 300 feet. Seventy feet lower is a level, east, 150 feet long, the back worked out ; an ore vein of eighteen inches in the floor the whole length. Sixty feet lower another level is being driven east ; the ore vein in the back and floor averages eighteen inches in width. In the shaft there are two feet of ore. West of the main shaft the mine is generally worked out to a depth of 400 feet and a length of 200 ; working down on this territory now. Half the length there is an ore vein of fifteen inches, the remainder in cap. This mine has yielded 500 ounces of gold per month for the past year. The west end of it has been more or less worked out by former owners, but has never been touched by the Company ; one shaft on it 100 feet deep, and one 280 ; both paid well on the surface. On the mine are shaft houses, smithshop, magazine, office, engine-house, with a 35-horse engine, and hoisting and pumping machinery complete. The Company have an old mill of eighteen stamps in Nevada Gulch, in running order, and sometimes in use ; they lease the New York Company's mill in Black Hawk. In 1864 they purchasd the machinery throughout for a 100-stamp mill, and built a stone building in Black Hawk 50 by 175. The stamps and batteries are at this mill building, but some portion of the machinery was sold to pay freight charges on the Missouri River. The mill is not likely ever to be completed, because the Company can get along without it until something better shall have been eliminated. John B. Fitzpatrick, of Black Hawk, is the agent of the Company.

The Central Gold Mining Company, own 200 feet on the Gunnell, and have a shaft 180 feet deep, with a crevice of fourteen inches of ore. The shaft is in good order, except that the whim-house has been blown off. The surface of the mine is pretty well hogged out, and it has not been worked for two years. The Company also own 200 feet on the Prize Lode, Gold Hill, on which are three shafts, 90, 165, and 185 feet in depth respectively. The vein of ore is generally from two to three feet wide, but badly broken up and mixed ; the deepest shaft shows it much better for the last ten feet. There are shaft-houses on the mine, and a whim for hoisting. Nothing has been done on it for fifteen months. The Company also own 380 feet on the Rhoderick Dhu, Quartz Hill ; three shafts, 100, 120, and 220 feet deep respectively. In about half the mine there is a two-foot vein of ore, but of the most refractory nature. Ninety feet from the surface is a level 250 feet long, showing an average vein of ore most of the way. On the mine are shaft-houses and a small engine for hoisting. Work was stopped in March, 1865. The Company have a 20-stamp mill at the mouth of Nevada Gulch, in complete working order, but idle ; also a pan mill, near by, with twelve pans, engine and gearing complete— has not been run for three years ; also complete machinery for a new mill of forty stamps and twenty pans, lying on Quartz Hill by the Rhoderick Dhu, not set up. All this property is lying idle, but is good, and probably will not long remain idle. J. B. Fitzpatrick is the agent.

The University Gold Mining Company own 143 feet on the Gunnell. A shaft, now 276 feet deep, in good shape, is being sunk, and there are about 600 tons of splendid ore out ; there is a two-foot vein of ore in the shaft, a little irregular. A 15-horse engine is being put up for hoisting. Two hundred feet from the surface, a level was run the whole length of the mine, showing an average ore vein of eighteen inches, which has been mostly taken out. The Company have 100 feet on the Fisk, and 100 on the Foote & Simmons, neither of them much improved ; also 200 feet on the Kansas Lode, in Nevada, the surface of which has been hogged out by former owners—not yet worked by the Company ; also a 15-stamp mill in Black Hawk. The Company will treat their ores by some of the improved processes—probably Keith's. Robert W. Mead, of Black Hawk, is the agent.

The Cook Gold Mining Company own 66 feet on the Gunnell ; have a shaft 250 feet deep, and sinking—in cap at present. The surface has been worked out to a depth of 150 feet. The shaft is doubtless on a pinch in the vein, as well as in cap. There is on the mine an engine-house, with engine and hoisting machinery—no mill. Charles Crosby is the agent. The Company have some other slightly developed mining property.

The Gunnell Central Gold Mining Company have 195 feet on the Gunnell ; two shafts, 180 and 220 feet deep. The surface is worked out to a depth of 180 feet. In the deep shaft there is a 12-inch vein of ore, and a level has been started in the bottom. There is an engine-house, with an 8-horse engine and hoisting rig complete on the mine. The Company also have 500 feet on the Casto—Wright's discovery—with a shaft 122 feet deep; three feet of pure ore exposed by the shaft for 80 feet in depth; also 500 feet on the Western Lode, between Prosser and Eureka Gulches—shaft 60 feet deep, showing a two-foot vein—the crevice developed in two other places. The Company have a mill at the mouth of Prosser Gulch, with 18-horse engine, 24 stamps, in running order; there is room in the mill for 24 Freiberg pans. Colonel James Baxter, of Central, is the agent; not now at work.

The remainder of the Gunnell Lode, we believe, is owned by individuals. Mr. Coleman has 155 feet, with a shaft 250 feet deep and in pay—also an engine-house and engine; has a 12-stamp mill, with a large engine and boiler, in Eureka Gulch, near the mine. Not at work now. No other parties are at work on the Gunnell save those mentioned.

THE BURROUGHS LODE.

The Ophir Gold Mining Company have 462 feet together on the Burroughs, including Discovery claim, and 100 feet toward the west end of the lode, undeveloped. The mine is considered worked out to a depth of 300 feet. It was the famous "Pat Casey Property," and produced immensely before the present owners purchased it. There are four shafts, A, 174, B, 343, C, 486, D, 320 feet deep. The Company are working now only in B and C.

In C they were in cap 150 feet; the last 70 feet show an ore vein from twenty inches to three feet wide. At the bottom of the deep shaft a level has been run 100 feet each way. West, the vein is badly split up; east, there is an average ore vein of thirty inches—they are now back-stoping this out. Shaft B is 72 feet east of C. At a depth of 300 feet they had a cap of twenty feet, and since then have had a vein of ore twenty inches in width. Shaft A is 115 feet east of B, and shows the same vein at 174 feet from the surface as B at 320, and C at 416. It is believed it strikes upward again west of the deep shaft, as the same vein is found 140 feet west at a depth of 320 feet. The west end of the mine has never been worked much. The B shaft is to be pushed down to the 480-foot level, and used while a pump is being put into C shaft. The old mill building in the gulch is to be moved on to the lode for an engine, pump, and shaft-house.* The present houses are of no account. A 12-horse engine does the hoisting. A railway four or five hundred feet long takes the ore to the mill in the gulch. The mill is of wood, contains 24-stamps and crushes forty to fifty tons a week, now yielding $35 to $40 a ton on the average. The Company also own a 20-stamp mill, steam power, in Chase Gulch,—in running order, though not now used. They have near by it a considerable property on Gregory Second, with two shafts, 80 and 150 feet deep, in good shape, but in cap; a wooden railway takes the ore to the mill. This property

---

* This calculation has been carried out during the past Winter.

has not been worked for two years. The Company have also 200 feet on the Kansas; a tunnel runs nearly in to it, striking the lode 50 feet from the surface; there are two shafts, each about 125 feet deep, which have never been worked by the present owners. They also have 400 feet on the Sullivan, and other slightly improved property. Altogether, this is one of the first properties in the country, at work and paying. Mr. E. Humphrey, of Nevada, is the agent, and he is a good boy.

The Gilpin Gold Mining Company adjoin the Ophir on the east; they own 262 1-2 feet, with two shafts, 350 and 420 feet deep. The latter has been for 25 feet in pay; has a drift in the bottom 50 feet west, disclosing a six-foot vein of pay-rock. This shaft was carried through a cap of 130 feet. The surface of the mine, to a depth of 80 feet, is worked out. Three hundred tons of pay-rock lie at the mouth of the shaft. The other shaft is in cap. The hoisting is done by a whim. The Company own a 22-stamp mill in the gulch at the foot of a compensation, wooden railway with a 36-horse engine, all in pretty good order. They had another 36-horse engine and a 10-stamp mill, which have been sold. Nothing has been done on this property since the Spring of 1864. The Company is represented by Colonel T. R. Tannatt, of Black Hawk.

The Colorado Gold Mining Company, of Boston, own 200 feet on the Burroughs, next east of the Gilpin Company; have two shafts, the west one 240 feet deep, and the east one ninety. In the

deep shaft are fifteen inches of what is considered
pay-rock; 160 feet from the surface a level is run
east 110 feet, under the east shaft, with an average
of two feet of pay-rock, the ground above slightly
taken out.   It is thought this is good nearly to the
surface.   There are eighteen inches of pay-rock in
the east shaft.   A whim-house and whim are on the
deep shaft, and a small engine, which is not set up.
There is a wooden railway to the mill.   The Company have also 240 feet on the Kansas, close by the
mill, and the same amount on the Sullivan, crossing
the Kansas—the two running much of the way
together.   The shaft where the lodes cross is five
by eleven in the clear, is in good shape, 45 feet deep,
with three feet of ore.   Eighty feet east is another
shaft of the same depth, with the same-sized pay-
vein.   The surface is not much worked out.   Further east they have another 140 feet on the Kansas,
with a shaft 90 feet deep, showing a five-foot crevice,
nearly all ore; also 166 feet on the Monroe,—which
is the Sullivan east of its crossing the Kansas—
with shaft 60 feet deep, out of which considerable
money has been taken.   They have a very nice
mill building, 70 by 100 feet, with a 100-horse
engine, Crosby & Thompson desulphurizer, Blake
crusher, Storer pulverizer, three ball-crushers, one
Hepburn pan, one shaking-table, and one Eaton
amalgamator, all in complete working order; the
mill was tried in the Spring of 1866, but did not
work satisfactorily, and so was shut down to await
developments.   The Company also own an old
12-stamp mill in the gulch, the engine belonging

to which has been taken on to the lode. J. F. Phillips, of Nevada, is the agent.

The Burroughs Gold Mining Company come next, and own 255 feet in two lots, C. P. Sykes, or the La Crosse Company, owning 50 feet between them. On their mine are three shafts, 43, 142, and 220 feet deep. The last been 100 feet in cap. The 142-foot shaft has a tolerable vein of ore, say twelve inches wide. One hundred feet from the surface the two deeper shafts are connected by a level. There is a 24-stamp mill on the lode, with a 25-horse engine, the machinery partially set up. Tanks are arranged for using the water over and over, as that article is somewhat scarce in the vicinity. The mill and mine are in good shape, and the Company have more than $20,000 in their treasury. Mr. DuBois, of Black Hawk, represents the Company. The Company have other mines,—200 feet on the Hubert, north of Nevada, with shaft 56 feet deep, &c. The works of the Company are well arranged to economize labor and team work, the main shaft opening in the mill just in front of the batteries.

The Hardesty Property joins the last above described on the east, and consists of 265 feet, on which are two shafts, 140 and 220 feet deep, each having an eighteen-inch vein of pure ore, which has produced $60 a ton under stamps. There are also two other shafts of a less depth, not in pay. This property has just been sold by Hardesty and is now owned by an association. There is a whim for hoisting but no mill nor machinery. J. A. Conlee

8

of Nevada has been appointed agent and instructed to commence work.

East of this the Burroughs vein seems to divide, and the branches take the names of Missouri and Baker.

The Pacific National Gold Mining Company own 550 feet on the Missouri—half of Discovery, and Nos. 1, 2, 3, 4, and 5 west; have a shaft on No. 3, 175 feet deep, with a crevice of good ore two feet in width at the bottom. On Discovery they have a shaft about 60 feet deep, with a fair show of ore, and on 1, 2, and 4, shafts from 20 to 30 feet deep. The discovery claim on the Missouri paid $85 a ton on the surface. The Company also have 142 feet on the Baker, adjoining, with one shaft 152 feet deep, just coming into pay. There is a whim-house on the mine 30 by 50, and a whim turned by a horse does the hoisting for the Baker and No. 3 Missouri shafts. The Company also have 1,345 feet on other lodes, partially developed; a new mill building, 75 by 101, in Spring Gulch, containing twenty-four 650-lb. stamps, a reverberatory de-sulpurizing furnace and a 30-horse engine. Work on the property was stopped in the Spring of 1866. Mr. John Young of Central is agent and part owner. Now we will trace the lode west of the Ophir. The First National Gold Mining Company of Colorado, own the first 183 feet.

The Gold Hill Gold Mining Company own the next 70 feet which are pretty much worked out to a depth of 200 feet. The Company used to get good ore but could not save the gold; it is thought to have been largely the fault of the mill. They have a 15-stamp mill complete and in running order, at the head of Nevada Gulch. The Company have no agent in Colorado and their mill and mine have been idle for the last two years.

The Baltimore & Colorado Gold Mining Company own the next 40 feet, and are represented by Mr, J. T. Simms of Nevada. They are now at work, down 160 feet, and getting out good ore. There is an engine, with hoisting apparatus, on the lode. The Company own and run the 8-stamp mill in the gulch near by.

The Quartz Hill Gold Mining Company own the next 90 feet, upon which is a shaft something more than 200 feet deep, well timbered, having two bucket ways, and a fair ore-vein in the bottom. Thirty or forty feet above the bottom of the shaft a level has been run the whole length of the mine and the back mostly taken out, paying in stamp mill, $35 a ton, average three feet of crevice crushed. The hoisting is done by whim. The Company have a compact 12-stamp, steam mill in the gulch near the mill, which commenced running in December 1864, and did well, producing in three months 480 ounces of gold. It was subsequently stopped together with work on the mine, because the whole institution was on too small a scale to work to advantage. The Company are understood to have since acquired other valuable mining property in the vicinity, which will enable them to enlarge their operations. They own a tunnel site pretty well up in the gulch, and have driven the tunnel 150 feet. It will cross six lodes in course of 900 feet, the last at a considerable depth. A. Mansur of Nevada is the agent.

Then come the First National again, owning 233 2-3 feet; then McCabe, 66 1-3 feet; then Andrews, 90 feet; First National again, 100 feet, and a half interest in the next 200, which takes the lode considerably beyond any development.

The First National Gold Mining Company have more than 600 feet in all, but it is badly divided. They have a shaft on each of the two eastern lots, about 240 feet deep, well timbered, of good size, and in complete order for working. The ground is somewhat worked out at the surface and bottom of each shaft. The west one is thought to be just "raising" the cap. The east shaft has a 7-foot crevice, through which the ore vein is scattered. There are other old shafts, of a less depth, not yet attacked by the present owners. The east shaft has a whim, the west one a 12-horse engine and complete hoisting works, with a good house. The Company have 450 feet on the Kansas, the east end of which is worked out 100 by 100 feet. The working shaft is 120 feet deep. A tunnel, from the mill in the gulch, in 225 feet, has passed the Kansas, which it strikes 50 feet from the surface, and is within 65 feet of the Burroughs, which it will strike 117 feet from the surface. They have had an enormous vein of rich ore in the ground worked in the Kansas,—in some places eleven feet wide. The hoisting works on the Kansas are driven by a line of shafting from the mill, which is 60 by 70, and

contains twenty-five 880-lb. stamps, eighteen Freiberg pans, and a 60-horse engine—all set up. This
splendid mill ran a few weeks in the Summer of
1866. Seventy tons from the Burroughs retorted
193 ounces of fine gold. The mill is now shut
down to wait for a process that shall save more of
the value of the ore. Thomas R. Rodman, of Nevada, is agent for the Company. The stockholders
are solid men, who have never offered their stock
for sale, and have but one object—to better themselves and the country by a legitimate development
of its resources.

We have now traced the Burroughs vein for about
3,000 feet. It is the king lode of Nevada, and perhaps second to none in the country but the Gregory
for strength, length, and value. It is a shame that
but a very small portion of it is at present productive.* In two places its very heavy cap has been
gone through, and a better vein than ever found
below,—which should encourage all others in cap,
not only on this but on all veins, to persevere ; and
the only way to prevent these caps and pinches from
eating up all the profits of the mines is to confine
operations *in them* to getting *through* them with as
few and small holes as can be got along with. As
an instance of the evil effect of the opposite course,
we might refer to Mr. P. F. Tobin's mine on the
Illinois. He has five shafts, all from 100 to 140

---

* This is so much the case that it was extremely hard in some
cases for the writer to find the owners or agents of the different lots
on the vein. It is quite possible that on this account some slight
inaccuracies may have crept into his report.

feet deep, and all in cap. As a consequence he is bankrupt so far as ready means goes, and the property is idle. One-third of the same work expended in one shaft would most certainly have taken him through the cap, and furnished him the means, *from the mine*, of making it productive, and the country by so much the more prosperous. This seems to us of enough importance to warrant its interpolation here.

OTHER MINES, COMPANIES, MILLS, ETC.

The American Flag Gold Mining Company, owning 530 feet on the American Flag Lode, Nevada, is considered one of the best companies in the district. There are seven shafts on the property, varying in depth from 70 to 230 feet, and it is estimated $200,000 have been taken from the mine. The crevice was enormous above the cap, varying from eight to eleven feet in width, and paying in a stamp mill an average of $30 a ton. In the Spring of 1864, the mine filled with water, and nothing was attempted until May, 1866. Then, machinery for pumping and hoisting, with pump, having arrived, Mr. James Clark, the agent, commenced work. On the 27th of July the engine and hoisting apparatus had been set up opposite the discovery claim, and the water was out and the shaft straightened and timbered 120 feet deep, ready for the pump, by the end of August. The Company intend to get the mine in order as fast as possible, selling the ores, which are very rich in lead as well as bullion, to the smelters meanwhile to meet expenses, and not indulge in the luxury of a costly mill of their own until progressing experiments shall have developed just what they need.

The La Crosse Gold Mining Company are confining their operations to driving a tunnel, intended to cut, at a considerable distance below the surface, property belonging to them on a number of lodes in Burroughs Hill running parallel with the Burroughs, some above, some below. They are now in more than 500 feet, and within a few feet of the Burroughs, upon which they own 50 feet, and which they will strike 200 feet from the surface. The Burroughs is half way from the mouth of the tunnel to the Rhoderick Dhu, which it is designed to reach eventually. The Company have a 12-stamp and four-pan mill at the mouth of the tunnel, in complete order, but not running. James Clark, of Nevada, is the agent.

The Kansas – Colorado Gold Mining Company have 400 feet on the Camp Grove and Kansas each, including the junction of the two lodes ; two shafts, 90 feet and 130 feet deep, with a fair crevice ;— 150 feet on the Sullivan—two shafts, 50 feet and 75 feet deep ; 100 feet on the Gardner, shaft 100 feet deep, with an average vein of ore ; 400 feet on the Cook County—two shafts, 30 feet and 50 feet deep ; 300 on the Cooper, with about the same development. The lodes are all in Nevada, and near together. The Company have a frame mill, almost on the Camp Grove, 50 by 100 feet, exclusive of a large stone engine-house, in which is set up as handsome a 60-horse engine as there is in the

country ; also machinery complete for a Crosby &
Thompson mill, purchased and set up, including
twelve stamps.   No results were obtained, and after
experimenting a few weeks in the Spring of 1866,
they shut down to await developments in the treatment of ores.   The mill can be easily adapted to
any process.   The Company have a six-inch pump,
not set up ; also an engine-house and small engine
on the shaft at the junction of the Camp Grove
and Kansas.   B. C. Waterman, of Nevada is the
superintendent, and T. R. Tannatt, of Black Hawk,
consulting engineer and managing director.

The Egyptian Gold Mining Company have 190
feet on the Egyptian, Quartz Hill ; shaft in the
centre of the mine 150 feet deep, just getting
through the cap, have ten inches of ore; shaft 30
feet east, 98 feet deep, in cap.   The hoisting is done
by hand.   They have also 100 feet on the Massachusetts, Nevada, shaft 40 feet deep; and a complete 12-stamp mill, four pans, at the upper end
of Nevada Gulch, leased and run by Thompson &
Deavor, of Central.   The Company were organized
in the Winter of 1865–6, and are represented by
C. C. Welch, of Central.

The Great Western Gold Mining Company have
190 feet on the Topeka, Russell Gulch ; four shafts,
20, 50, 150 and 180 feet deep.   The working shaft
opens into the mill ; there is said to be a good ore
vein in the deep shafts.   They have also 200 feet
on the Bench, near by—two shafts, 50 and 130 feet
deep, in good pay ; and over 8,000 feet of undeveloped property on the best lodes in Russell Dis-

trict; an old 12-stamp mill in Russell Gulch, run in 1865 by lessees, — idle and somewhat out of repair now; a new frame mill on the Topeka Lode, with a 40-horse engine, 20 stamps and some pans. The Company are not now at work. B. C. Waterman is the superintendent, and T. R. Tannatt, managing director.

The Alps and Granada Gold Mining Companies are composed of pretty much the same men, and are located on the same vein on the top and southern exposure of Quartz Hill, the Granada Company holding 800 feet under the name of Mackie, and the Alps Company holding the 700 feet adjoining, west, under the name of Alps. The Mackie has four shafts, 44, 56, 105, and 175 feet deep respectively. The ground worked is all on the west end of the mine. At the bottom of the deepest shaft a level is started either way, and the shaft kept sinking; there is an ore vein in both levels eight inches wide. There are three shaft-houses, and an engine-house 40 by 40, half on one mine and half on the other, owned by the Alps Company, but used by both, with a 25-horse engine and very complete hoisting tackle. On the Alps the ground worked out is on the east end. There are two shafts 90 and 170 feet deep, and two or three others from 20 to 35 feet deep, just down to the crevice. In the bottom of the deep shaft a level is started each way, showing an ore vein ten inches wide. Three hundred and sixty-five tons of gossan from the surface of this vein, taken out in 1863–64, yielded over $32,000 in gold. Its profits for the

8*

first four months it was worked, amounted to
$40,129.18.   The Granada Company own a magnifi-
cent mill-building in Russell Gulch, 65 by 100, containing a 100-horse engine and all the machinery
for a 30-stamp mill.   The engine and boilers are set
up, but the remainder is not—now waiting for a process, to any of which the mill can be easily adapted.
Good roads lead from the mine to the heads of Nevada, Russell and Leavenworth Gulches.   George
R. Mitchell of Nevada, is the agent.*   The works
on the mine, the shafts, etc., are in tip-top order.
The shafts are being sunk by contract for $30 a
foot, the Company hoisting and doing the smithing;
drifts on the same terms for eight and ten dollars.
The mines are in the most delightful situation, near
the highest point of that mountain tongue which
extends clear down to the junction of North and
South Clear Creeks,—where all the world seems
tributary to the eye, and yet quite well sheltered
on the north and west.

The Nottoway Gold Mining Compnay have 800
feet on the Nottoway, on the north side of Russell
Gulch, half way from its head to Pleasant Valley;
three shafts, each more than 100 feet deep.   The
ore has paid in a stamp mill $70 a ton.   The lode
has a very strong vein of ore.   The hoisting is
done by hand.   The Company have a mill in the
gulch at the foot of the lode, intended for the Dodge

---

* He since leased an old 12-stamp mill in Leavenworth Gulch,
and, selling his best ores to the smelters, took 1,197 ounces of gold,
$18,896.30, from 1,360 tons of second quality ore; this between
August 11, 1866, and February 2, 1867.

process, but the machinery is not put up.   Eben Smith, of Central, is the agent.   Not at work.

The King Gold Mining Company have No. 5, and half of No. 6 west, and No. 3 east on the Nottoway; two shafts on the west mine, 130 feet deep; hoisting done by rope from the mill engine; no improvement on the east mine.   They have also 200 feet on the Dorchester—50-foot shaft; 300 feet on the Golden Wedge,—30-foot shaft; all near together, and looking encouragingly for pay: a 12-stamp mill in the gulch, near the mine, in running order, we believe.   Mr. W. A. Abbee, of Central, is agent. The Nottoway is opened from 5 east to 15 west, and is considered one of the best veins in the country.

The Rochdale Gold Mining Company have 800 feet on the Harsh Lode, Leavenworth Gulch; four shafts, down on to a three foot ore vein—average depth, 50 feet; deepest, 80 feet; four other shafts not yet down to the ore, still in quartz.   About 50 feet from the surface is a drift 250 feet long, west from the deep shaft, showing an average ore vein of three feet; 80 feet from the surface, is a drift west 40 feet, on a crevice of ore of three to four feet.   The hoisting is done by hand, and they are not troubled with water. The Company have also 550 feet on the Calhoun, in the same vicinity; one shaft 125 feet deep, which has gone through a vein of pure and rich ore eighteen inches thick for 60 feet; there are 85 tons of ore out.   The surface of the whole mine has been worked out to a depth of 40 feet, and paid largely.   The hoisting is done by hand.   The ore

is considered as rich as any in the country. They
also have 600 feet on the Wood, in the same vicinity,
including all the developed part of the lode ; one
shaft 80 feet deep, which exposes an ore vein of
fifteen inches—the material taken out of this shaft
more than paid for the sinking ; one shaft 60 feet
deep also in pay. The hoisting is done by hand.
The surface has been worked out 40 by 300 feet,
and paid largely. The Company have a frame mill
60 by 100 on the Harsh, about half of it two-story,
containing a 60-horse engine, two Dodge crushers,
and two Cutler mills, such as are used in the zinc
works at Jersey City. They have made some experiments in amalgamating, but have not yet decided on a process. Their mill is easily adaptable
to any. With a satisfactory treatment for the ores,
the Company must be successful, for they own extensive, strong, and rich veins, in good shape, easily
accessible, with a mill conveniently located. S. P.
Lathrop, of Black Hawk, is agent and part owner.

The Prometheus Gold Mining Company own 500
feet on Prometheus, in Russell Gulch ; shaft 55 feet
deep, with fourteen inches of ore ; four other shafts,
from 25 to 40 feet deep, all showing a good ore vein.
Their hoisting is done by hand. They have no mill
nor machinery ; $30,000 of their capital is to be
devoted to mining. Col. Char.es H. Lewis, of
Central, is the agent. Now at work.

The Empire Gold Mining Company have 1,400
feet on the Empire Lode, which is an extension of
the American Flag ; four shafts, from 80 to 90 feet
deep each—two of them on the west end of the

mine, down to a two-foot vein of galenous ore. They are putting up a whim, and mining; have no mill nor machinery; working capital of $30,000. Col. Charles H. Lewis, agent.

The King Gold Mining Company have 1,600 feet on the King Lode, Nevada Flats; one shaft 80 feet deep, one 93, and the crevice struck on nearly every 100 feet. The ore vein is galenous, twelve inches wide. A contract is let to sink the deepest shaft—on the discovery—100 feet. The hoisting is done with a whim. The Company will probably sell the ore to the smelters, or keep it for the future. They have a mill building 35 by 70, in Eureka Gulch, 80 rods from the mine, intended for a Crosby & Thompson mill; was tried and failed. They will mine, and await developments as to treating processes. They have a fine dwelling and boarding-house, 24 by 36, two-story, painted and well-finished. Col. Charles H. Lewis, agent.

The Monitor Gold Mining Association have 400 feet on the Canton Lode, Leavenworth Gulch; two shafts, 80 and 100 feet deep, connected 50 feet from the surface by a level. Twenty feet lower is another level, not run clear through; twenty feet lower a third level is started. There is an average ore vein of three feet in the shafts and levels; 700 tons of ore out. They also have 600 feet on the Pennsylvania, at the head of Virginia Kanyon; two shafts, 40 and 100 feet deep, in cap; other less developed property, considered first-class. The hoisting all done by hand. The Company have a stone mill 65 by 80 in Russell Gulch; tried the Crosby

& Thompson process thoroughly, and it utterly failing, gave it up; have adopted nothing yet in its place. In the mill are a 40-horse engine, a Dodge cracker, two ball pulverizers, one shaking-table, and one set of Peck pans. The mill could be adapted to the Keith process by building a furnace. A. S. Cobb, of Russell Gulch, is the agent.

The Keystone Mining Company have 200 feet on the Calhoun, Leavenworth Gulch, with a shaft 140 feet deep, just through a cap of 80 feet, and showing eight inches of ore; 100 feet on the Wood, in the same Gulch, shaft 60 feet deep, sixteen inches of ore; 700 feet on the Cisler, south of Russell Gulch, shaft 140 feet deep, ore vein of two to three feet; 600 feet on the Rockford, at the head of Russell, shaft 40 feet deep; and some other less improved property. They have also a stone mill building in Russell Gulch, 45 by 100, exclusive of engine-room 34 by 60, partly finished. The machinery is on the ground for 30 stamps and 20 pans, but none of it set up. The Company have as good a mining property as any. Not at work and no agent.

The Philadelphia and Colorado Gold Mining Company have 300 feet next east of the Clark-Gardner, on the Gardner ; one shaft 250 feet deep, one 80 ; a drift 220 feet from the surface, run 25 feet either way, exposing a pay-vein eighteen inches in width. On the mine is an engine-house, with a small engine for hoisting. They have beside much other property, less improved ; a large stone mill in Nevada Gulch, 70 by 70 in the clear, exclusive

of engine-house, 34 by 35, an assay office in connection with it, 20 feet square, and a recess on one
side for a quartz room. The mill is intended for 50
stamps, 12 pans—only 25 of the stamps now put
up—and two Cornish buddles. They ran the mill
a few weeks in the Spring of 1866, and shut down
to put up a Monnier muffle. They built a *leanto* on
the side of the mill 25 by 112, and a brick muffle
80 feet long, six by nine feet in size, with a stack 50
feet high.* The ore is introduced at one end, with
one-tenth of its weight of sulphate of soda, and
worked to the other with shovels, then lixiviated
for the copper and silver, and amalgamated for the
gold. They have a small drying furnace besides the
muffle. The muffle was commenced September
1st, 1866. The mill is in good order, a fine structure, and contains an 80-horse engine. Henry A.
Vezin, of Philadelphia, did this last work. The
Company have no agent in Colorado at present.

The Clark-Gardner Gold Mining Company have
200 feet on the Gardner, Quartz Hill; two shafts,
200 and 182 feet deep,—the last opening into the
mill—connected by a drift 182 feet from the surface. In both shafts and the level is an ore vein,
averaging four feet in width. There are 350 tons
of ore out. They have a stone mill building on the
lode, 40 by 80 feet, with a Little-Giant engine
of 40-horse power. The only machinery at present
in the mill is a set of Cornish rollers, which is not

---

*This was done by the Monnier Metallurgical Company of Colo-
rado—headquarters in Philadelphia—and this Company together;
that is, each sharing equally in the expense.

yet set up. The hoisting works were constructed by Joseph F. Sanderson ; an iron skip raises two tons at once ;—it is the best hoisting apparatus in the country. The Company shut down in July, 1866, to await developments in smelting. Alfred Clark, of Nevada, is the agent.

Next west of the Clark-Gardner, Frank Gravitt owns 100 feet on the Gardner Lode, not much improved. Next come the Hawley-Gardner Company, owning 200 feet, undeveloped ; expect to commence work in the Spring of 1867. S. B. Hawley owns the next 300 feet ; two shafts, 115 and 180 feet deep ; the deep shaft is just through the cap, and has fourteen inches of ore ; above the cap, which is 70 feet deep, the crevice is from three to five feet wide, and the ore and quartz yielded from $25 to $225 a ton under stamps. B. C. Waterman owns the next 100 feet, has a deep shaft, whim and whim-house. The Gardner is considered one of the best veins in the country. It is wide and soft, and rich. The Philadelphia and Colorado Company once took out 420 tons with only $800 expense for powder and blasting.

The Congress Gold Mining Company have 300 feet on the Saratoga, between Russell and Willis Gulches ; three shafts, 145, 115, and 100 feet deep respectively. The two deepest shafts are timbered for 100 feet ; all the shafts are in pay. More than $50,000 have been taken from this mine. They are now putting up a 50-horse engine—large enough to run a mill and the mine ; also a six-inch pump. They will sink the two east shafts to a depth of 200 feet, and connect by drift. The material now coming out is worth $30 a ton by stamps. The Company own no mill, but are thinking of putting up a small stamp-mill on the mine, the latter furnishing water to run it. The mine is in first-rate shape. James S. Sheafe, of Russell Gulch, is the agent.

P. F. Tobin owns 310 feet on the Illinois Lode, Quartz Hill, supposed extension of the Mammoth; two shafts opening in the mill, one 90 feet deep, one 190, drifted together 80 feet from the surface; ten feet from the bottom of the deep shaft is a drift 43 feet east. These shafts are in cap, and show about 6 inches only of galenous ore. Fifteen feet east of the mill is a shaft 130 feet deep; 20 feet further east is a 120-foot shaft; 30 feet further a 140-foot shaft—all in cap. The surface of the mine is pretty well worked out. On the mine is a frame mill, 30 by 75, containing a 20-horse engine with hoisting apparatus complete, and twelve stamps, all in running order.

The Ford Gold Mining Company own 600 feet on the Jefferson Lode, at the head of Russell; one shaft 130 feet deep, one 50; the surface is stripped for 150 feet. The crevice is three feet wide, and the surface quartz is very heavy with galena. The vein is even, and descends vertically between smooth, solid walls about three feet apart. The Company have also 600 feet on the Goldsborough, in the same vicinity, not much improved; also 400 feet on the Stewart, same vicinity, one shaft 100 feet deep, one 40 to 50—the crevice in the deep shaft three feet wide, half of it very rich and heavy galena ; a wooden mill, just below the lodes in the gulch containing a reverberatory smelting furnace ready to run, of six tons a day capacity—a Dodge crusher, Blake crusher, two sets of burrs, a Collom separator, and a 40-horse engine, all in running order. The Company are not at work, on account of temporary pecuniary embarrassment. Francis R. Ford, of Russell Gulch, is the agent.

The Hill Gold Mining Company own 500 feet on the Fairfield, south from discovery, at the head of Russell—a north and south lode. The surface of No. 1, is worked out to a depth of 40 or 50 feet ; a shaft 120 feet deep on No. 1, in cap. The hoisting is done by hand. There is a mill in the gulch near the mine, containing twelve 600-lb. stamps, a 15-horse engine, not set up ; foundation for the batteries laid. The Company have not been at work for three months, as their prospects were not considered encouraging enough to warrant going on until mining should be less expensive. Iron pyrites from the lode prospects extremely rich in gold pan, and assays $75 a ton, coin value, but they have not yet enough of it to pay. John H. Barlow of Russell Gulch is the agent.

The Fairfield Gold Mining Company have 500 feet on the Fairfield, just north of the Hill Company ; one shaft 70 feet deep, timbered and in good shape ; other shafts just down to the crevice the whole length of the mine. The last 30 feet of the deep shaft show a crevice from eighteen to forty inches in width ; a level is run 70 feet long, 25 feet from the surface, on an average vein of two feet. The hoisting is done by hand. The Company also have 300 feet on the Leavenworth, in Leavenworth Gulch ; shaft 80 feet deep, well timbered and in good shape ; the vein underlies so that the shaft at 80 feet depth just strikes the crevice, which contains two feet of ore ; another shaft 65 feet deep— the surface a good deal worked out, paying largely ; other less improved property. They have an old 8-stamp mill at the head of Russell, somewhat out of repair. The Company stopped work in May, 1866, like many others, to await developments. O. H. Harker of Central, is the agent.

The Kershow Gold Mining Company have 200 feet on the Bench Lode, near the Topeka, Russell Gulch ; two shafts one 155 feet deep, the other 85. The surface is worked out for 40 feet in depth. From the bottom of the 85-foot shaft is a level, driving both ways, now in 20 feet in each direction ; there are from four to five feet of ore in this drift. In the deep shaft they were in cap 80 feet, but now have three feet of rich ore. Both shafts are well timbered and in good shape. On the mine are an engine-house, containing a 20-horse engine—rented, and two shaft-houses. They have about 300 tons of ore out ; machinery for two Crosby & Thompson mills, complete ; a 100-horse double engine, two desulphurizers, two Storer beaters, Blake crackers, &c., all on the ground, but none of it put up. The Company have considerable other mining property, not improved, among it 600 feet on the Tuscola, in the same vicinity ; two shafts, each 30

feet deep, connected by a drift, showing three feet
of ore.   They do not know whether they will adopt
smelting or the Keith process for treatment.   An-
drew J. Ames, of Russell Gulch, is their agent.

John M. Osborne, represents a partnership mining
concern, the partners living in New Jersey.   He is
running a tunnel into the big hill south of the head
of Russell Gulch, which rises at an angle of 45°
to a height of more than 700 feet, and intends to
cross the rich belt of lodes running down the gulch,
the same as that containing the Pewabic, Iron,
Kingston, Nashville, White Cloud, Clinton County,
&c., all of them known to be rich.   The tunnel is
now in 80 feet, and is to be driven without cessation.   The partnership own a good deal of the best
property in the head of Russell Gulch, more or less
developed, but are now confining themselves wholly
to driving the tunnel.

Joseph Briggs and John W. Zehner own 600 feet
on the Kingston Lode, Russell Gulch, including the
discovery, they being the discoverers ; four shafts,
55, 35, 20 and 40 feet deep respectively ; the crevice
of ore in the discovery shaft is three feet wide,
nine feet between walls.   The first seven tons of
ore yielded $480 ; seventy tons from the different
shafts, quartz and iron, 10 to 55 feet from the surface, averaged $36 a ton in gold.   Four hundred
feet are open.   The lode is not yet struck beyond
this property.

The Pewabic Lode is all owned by the original
pre-emptors, and is opened by seven shafts from 30
to 60 feet deep, for 900 feet in length.   It is consid-

erably worked out on the surface and by drifts. It is estimated that 1500 tons of material have been taken from the lode, averaging $30 in gold per ton. One run of 21 tons averaged $57 a ton. The crevice varies in width from five to ten feet.

The Clear Creek Tunnel Company own 600 feet on the Kinney Tunnel Lode, on North Clear Creek, in Black Hawk. Adit driven in on creek level and on vein 60 feet, crevice of gossan six feet wide, with thin streaks or formations of very rich ore, assaying as high as $600 per ton in gold, improving rapidly. Also a mill-site on the creek at mouth of adit, dwelling-house and lot near by, and 25-horse engine now in use in a saw-mill at Guy Hill.

The Kip & Buell Gold Mining and Tunnel Company, have 600 feet on the Kip Lode, crossing Gregory Gulch just above Mountain City ; one shaft 235 feet deep. Two hundred feet from the surface a level is run east and west 100 feet long ; the crevice between the walls is eight feet, with twenty inches of tolerably clear ore. From the level downward, the vein will probably pay for taking out. An engine-house, containing a 10-horse engine, is on the shaft. This Company also have 350 feet on the Leavitt, crossing Gregory Gulch, parallel with and not far from the Kip ; two shafts, 75 and 90 feet deep, with a crevice of six feet, mixed ore and rock in the west shaft,—the east one being on a pinch occasioned by a cross-course. They are now sinking the west shaft, with good indications. They have leased 150 feet east for two years. The ore is raised within four feet of the new mill.

The Company have a log 12-stamp mill, built in
1860, which they have been running on custom
ore.*   They have a stone mill-building 45 by 100
feet, containing two upright engines, of 75-horse
power, a five-inch pump and hoisting gear, at work ;
they had some other machinery, which seems to
have been proven worthless before it was put up.
The mill is a splendid one, built, says Mr. Kip, at a
cost of $15,000, and adaptable to any plan of treat-
ing ores.   John Kip, of Central, is agent and also
a considerable owner.

The Montezuma Gold Mining Company have 300
feet on the Newfoundland, in the lower part of Nevada Gulch ; a shaft nearly in the center of the
mine, well curbed and in fine shape.   The vein is
regularly irregular—that is to say, they have it about
half the time, and four feet in width if at all.   Sixty
feet west is a shaft 140 feet deep, drifted to the
other shaft.   This shaft and drift have not yet been
worked by the Company.   There are several drifts
on pockets from the main shaft 15 to 40 feet long.
They are now sinking the main shaft, and running
a level east, 300 feet from the surface, on a 20-inch
vein.   On the mine is a shaft-house 18 by 30, with
a 10-horse engine and hoisting works complete—no
pump, but a bucket of water can be raised every
two minutes.   Three hundred feet from the mine is
a new frame mill, irregular in shape, about 70 by
100 in size.   It is intended for a Crosby & Thompson outfit entirely ; contains one of Otis Tufts'

---

* It has latterly been doing very well on the Company's ore from
the Leavitt.   Such is the tenor of our advices from Colorado.

120-horse engines, thought (by Mr. Cushman) to be the finest in Colorado; a Blake crusher, Crosby & Thompson desulphurizer, 4-foot ball pulverizer, 30-inch ball pulverizer, three Hepburn pans, two shaking-tables, all put up in the best of style. The mechanical arrangement for handling the ore is perfect. They have just started and are depending on the Crosby & Thompson process for success; could easily substitute Keith's, or any other, should that prove worthless. The capacity of the mill is 15 tons a day. Samuel Cushman, of Central, is the agent.

The Gregory Gold Mining Company have 160 feet on Gregory Second, Mountain City; one shaft 160 feet deep, with a three-foot vein of ore. The last run of 15 or 20 tons produced about an ounce of gold to the ton under stamps. They have another shaft 95 feet deep; the mine is worked out above that depth, and there is a pinch below: the deep shaft is just through it. On the mine is a new engine-house, with engine and hoisting machinery, in good trim. The Company also own 200 feet on the Gregory Extension, running from the United States Company's mine to the Manhattan Company's, but slightly improved; also 50 feet on the Bobtail, on No. 3, west—shaft 230 feet deep, with rather a pinched crevice, engine-house and engine on it; also 360 feet on the Fisk, no improvements; one 60-horse engine, and a set of the Dodge machinery of 1864, not put up or likely to be. William Mc-Cleary, of Black Hawk, is the agent.

The Montana Gold Mining Company have 200

feet on the Kansas, 200 on the Kent County, and 500 on the Illinois, all on Quartz Hill. On the Kansas they have one shaft 50 feet deep, with an 8-inch vein of ore ; on the Kent County one shaft 40 feet deep, crevice of gossan three feet wide, ore just coming in ; on the Illinois two shafts, 40 and 60 feet deep, ore vein 24 inches wide. They stopped work on the mines in the Fall of 1864. They have a large frame 30-stamp mill at the mouth of Spring Gulch, Central City, containing 15 stamps and a 100-horse engine, set up and run a few days in 1865. P. L. Sherry, of Central, is the agent.

The Manhattan Gold Mining Company have 350 feet on the Fisk ; two shafts, 130 and 214 feet deep. In the shallower there is a vein of ore four feet in width for the last 40 feet, and a level in a few feet each way shows no diminution. There are nearly 300 tons of ore out. In the deep shaft is about a six-inch vein ; they have never had any larger from the top, and the shaft is thought to be off the crevice. On the mine are a whim-house, and an engine-house containing a 25-horse engine. The Company have further 200 feet on the Gregory Extension, shaft 50 feet deep, with not much show yet ; own property besides on the Bobtail, Tucker, Ground-hog, Enterprise, Cotton, Kip, Galena, etc., none of it much improved ; have a frame mill in Black Hawk 40 by 100, containing a Keith furnace, Ingersoll crusher— which takes the ore wet or dry equally well—ball pulverizers and twelve shaking-tables. The estimated capacity of the mill is twenty tons a day. There is a large stone engine-house a little removed from the mill, with a handsome double engine of 80-horse power, stable, &c. They expect to start the mill and make it pay from the 1st of November. Col. Thomas R. Tannatt, of Black Hawk, is the agent.

The Rocky Mountain Gold Mining Company have 250 feet on the Bates, immediately in Gregory Gulch ; three shafts, 150, 175 and 150 feet deep respectively. In two of them they have three feet of ore. The deepest is the main shaft, now receiving a six-inch pump and being driven down. They have a stone engine-house 30 by 32, and a mill adjoining 50 by 85 ; also a 40-horse engine, expected to drive the mill, pump, and hoisting rig. Dodge machinery was purchased for the mill, but is thrown aside and will not be put up. They do not yet know what they will adopt,—but probably Keith's process, should it give satisfaction in the Manhattan mill. The Company own other undeveloped property, including 3300 feet on the best lodes in Empire District, Clear Creek County. They are now putting up their engine, pump and hoisting works, preparatory to mining on the Bates. Thomas R. Tannatt is the agent.

The Standard Gold Company have 175 feet on the Fisk ; one shaft 125 feet deep, three-foot vein of ore ; hoisting by whim ; stopped mining in the Winter of 1864-5. They have also a mill site and 750 feet of water power on North Clear Creek above Black Hawk. A 40-horse engine, and machinery for a Dodge mill have just arrived, after being on the road two years, but will not be set up.

9

The Company own 3,000 feet on veins in Ohio District, Clear Creek County. They are not now at work. Col. T. R. Tannatt is the agent.

The Alliance Mining Company, organized in the Spring of 1866 by the consolidation of "The Eight Associates," "The Crawford & Coin," and "The Leavenworth Companies," have 400 feet on the Harsh, including discovery; two shafts, each 60 feet deep, and one 120 feet, with a good crevice in all of them; 600 feet on the Crawford County, in Russell District—two shafts, 40 and 70 feet deep, good crevice in both; 300 feet on the Carolton, Leavenworth Gulch—shaft 80 feet deep, 18 inches of ore; 700 feet on the Huber, same vicinity—two shafts, 120 and 180 feet deep, in the latter two to three feet of ore, in the former eight feet; 400 feet on the Stump, Russell District—two shafts, each 40 feet deep, and one 130, two feet of ore in the latter; 500 feet on the Coin, Mountain City—shaft 80 feet deep, ore vein two feet wide; 300 feet on the Berry, Gregory Hill—shaft 70 feet deep; 700 feet on the Alliance, Gregory Hill, shaft 124 feet deep; other less developed property; no hoisting machinery but whims and windlasses. They have two stone mill-buildings in Russell Gulch, 50 or 60 by 150, calculated for 40 stamps and 20 pans each, with engines, shafting, etc., for complete mills, the machinery not put up; also the Excelsior mill, a mile below Black Hawk, steam and water power, 20 stamps and eight pans, all in working order, which has been leased to the Cook Company, who have been trying to run a Crosby & Thompson desulphurizer, but so far without much success ; the mill also contains a reverberatory desulphurizing furnace. The Company are not doing much at present, but anticipate erecting smelting works another season.   D. W. Wise, of Central, is the agent, and Robert Teats, of same place, acting superintendent.

The Corydon Gold Mining Company have 600 feet on the Corydon, lower part of Nevada Gulch ; discovery shaft, near the east end of the mine, 275 feet deep, three feet of ore in the bottom.   One hundred feet from the surface is a drift west 140 feet, with fifteen to forty inches of ore in the floor ; 250 feet from the surface is another drift 40 feet long, on an average 30-inch ore vein ; in the shaft below is the same sized vein.   One hundred and fifty feet west is a shaft 99 feet deep, which has been in cap, but now has a fair crevice of ore.   There are 1500 tons of ore out.   Levels are to be run the whole length of the mine.   The ore has yielded from $12 to $37 a ton in a stamp mill.   The main shaft is in as good shape as any in the country.   On the mine is an engine-house, with a 16-horse engine and hoisting rig complete.   The Company also have 400 feet on the Newfoundland, near by, undeveloped ; 400 feet on the Lyman, same vicinity,—shaft 110 feet deep, two-foot ore vein, the ore from which yielded $100 per ton by the Keith process—three other shafts, from 30 to 85 feet deep ; 400 feet on the Excelsior, the crevice simply struck on each claim ; and an 8-stamp mill in Nevada Gulch, near the lodes.   Mr. H. M. Teller, of Central, who is part owner and represents the Company, has dissuaded them from investing their working capital in machinery by dint of strong and persistent effort. He is mining simply as yet.

The Cook & Kimball Gold Mining Company have a large Bertota mill in Gregory Gulch, near the heart of Central City. It contains a 20-horse portable engine, two batteries of four 320-lb. stamps each, six small iron Chilian mills, and eighteen pairs of Bertola pans—iron, with stone mullers—all in running order, and in use by Mr. George L. Cook, son of Cook, of Cook & Kimball, on his own account. He says it is an improvement on the stamp mill. The process consists substantially in amalgamating in iron pans, after subjecting the pulverized ore to a chemical steam bath, the exact components of which are as yet a secret so far as the public are concerned. This mill is supplied with water from the Gulch Lode, under the mill, considerably improved, but never worked by the present owners. What little ore they have treated has been for other parties. The Company are not doing anything.

The Lode Star Gold Mining Company have 1600 feet on the Pacific Lode, Illinois Central District ; one shaft 80 feet deep, one 60, and other shallower shafts. The vein is struck for 500 feet. The deepest shaft is in cap ; the others show a crevice of from two to four feet. They are working on this lode. They also have 400 feet on the Metropolitan, Quartz Hill, shaft 55 feet deep, being sunk ; also 1600 feet on the Atlantic, in Russell, not much improved. The Company have a mill at the mouth of Excelsior Gulch, frame, 50 by 60 in size, containing a 50-horse engine, a Kingsley's crusher—worthless—a Crosby & Thompson desulphurizer, four-foot ball pulverizer, three shaking-tables, all set up; started, and stopped. The Company are mining, and intend to let the mill stand still and await developments. Capt. George K. Kimball, of Central, is their agent.

The Columbia Gold Mining Company have 1600 feet on the Wall Street Lode, near the mouth of Nevada Gulch; shaft 40 feet deep, vein of ore one foot in width; a full Dodge and Crosby & Thompson mill, the machinery, including a 50-horse engine, all set up and in working shape. George K. Kimball is the agent.

The Thurber Gold Mining Company have six full, or nearly full, lodes (1600 feet), in Spring Gulch, none of them worked but one—the Grace—which has a shaft 60 feet deep, with a five-foot crevice, but no defined vein of ore yet. They have also 1000 feet on the Burton, Illinois Gulch, with a shaft 96 feet deep, ore-vein two feet wide, now being sunk; and some other lodes, not at present worked; no mill; a small engine and rig for hoisting. Their operations are confined strictly to mining. Col. W. A. Arnold, of Central, is their agent.

The Whipple Gold Mining Company have 100 feet on the Bobtail—No. 4 west—and 200 on the Fisk—Nos. 4 and 5 west—at what was once supposed to be the crossing of the two lodes; it has been demonstrated that they do not cross on this property, but further west, if at all. They have a shaft on the Bobtail claim 85 feet deep, with an ore-vein 18 inches wide—the surface somewhat worked out; at the bottom of the shaft a cross-cut, 24 feet long, strikes the Fisk in the centre of the Company's 200 feet, in a shaft 150 feet deep. A level is run, 110 feet from the surface, on a three-foot ore vein, and considerably worked out in the back; below this level the ore vein is from two to three feet wide. There are 300 tons of ore out. A large whim-house answers for both shafts. The Company are sinking on the Fisk now. They have a mill and water-power in the lower part of Black Hawk; the mill containing a Dodge crusher and desulphurizer, Cornish rollers, eight Dodge pans, a Dodge amal-gamator, and a large oscillating engine, all set up, and run a few weeks in the beginning of 1866; not working satisfactorily it was shut down. M. A. Arnold, of Central, is the agent.

The New England Mining Company of Colorado have 900 feet on the Running Lode, a strong vein about half a mile south-east of the Bobtail. There are several shafts on the property, varying in depth from 20 to 120 feet. In the bottom of the latter shaft is a vein of ore two feet wide. There are 150 tons out. On the mine is an engine-house, with engine and hoisting rig complete. The Company have a mill in Black Hawk, containing eight stamps, two pans, and a small engine. They are represented by Com. Rodney French, of New Bedford, and have been principally engaged during the last two years in experimenting with their ores with a view to adopting the best treatment known. The former owners claim to have taken $75,000 from the mine.

The Fisk Gold Mining Company have 200 feet on the Fisk, No's 1 and 2 west; a shaft on No. 1, 155 feet deep, showing three feet of ore mixed through a seven-foot crevice; shaft on No. 2, 75 feet deep, with a four-foot crevice of ore and rock, well mixed. On the mine is an engine-house, with a 15-horse engine and hoisting works in good order. The Company are taking out ore, and selling it to the Mammoth (Keith) mill. They have also 500 feet on the Running Lode, but slightly improved; a stone mill building in Black Hawk, about 80 feet square; a 75-horse engine, forty 880-lb. stamps, and 20 Freiberg pans, on the ground, but not put up. W. N. Dickerson, of Black Hawk, is the agent, and a large owner of the stock.

The Jaques Gold Mining Company have 300 feet on the Mercer County (extension of the Flack)— Nos. 3, 4 and 5 east; a shaft on No. 4, 172 feet deep, with a vein of ore thirty to forty inches wide, assaying $120 a ton; shaft on No. 5, 142 feet deep, with two feet of ore. A drift 130 feet from the surface connects the two shafts, and runs west 53 feet on No. 3; a shaft on No. 3, 40 feet deep—no ore yet. A whim and two shaft-houses are on the mine. The Company have also 700 feet on other lodes, less developed; and a mill in Nevada known as the "Stoner," containing twelve 600-lb. stamps and an engine. John Young, of Central, is the agent. Not at work.

The Sierra Madre Gold Mining Company have

600 feet on the Eureka Lode, at the head of Prosser Gulch, in a body, and 66 2-3 feet in another place. The main shaft, 142 feet deep, opens into a wing of the mill ; 150 feet east is another shaft 87 feet deep, five feet between walls, with strong seams of ore coming in. There are 80 tons of ore out. The Company have a frame mill 40 by 60, containing a 35-horse Patterson engine, a Thunderbolt crusher, and ore dressing machinery after the plan of the Royal Hanoverian works in the Hartz Mountains. The intention of these works is simply to crush and dress the ores preparatory to smelting : after being reduced to an even fineness, the ore, except the dust or slimes, is carried by a stream of water to a continuous German jigger, the capacity of which is 650 cubic feet in twenty-four hours, the result being perfectly clean ore. The fine ore, cr slimes formed in crushing, pass to the German buddle, where they are cleaned. The tailings from the jigger pass over a blanketed shaking-table, and are afterward finish-ed on a shaking-table without blankets. The head of the buddle collects the clean ore, the tailings pass over a blanketed table on to a shaking-table without blankets as above, which finishes the oper-ation. There are other blanket tables for these tailings, so that the ore is all saved, perfectly clean-ed, and the only manual labor required is in remov-ing it from the different machines. The capacity of the dressing works, all in complete operation, is 50 tons in twenty-four hours. The Company are thinking of building a set of furnaces for what is called the "Roast Reduction Process," as carried

on in Europe. The capacity of the furnaces to be ten tons each of dressed ore in twenty-four hours. There is a four-inch Cornish pump in the main shaft, and this is being sunk at the rate of ten feet a week, and at an average cost of about $30. Wm. H. Doe, of Central, is agent and large owner.

The Eureka Gold Mining Company have the discovery claim on the Eureka, and considerable undeveloped property on the east end of the lode; a shaft 160 feet deep, 10 feet between crevice walls, 5 feet of solid ore; 40 or 50 feet west a shaft 90 feet deep, in cap; engine house, engine and hoisting rig on the shaft; no mill. The lode has been gouged out on the surface 400 feet in length and paid well. It is considered one of the strong veins of the country. Wm. H. Cushman is the agent.

The Chicago Gold Company have 200 feet on the Kansas, not much improved; 100 feet on the Burroughs—No. 6 west—not developed; 133 feet on the Monroe, considerably developed; 400 feet on the Buckeye, shaft 80 feet deep, with one foot of ore—now being worked; other scattering property, not worked; no mill nor machinery; will *mine*, that is all. They are represented by George L. Cook of Central.

The Morrell Gold Company have 460 feet on the Morrell Lode, Russell Gulch; shaft 50 feet deep, ore vein of galena 24 inches in width, assaying $300 a ton; no mill nor machinery. George L. Cook is the agent. These two Chicago Companies have started in on a correct basis, and will confine themselves to mining for the present.

9*

The Merchants' Gold and Silver Company have four full lodes (1600 feet each)—the Senator, Merchant, Commercial, and Oscar, on Enterprise Hill, near Black Hawk.   The two first are being worked. There is a shaft on the Senator 70 feet deep, with a seven-inch vein ; shaft on the Merchant 55 feet deep.   Three-foot crevice of mixed ore and quartz. There are 70 tons of pay material out.   The Company have no mill nor machinery, and are mining at present.   W. L. Thompson, of Black Hawk, is the agent.

The Fisher Gold Mining Company have improved property on the Quartz-Mill, Leavenworth, Wood, Calhoun and other lodes in Leavenworth Gulch ; a Bertola mill in Black Hawk, containing a 20-horse engine, six stamps, twenty pairs of Bertola pans, and two Chilian mills ; also a reverberatory furnace for desulphurizing.   They used the Bertola process, but could not make it pay—either because they did not know how to use it, because it is not adapted to the purpose, or because there was nothing in their ores.   They have no agent in Colorado at present.

The Chase Gold Company have 500 feet on the S. P. Chase, between Russell and Willis Gulches ; two shafts, 70 and 130 feet deep, the latter sinking ; a whim-house and whim ; a 10-stamp steam mill in Russell Gulch, in working order, but not running. E. J. Sweet, of South Boulder, is the agent.

The Bates & Baxter Gold Mining Company have 300 feet on the Bates—No's 1, 2, and 3 east ; shaft on No. 1, 380 feet deep, in lean ore ; shaft on No. 2, 250 feet deep, also in lean ore.   Two hundred feet

from the surface the shafts are connected by a drift
150 feet long. Very little ground has ever been
worked out ; the vein is superlatively "pockety."
The former owner took out a pocket 40 by 40 feet ;
it and the above level are about all that has ever been
worked out. On the mine are a whim-house, and a
whim for hoisting. The Company have a 15-stamp
steam mill in Mountain City, rented ; have done
nothing since October, 1865.

The Union Gold Mining Company have 250 feet
next west of the above on the Bates ; two shafts,
50 feet apart ; west shaft 270 feet deep, east, 230 ;
drifted together 200 feet from the surface, and again
at 230. Both shafts expose the faces of fair average
veins of ore for the last hundred feet of their depth.
There are two drifts from west shaft to west end
of mine, both well toward the bottom of it and
having good veins of ore. The Company at one
time had out a large pile of ore ; it has been crushed
in a stamp mill, we know not with what result.*
There are steam-hoisting works on the mine, and
in Mountain City, close by, a mill building and machinery for 15 stamps, not in running order. S. P.
Lathrop of Black Hawk is agent.

The United States Gold Mining Company have
262 feet on Gregory Second, and 250 on Gregory
Extension ; a shaft on Gregory Second 170 feet
deep, with 14 inches of ore, pyrites and sulphurets, in

---

*Late advices state that this Company have ground in sight to
last eight or ten months ; that they were selling their first quality
ore to the Smelting Works at $60 per ton, and getting about $30
per ton from the second quality under stamps.

the bottom—has gone through a stratum of galenous ore 110 feet, the vein averaging ten inches in
width; another shaft on the same 140 feet deep, 18
inches of ore in the bottom, of the same character
as in the deeper shaft ; a whim for hoisting; 30 or
40 tons of ore out. On the Gregory Extension
they have a shaft 172 feet deep, forty inches between walls, the gangue a white, soft quartz, carrying considerable pyrites,—no defined ore vein ;
another shaft 56 feet in depth. The Company own
mill site and water power on North Clear Creek,
430 feet long and from bank to bank ; no mill nor
machinery ; have done nothing since August, 1865.
J. M. Smith, of Black Hawk, is the agent.

The Josephine Gold Mining Company have 600
feet on the Granite, Mammoth Hill ; all opened,—
one shaft 85 feet deep ; 300 feet on the German,
slightly improved ; 200 on the Peck & Thomas,
shaft 30 feet deep ; 250 feet on the Ogden, shaft 40
feet deep—and other property ; no mill nor machinery. The Company were organized in 1865,
but have never done anything.

The Susquehanna Gold Mining Company have
700 feet on the German, near Central City, supposed
extension of the Bates ; a shaft 140 feet deep, with
an ore vein of 17 inches, and widening ; a shaft
nearly in the centre of the property, 50 feet deep,
being cribbed,—five by eleven in the clear, and
sunk for a main shaft—shows the same vein as the
other shaft. The surface quartz yielded $45 to $70
a ton by stamps. The Company were but recently
organized, but have gone to work right, and are not

wasting or misapplying a dollar.   S. B. Morgan, of Black Hawk, is the agent.

The Rochester City Gold Mining Company have 217 feet on the Borton, supposed to be the Gardner and Rhoderick Dhu crevice in one; a shaft 200 feet deep, crevice between walls six feet, with ore all through it, hoisting by whim.   They have 300 feet on the Buford, and much other outside property. The Borton promises to be a mine of value.   Wm. A. Abbe, of Central, is the agent.

William N. Dickerson is working 600 feet on the Stonewall, near the Fisk ; has a shaft 75 feet deep, 50-inch crevice, with 20 inches of ore, which runs $12 to $15 gold per ton under stamps ; a 12-stamp water-mill, containing also four pans, in Black Hawk, running.   The mill building is 30 by 76 feet ; the water-power 40 feet head.

E. K. Baxter is working the Baxter & Crispin, on the eastern slope of Quartz Hill ; has the whole lode ; a shaft 80 feet deep, four feet between walls, ore about eight inches in width, and improving ; another shaft 40 feet deep, with three feet of quartz, which yields $20 a ton.   He is also working the Myers Lode, in Lump Gulch—shaft 40 feet deep, with three feet of ore ; also owns 300 feet on the Baldwin, Russell Gulch—shaft 115 feet deep, four feet between walls, in lean ore for the last 70 feet. Five wagon loads of ore from the last-named vein yielded thirty-six ounces of gold.   Mr. Baxter has no mill nor machinery.

John P. Bruce is mining on the Foote & Simmons ; has 100 feet, near the Gregory ; shaft 270

feet deep, two-thirds of the ground above yet un-
touched; levels have been started for back-stoping
100 and 200 feet from the surface; the crevice
averages twelve inches; the hoisting is done by
whim. He is also working the Bruce Lode, east
of North Clear Creek, in Black Hawk; has a shaft
50 feet deep, and is getting out good-looking stuff.
He has a water and steam mill, of twelve stamps,
in Black Hawk.

J. F. Field owns 33 1-3 feet—the west end of
No. 5, east,—on the Bobtail, being the discovery;
it has been worked out for 375 feet in depth, the
crevice having averaged 20 inches. Twenty feet
of picked ore from this mine once produced $740
under stamps. It yielded $145 per ton in a stamp
mill all one Summer. The shaft is well cribbed to
the bottom. The ore is raised by power from the
Black Hawk Company's engine. Work was stopped
in June, 1866, on account of water. During three
weeks in June 150 tons of selected ore were taken
out. Mr. Field has a steam mill in Black Hawk,
containing twelve 600-lb. stamps, in good order.
It is estimated that $150,000 have been taken from
the claim. Mr. Field is also working the Field,
Cotton, Nemaha and Log Cabin Lodes, all near the
Bobtail, and developed from 30 to 135 feet in depth.
The Cotton has three shafts on it, and is stripped
to iron, having produced $20,000. All these are
worked by whim or windlass.

The Mystic Tunnel Company are running into
Quartz Hill from a point low down on Nevada
Gulch. On the 1st of August, 1865, they were in

85 feet, and had struck one lode 25 feet from the surface, with 20 inches of ore. The tunnel will strike the Burroughs 800 or 1000 feet from the surface. R. G. Kellett, of Central, is the agent.*

William Pritchard is mining on the S. P. Chase, the Tuck, and the Whalin. On them all he has encouraging prospects, in shafts from 40 to 80 feet in depth.

The Colorado Ore Reducing Company, were organized in the Spring of 1866 with $65,000 capital, to build a Keith mill for manufacturing custom ores. The mill is in Black Hawk; the whole structure being 60 by 90 feet. The furnace is 9 by 18, and 26 feet high outside, the stack of stone and brick, rising 60 feet; the Keith process complete, with all the improvements up to the moment of building adopted. Capacity, with sixteen shaking tables, 25 to 30 tons a day. The works are complete, and ready to start on their trial trip. Mr. Du Bois, of Black Hawk, is the agent.

The Roxbury Gold Mining Company own 856 claims of 100 feet each, scattered all over the county. They were recorded on the ends of lodes, and bonded to the ex-Rev. W. W. King, at one time of Chicago, who, we are informed, sold the outfit in Roxbury, Mass., for $60,000. Theodore B. Moses was hunting for the property during

---

*This must be the same as the Quartz Hill Tunnel Company, of which a Colorado paper of late date says: "It was organized one year since with a capital of $50,000; its tunnel is now 200 feet long, having already crossed two lodes, and its cost has been less than $10,000." The stock is owned in Central City, and work is carried on by regular assessments.

the entire Summer of 1866, but without any alarming success. People who allow themselves to be swindled in so outrageous a manner have really but themselves to blame. It is doubtful if this batch of so-called mining claims, sold for $60,000, is really worth sixty cents.

The Great Eastern Gold Mining Company are mining on the Hoosier Lode, near the Running; one shaft 145 feet deep; have other property on South Clear Creek; no mill nor machinery. S. B. Morgan, of Black Hawk, is the agent.

Truman Whitcomb has 100 feet on the Kansas; worked out 90 feet in depth, 16 inches of first-class ore one-half the way, the rest pinched up. He has also 150 feet on the Indiana, extension of the Gardner west; one shaft 145 feet deep, with two feet of ore, and another 55 feet deep, 70 feet east, drifted together; 12 inches of ore in the drift,—ore, copper, zinc and galena, with a fair proportion of bullion. He has much other undeveloped property, and a 12-stamp steam mill, running on custom ore. The Indiana and Kansas are both almost impossible to work to profit in a stamp mill. Mr. Whitcomb is one of the oldest miners in Nevada, and considers that the Kansas is to Nevada what the Gregory is to Black Hawk.

The Flack Lode is one of the best in Nevada. It has been worked out considerably for 400 feet in depth. One shaft is 345 feet deep, another 250. Nothing has been done on it since 1864. An association owned the 700 feet on which most of the work has been done, and they got into a quarrel, and one of the partners prevented the rest from working ; but they all agreed to bond it for sale. Negotiations for its sale to Vivian & Sons have been long in progress ; what the probabilities of success are, it is impossible for us to say. The consideration asked is £40,000.

The Forks Lode, of Nevada, is one of the best in the country ; paid well in early times in stamp mills. The surface is worked out for 500 feet in length. The deepest shaft is about 300 feet ; there are several shafts from 120 feet to that depth. The Denver Mining Company had 400 feet on it, which was sold out by the sheriff, in the Summer of 1866, together with an 18-stamp mill in Nevada Gulch, in working order, and machinery for a new mill. The property is as good as any, but the Company never did anything with it, although they did declare a dividend once.

The Crozier Gold Mining Company are mining in Quartz Valley, on the Mitchell, of which they have 400 feet. They have also 275 feet on the Des Moines, in Russell District, property on the Perrin, in Eureka, and much other undeveloped property, including 200 feet on the Freeland and 300 on the Vanderbilt, in Trail Run District, Clear Creek County. They have no mill nor machinery. H. M. Orahood, of Black Hawk, is their agent.

The Commonwealth Gold Mining Company have 500 feet on the Prize, and 800 on the Crosby, a branch of the Prize. They have a shaft 100 feet in depth on the Prize which they are sinking. Samuel Tidd is their agent. They have no mill nor machinery.

The Kenyon Gold Mining Company have a very large Bertola mill in Black Hawk, run by steam, put up late in 1863, but never much in operation, and a great amount of mining property, more or less developed, in the best districts of Gilpin and Clear Creek Counties. Joseph Kenyon, of Black Hawk, is their agent.

The Empire Gold Mining Company have an 18-stamp steam mill in Black Hawk, leased and at present running for the Smith & Parmelee Company. They have some considerably developed mining property on the Foote & Simmons, and other lodes in the vicinity of Black Hawk and Gregory Point. Maj. O. P. Rand of Boston, formerly represented the Company in Colorado, but they never did much, and latterly have done nothing.

Mr. J. B. Fitzpatrick owns an 8-stamp, steam mill in Black Hawk, leased and running for the Smith & Parmelee Company.

There are three or four other mills in Black Hawk including the Idaho Mill, which have been idle a long while and do not seem to have any owners. The Idaho Mill, however, has lately passed into the hands of an association of Judge G. B. Backus's friends in Pennsylvania, and is liable to be started most any time.

The Loker Gold Mining Company own 400 feet on the Bates, on both sides and crossing Chase Gulch not far from its mouth. F. W. Page, the agent, sunk a shaft on it to a depth of 150 or more feet, and was getting out some very fair ore when they stopped work last Spring. Doubtless the Company own one of the idle mills in the gulch near the lode ; we know not for certain.

The foregoing comprises nearly all the companies with their most important properties and operations, in the Gregory Diggings. It is possible some have been overlooked, and that some inaccuracies have crept in, but such has not been the intention. Lodes known to be very valuable, discovered within the last three years, we hardly know how to notice without seeming invidious, since we cannot notice them all.

The Pierce Lode is considered one of the strongest gold veins in the county. It is situate in Central City, crossing Nevada Gulch just below its junction with Spring Gulch, and seems to be formed by the junction of the Adeline, New York, Cork, Rich, and John Phœnix Lodes. The crevice is very wide—16 1-2 feet—and it is being worked, shaft 60 feet in depth.

The Adeline, a little further up and on the south side of Nevada Gulch, supposed extension of the Corydon, is another strong, rich vein. John Shumar is working it and recently got 96 ounces of gold from 50 tons of quartz.

On the eastern point of Quartz Hill is the Ulysses Lode, opened for 600 feet, and having four to five feet of solid ore, pyrites of iron and copper, at a depth of 50 feet, in Discovery shaft.

Near the head of Spring Gulch is the Wapello County Lode, shaft 100 feet deep, fair average crevice of ore.

In Spring Gulch, close by McIntyre's mill, is a new lode belonging to John Shumar, having a large ore-crevice almost on the surface, yielding by Keith process between $50 and $70 a ton.

Between the Bates and Gregory Extension, south side of the hill, is the Hope Lode, owned by John Tierney, opened for 500 feet by shafts from 25 to 188 feet in depth, vein five feet in width, paid in stamp mill from $18 to $25 a ton.

In Chase Gulch, half a mile from its mouth, on the south side, is the Etna, one of the strongest and richest and most promising veins in the county.

Near the head of Russell Gulch is the Jersey City, opened on four claims, to a depth of 30 to 50 feet, each shaft developing a strong rich vein of iron pyrites.

In Russell are also the Federal, Iron, General Birney, Jo Watson, H. D. Towne, Nemaha, Washcash, White Cloud, Sangamo, Watch, Banker, Rock Island, Pennsylvania, Nashville, Clinton County, Gorham, Sam Hackly, Timbuctoo, Windsor County, Prometheus, Big Horn, Pewabic No. 2, General Butler, and others, all of them developed to a good ore crevice, which is generally struck in Russell Gulch if at all within 50 feet of the surface.

In Saw Pit Gulch is the Genesee County, opened for 500 feet, showing a quartz crevice everywhere from six to ten feet wide ; and in the Discovery shaft, at a depth of 30 feet developing a vein of solid, beautiful ore three to four feet wide. Saw Pit Gulch is a tributary of Russell Gulch.

But we cannot particularize further.   If the reader

fail to get some idea of the net-work of gold veins that covers a circle three miles over of which Central City is the center from all we have said in this chapter, we despair of giving it. And there are perhaps a hundred good lodes in the space mentioned which are not named in this book at all.*

---

* On the 1st of February last, forty mills and treating establishments were at work in Colorado. It may seem like a small proportion of the whole to strangers, but not to Coloradans. There was hardly ever a time when a larger proportion of the mills was in operation, and since the era of high prices, deep mining, and worst of all, *speculation*, set in—beginning of 1864—there has not been, as a rule, half so large a proportion at work. It indicates a great decline in the cost of living and working, and more and better than that, it proves that the mines are equal to their own development when extraneous help, which has really been a curse instead of a blessing, is withdrawn.

CHAPTER VIII.

Gilpin County Continued—Swinging Round the Circle—Independent, South Boulder, Central, Wisconsin Districts, Peck and Missouri Gulches—Their Improved Mines, Mills, Companies, Processes, &c.

As we have said before, the mines noticed in the last chapter, occur on that high tongue of land which comes down from the Range between the principal forks—called North and South—of Clear Creek. They are accessible from the Valley over three wagon roads, one entering the Foot-hills at Boulder City, one at Golden Gate, the other at Mt. Vernon, each about twenty-five miles in length. From Black Hawk on North Clear Creek, a wagon road winds up through Gregory and Spring Gulches, crosses the heads of Leavenworth and Russell Gulches and goes down Virginia Kanyon to Idaho on South Clear Creek, the distance about six miles, the elevation overcome, two thousand feet, the route toward the south-west, and passing through the improved mines of the old Gregory and Russell Districts. Another wagon road crosses the divide higher up—at the head of Nevada or Eureka—descends on to Fall River, and follows that stream down

to South Clear Creek ; or, branching to the right
when the summit is attained, it follows the crest of
the divide north-west to Peck Gulch, the upper portion of Chase Gulch, and soon thereafter enters Wisconsin District, embracing the extreme sources of
North Clear and South Boulder Creeks, ten or twelve
miles north-west from Central City, and right at the
foot of James Peak. Doubling and proceeding down
the South Boulder on the arc of a circle of which
Central City is the pivot, we shall pass through
South Boulder District and arrive in the course of
about twelve miles at the mouth of Gamble Gulch,
coming down from the south. Turning into this
we ascend about two thousand feet in two miles,
and find ourselves in a patch of gold veins, called
Independent District, of which the Gold Dirt and
Perigo are the principal, so far as known. Adjoining Independent on the east is Central District,
lying at the head of Lump Gulch, a tributary of
Gamble Gulch. Where the two form a junction is
what used to be called Deadwood Diggings, the
place where gold was first discovered in the Mountains. From the head of Lump Gulch a fine road
leads out to the Denver and Central City stage route.
Crossing the crest of the divide from Independent
District, south, we are in Wide Awake District, at
the head of Missouri Gulch, seven miles north of
Black Hawk. So that we have "swung round the
circle" of the Gilpin County Mining Districts, and
will now swing back, if the reader please, and give
all the information we have concerning these districts "into his hands."

Independent District, or Gold Dirt, with its ten or dozen stamp-mills and its town of log-houses along Gamble Gulch, was by no means an inconsiderable competitor with Gregory in 1860, as a place of importance among the mines. Now, but four or five companies are operating here. The Gold Dirt Lode crosses Gamble Gulch about two miles above its junction with South Boulder. It is struck for a distance of two thousand, and has been developed to a depth of four hundred and twenty feet.

The Hope Gold Company own 2200 feet on the vein, their improvements being, however, chiefly confined to No's 3, 4, 5, and 6, east, and 3 west. No. 3 is worked out to a depth of 380 feet, and is now rather pinched in the shaft, which is 400 feet deep, and is near the east end of the claim, about 20 feet from the main shaft, on the boundary between 3 and 4. The main shaft is 420 feet deep and being sunk, cribbed for 300 feet, four by eight in the clear, well timbered the rest of the way, and contains a four-inch pump which has been working a long while to perfection. Starting near the present bottom of this shaft there are three levels, perhaps 80 feet apart, the lower one running east 130 feet, the middle one 200, and the upper one 230. Nearly all the ground has been worked out in the backs of these levels for a distance of 120 feet east of the shaft. One hundred feet east, the crevice is 15 feet between walls, with a vein of ore from 12 to 18 inches in thickness on each wall. Here, in the two upper levels, the best vein jumps off at the interruption of a cross vein, from the north to the south

Wall In the upper level they are now taking out the vein on the north wall; in the two lower levels on the south wall. The crevice matter, as taken out, is worth only $15 a ton, but only 20 per cent. of it is ore. The base of the vein, like that of all others in the country, is copper, and it seems to lie at a greater depth than in the veins about Gregory, eight miles to the south and of a good deal less altitude. Wherever the cupriferous ore is found, it is rich in gold and silver and the veins are regular, not pockety nor displaced and split up. As yet but little of it has been found in the Gold Dirt vein, hence its great irregularity in every respect. In the mine under consideration it occurs sparingly in the upper level, from 200 to 250 feet from the surface. Then for a depth of 150 feet comes very coarse iron pyrites, streaked with hematite iron ore. By going deeper the copper ore will doubtless again be struck, and mining on the vein be attended with the rich results realized from its surface quartz. There is no surface crevice for 200 feet depth east of the main shaft, so far as known. A shaft has been sunk at the corner of the mill on No. 6, 90 feet in depth, but nothing satisfactory was found. Fifty feet south of this shaft, one was sunk on a spur, thought at the time to be the main crevice, 120 feet; it is cribbed clear down and is in good shape, but no pay-ore was got out of it, and it was long since abandoned. There is also a shaft 120 feet deep on No. 3 west, cribbed clear down, 18-inch vein of ore, not worked. There is an irregular shaft-house on No's 3 and 4, 100 feet long, from which

10

a wooden railway conveys the ore into the third story of the mill. Timber is on the ground for a quartz-house 80 feet long for drying the material; will not be put up at present. The mill is on No. 6, and is a three-story frame, 60 by 75 feet, engine-room 40 by 50, uses the Keith process. The furnace and stack, with a large cooling room, occupy a great proportion of the body of the mill. There is a Blake cracker, three large-sized ball-pulverizers, the desulphurizing furnace, three large burnishers, dolly-tub, and fifteen shaking-tables. The engine is 100-horse power, and with the addition of a little more burnishing machinery the capacity of the mill would be thirty tons a day. The process, says the agent, Col. C. L. Grafflin, after a trial of six months, gives entire satisfaction, saving 80 per cent. of the gold even in poor ores. The Company have 1750 tons of tailings, considered worth $20 a ton. Also a 16-stamp, steam mill in running order in Gamble Gulch, half a mile from the lode. Also a great deal of undeveloped lode property, ranches, buildings in Gold Dirt, Sonora, &c., &c. The agent is a model man, and has almost worn his life out trying, for the last three years, to make the enterprise a success for its owners.

The Eagle Gold Mining Company own Discovery, No's 1 and 2 east, and No. 5 west on the Gold Dirt Lode. On No. 1 they have an engine-house and 50-horse engine, shaft 180 feet deep, cribbed four by nine feet in the clear, to the bottom, now sinking at the rate of a foot a day and to be sunk in future without cessation. Discovery shaft is 150 feet deep, cribbed four by eight feet, not worked. Have shaft on No. 2, 185 feet deep, cribbed four by eight feet, not worked. There is a line of shafting to the wing shafts, houses and hoisting rig complete. The vein is about two feet wide, and considered worth $40 to $50 a ton. The ore is badly streaked with hematite iron, and has nothing in it that can be got with stamp-mill. One hundred and forty feet down, the mine is drifted from end to end, and above that the ground was worked out in 1860 by Sweet & Hollister, yielding $150,000. They calculate to find a vein of the same richness as the surface by going deep enough and they have started for it. No. 5 has never been opened; neither has any of the rest of the Company's lodes. They have a first-class 50-stamp mill at the mouth of Gamble Gulch. The building is 75 by 90 feet, contains the batteries, plates, 60-horse engine and boilers, and that is all. It was run through June, 1865, but without paying result. It was shut up and is likely to remain so until further developments in the art of treating Colorado ores. The Company have a boarding-house, barn, and other necessary buildings near their mill on South Boulder. E. J. Sweet is their agent, a man whose experience in Colorado mining and milling is perhaps second to that of none.

The Rollins Gold Company own 400 lode claims in Independent and South Boulder Districts. On the Maurer, which is not far from the Gold Dirt, they have two deep shafts and a very large ore crevice, an engine-house 40 by 50 feet with engine and hoisting rig complete, and a shaft-house 35 by 40 feet. On the Perigo, which is top of the hill opposite the Gold Dirt and a mile distant, they have four deep shafts, an engine-house 40 by 50 with engine and hoisting works. On these as well as on the New York & Benton, the Company are mining with energy. Among their less developed lodes, considered good if not first-class, are the Bateman, Wisconsin, Boston, Subterranean, Kansas, and War Eagle. On the South Boulder, just above the mouth of Gamble Gulch, the General Director of the Company, J. Q A. Rollins, has laid off a town-site, and called it South Boulder. The main street curves regularly with the creek, and along its lower side a race has been located, five thousand feet long, calculated to carry the entire Boulder, and furnishing 15 water-lots of 300 feet front each with power for mills. On the other side of the street, which is 60 feet wide, a tier of building lots, each 40 by 80 feet, has been surveyed. Beyond this is another street parallel with the first with its double tier of building lots the same size as the above. The spot is 25 miles from Golden Gate over an excellent wagon-road ; 20 from Boulder City over the old Gordon Road, ten north from Central City ; and on any road that shall ever enter the Middle Park via. the Boulder Pass. This town-site covers a beautiful, natural park, about half or three-fourths of a mile wide by a mile and a half long, the north side of it, along which are the surveyed streets, most delightfully turned up to the kiss of the sun. They have made forty tons of hay along the creek bottom this season, and a crop of 3000 bushels of vegetables. The Company's mill and other buildings are located in this park. The mill is 76 by 90 feet in dimensions, built like a pair of stairs against the creek bank, each bent forming a step. It has two sets of Gardner's quartz machinery in it, one for dry, the other for wet crushing. The wet side has been in operation since the 18th of July and gives perfect satisfaction to Mr. Rollins. First there is Gardner's Thunderbolt crusher; on the next story, or bent, or step below, Gardner's Thundermug pulverizer, a huge cast-iron pan with an oscillatory motion rolling round a 6000-lb. ball, a perfect triumph of mechanical skill; on the next story below a set of concentrators, small round iron boxes with screen-blowers in them, designed to beat up the clay and liberate and catch the coarse gold in little pockets attached to them; on the next story below a Gardner's amalgamator, an iron bowl of peculiar construction whirling rapidly within a bowl, the motion expected to keep the "quick" on the sides of the bowl and throw out the slimes over the edge. This is found to work well. They have added two shaking-tables to all this, on which they get very little. The dry side of the mill has the Thunderbolt crusher, a huge mortar with a 6000-lb. pestle turned by the handle, a set of Wilson's fire-clay cylinders for desulphurizing, an iron dolly-tub, another mortar like the one above for burnishing, another dolly-tub, then the Evans amalgamator, a segment of a circle rocking on its periphery. This was started in July last, but the reels in the fire retorts were soon eaten up, and it could not run. New reels, coated with porcelain, are *en route*, and much is hoped from the process when they shall have been put in. The machinery in this mill is of the best make and well put up. The Company have a steam saw-mill at the mouth of Gamble Gulch, quartz-house, 60 by 80 feet, barn, boarding-house, smith-shop, market-house, and four or five log dwellings. They have constructed several miles of wagon road in the vicinity. They have also a 6-stamp and a 12-stamp mill in Gamble Gulch, not in repair nor used. John Q. A. Rollins, of South Boulder, the most energetic man in the whole world, is General Director.

The Perigo Mining and Tunneling Company have several hundred feet of improved property on the Perigo Lode, an engine-house and hoisting works, mine pump, and two or three deep shafts.*

The Excelsior Gold Mining Company are tearing out forty stamps, which have never been used, and a Crosby & Thompson furnace, which has not been much used, from their mill in South Boulder Park. It is the intention of the Company to soon put up another set of the Crosby & Thompson machinery, with some important modifications.*   The Excel-

---

*This Company have leased their mines and premises to W. E. Darby, of Gold Dirt, for a term of two years. He proposes to get out ore and have it treated by the Keith machinery in the Hope Company's mill, about a mile distant.

†Under the head of Processes for Treating Ores, will be found the latest ideas of these gentlemen with regard to desulphurizing and amalgamating. They believe that after three years of trial and difficulty, they have at last perfected what is called their process.

sior Company own property on the Parker, Thomas,
and Hope, in Phœnix District, adjoining South
Boulder on the north. They are considered good
lodes. They also have property on the Revenue,
in South Boulder, and the Illinois, in Central District (Lump Gulch).

The Illinois Gold Mining Company, represented
by Crosby & Thompson, are mining and have built
a mill building on the Illinois Lode; none of the
machinery set up but the engine, which is used
simply for hoisting. Have one shaft 80, and one
60 feet deep, drifted together 40 feet from the surface, fair show of ore, lode reputed very rich. Aus-
tin, DuBois & Co., long ago used to run a mill on
quartz from the Illinois, and other lodes in the
District, with fair success. No one is now operating in the District but the Illinois Company.

Horton, Frothingham & Jones, have tried very
hard to succeed with the Crosby & Thompson
machinery, but as yet to no purpose. They are
now using one of the cylinders as a burnisher,
filling it half full of small boulders and passing the
desulphurized ore through it from one end to the
other. This seems to us to answer its purpose the
best of any machine we have seen. They are also
trying the Crosby amalgamator, consisting of a
cast-iron mercury tank holding 1000 pounds, connected with a hollow wooden column, perhaps eight
feet high. Conveyed into the top of this column,
the ore is forced by its own weight up through the
mercury tank, as the easiest escape. In the mercury play back and forth slotted copper-plates,

evolving electricity, which purifies and enlivens the quicksilver, and securing, by a minute division of the ore, perfect contact. When they first started this machine, careful tests indicated that they were doing well; but after a certain period the longer they ran the less gold was there in the quicksilver.* So they have stopped work and are going East for the Winter. Whether the Crosby & Thompson cylinders can be made to thoroughly calcine ores without destroying them by the heat and gases liberated, yet remains to be proven in Colorado. Horton, Frothingham & Jones have property on the Revenue and Illinois Lodes, considerably improved but not worked at present.

The National Gold Mining Company, arose on the ruins of "The Pittsburgh and Rocky Mountain Gold Mining Company," which was organized on property in Wisconsin District, better known perhaps as Mammoth City, in Boston as early as 1862. They brought on a 50-stamp mill, but before they got into operation ran out of money, fell to quarrelling, and were sold out by the sheriff. The present Company own some 300 lode claims in the District and in 1865 built a complete Crosby &

---

* From this most astounding and perplexing, not to say provoking, circumstance, repeated a few times, Crosby was led to the belief that the gold, after chemically uniting with the mercury, commenced oxydizing and escaping in an impalpable form. Careful experiments seemed to confirm the idea, and finally, so far as he was concerned, establish the fact. A patent was taken out covering the supposed discovery, and, of course, the proposed remedy, and in the beginning of February of the current year, Crosby went back to Colorado from Boston to put new works in operation. But of this more hereafter. See the chapter on Processes.

Thompson mill. Before it fairly started, the Company shut down. They have driven a tunnel into each bank of the creek about 160 feet, designing to strike with each eight or ten of their best lodes at great depths. On one lode they have a shaft 90 feet deep, good whim-house and whim, and an ore vein two feet in width. They have also a barn, boarding-house, store, etc.

The Invincible Gold Mining Company, represented by C. C. Welch of Central, divide the best property of the District with the National. They have six to seven thousand feet of lodes, one of which they are working, saw-mill, water powers, &c. The Sampson is on the extreme head of North Clear Creek, has a shaft 60 feet deep, two feet of ore, assaying $40 to $50 a ton. It is being developed by Mr. Welch.

Peck Gulch lies between Wisconsin District and Central City, and is the extreme head of Chase Gulch. Its chief vein is the Mann, owned by W. J. Mann, and B. F. Pease, developed to a depth of 60 feet, where its crevice is eight feet wide, two-thirds of it ore. Mann & Pease have a 12-stamp steam mill near the lode, in running order, and in which the surface quartz paid from $5 to $18.50 a ton. The ore they could not make pay. It prospects very rich. They have about 300 tons of ore out and design to soon start the mill again on surface quartz. There are several other lodes in the vicinity, less developed but considered good.

The Caledonia Gold Mining Company own 361 feet on the Caledonia, the great lode of Wide

10*

Awake District, which the reader will remember is seven miles North of Black Hawk at the head of Missouri Gulch. Have one shaft 267 feet deep, one 140 feet, and four others, 25, 45, 90, and 130 feet, some showing a good vein, and some not. Shaft-house 30 by 30 feet, 10-horse engine, complete hoisting rig for two shafts, smith-shop, &c. Have an old 6-stamp, steam mill, also a new mill, 30 by 50 feet, 40-horse Little Giant engine, and Crosby & Thompson machinery throughout; mill built, machinery not set up, not at work. Sam Cushman of Central, agent.

The Washington and Wallace Companies, own property considerably developed, on the Wallace, Washington, and Wide Awake lodes. Neither have mill nor machinery, nor are they at work at present. Sam Cushman of Central, agent.

The Mountain Eagle Company—property on the Caledonia. Have a 9-stamp, steam mill, are mining and running mill, quartz yields about $15 a ton. S. B. Morgan of Black Hawk, agent.

David Clow has a new 12-stamp, steam mill and property on Caledonia. Is at work with average success.

All these districts have the advantages of cheap fuel, lumber, and mine timber, of pasturage, and most of them of water power.

CHAPTER IX.

CLEAR CREEK COUNTY is so located as to just
embrace the country drained by *South* Clear Creek.
The reader will please remember that Clear Creek
forks fourteen miles within the Foot-hills from
Golden City. At that point corner Gilpin and
Clear Creek Counties, one meant to cover the
north, the other the south fork of the Creek. From
this point to the crest of the Range, South Clear
Creek forms a gigantic tree, as it were, forty miles
in extreme length, worn down into the surface of
the wilderness of upward-sweeping hills and ridges
from one to five thousand feet in depth. All along
its trunk and throughout its main limbs and smaller
branches, Nature has hidden her treasures of gold
and silver, her jewels and precious stones ; and as
if determined for once to be magnificent, has not
only well-marked her *cache*, but grouped here the
indispensable means of unearthing and rendering
them useful to man. The enclosing hills are low

and often smooth, grassy, and sunny, receding and ascending gradually and affording means of easy access. There are many bars of considerable size, smooth and pretty, offering delightful sites for towns, excellent places for mills and mining works. There is abundance of fuel, and unlimited "range" on the hill-sides for stock. Six hundred feet of the creek gives, with the volume that may be used, on a turbine wheel, a power of one hundred horses, and the valley is so open that there is hardly any point for ten miles where powers can not be taken out on both sides, making for this distance, one hundred and eighty in all. Taking the two forks with their forks into the calculation, it is not too much to say that they and the main stream furnish, from Grass Valley Bar to their sources, six hundred first-class water-powers. The bars were somewhat mined in the early days of Colorado, but that, as has been before observed, has now pretty much ceased.

The quartz mines now engage the principal effort. These are considered first-class, and are almost universally well located for tunneling. The advantages of tunneling where the ground will permit — for instance, where there is ample room on the creeks for the rubble, and where the hills rise at an angle of 45° or more from the streams to a great hight — can hardly be overestimated. Its cost in Colorado at present is between $25 and $30 a foot. All ground above the tunnel may be broken *down* instead of *up*, which in itself is a great saving of time, labor, and powder, as every practical miner knows. The water runs off through the tunnel and the ore may be conveyed on dump cars through the same channel into the mill, saving costly hoisting and pumping machinery and power, the construction of surface roads, a great deal of heavy teaming, and excavating for whim and shaft houses. And in the mill which uses hydraulic power, fuel and machinery are economized. It would seem that mining by means of tunnels and treating by water instead of steam mills, ought to pay handsome dividends on unwatered capitals on ten-dollar rock, provided the veins are of average size, regularity, and richness. And where a tunnel can attain a depth of one, two, or three thousand feet in the course of a reasonable length, the ground above will be seen to be clear gain when it is remembered that beyond a certain depth it is unprofitable to mine, because the expense of hoisting the ore and water overbalance the value of the ore. The advantages of unlimited water power and mining by tunnels are common to every part of Clear Creek County.

Idaho, the county-seat, is situate on Payne's Bar, at the mouth of Virginia Kanyon, seven miles above the junction of North and South Clear Creeks. Good wagon roads radiate from Idaho to Denver, thirty-five miles east, to Central City, six miles north, and to Empire and Georgetown, twelve miles west. It is nearly 8000 feet above the sea, and is noted not only for its mines but for its hot soda springs, which have been improved until they are a most delightful place of resort. The waters, internally or externally, or both, have valuable medicinal properties, especially in rheumatic and cutaneous ailments. There is a large, pleasant hotel, owned and kept by F. W. Bebee in the best style. Payne's Bar is expansive and smooth, and the hills opposite on the south are toned down by the channels, near together, of Soda and Chicago Creeks, the latter the first place where gold was discovered in the county, and its surroundings scarred by the operations of the early miners. These hills are covered with the finest turf and in the right season are one bed of flowers. They are topped out by mountains rising to a hight of 11,000 to 12,000 feet, locally named "Old Chief," "Old Squaw," and "Papoose." It is about two or three miles below Idaho where the mines begin, extending thence on the main stream to Empire, thirteen miles above, and on the left fork to its extreme sources, twenty-five miles.*

At the mouth of Fall River, three miles above Idaho, there is a post office, hotel, and stores; at the mouth of Mill Creek, four miles further up, another post office, hotel, stores, &c.; two miles above the Creek forks, and two miles still above is the town of Empire.

Of all the towns brought into existence by the fame of Cherry Creek sand, Empire bears away the palm for a pretty location and picturesque surroundings. Imagine a lively stream, a hop-step-

---

*Between North and South Clear Creeks, below Idaho, occurs a vein or deposit of milk opal, some specimens having caught the slightest breath, perhaps, of a flame. No valuable opals have been found as yet, but that is not saying that there will not be.

and-jump over, tumbling and rushing toward sunrise forever at the bottom of an open kanyon two
thousand to four thousand feet in depth. Formed by
million trinklets from thousand heavy snow wreaths,
in sight, it is pure, clear, and cool. Two brooks,
Lyons' from the north, and Bard's from the south,
flow into the main stream opposite each other, their
deltas, with the natural bars of the creek, forming
the town-plat. With a little trimming it would be
square, the corners toward the cardinal points.
Four mountains, Lincoln, Douglas, Covode, and
Eureka, constitute bold promontories, perhaps a
thousand feet in altitude, between the creeks. Ascend either of these, and from the successive hights
still before you, you seem yet in the valley, and so
you are comparatively, although 10,000 feet above
the sea. The scenery is Alpine, and the elevation,
being 8,871 feet above sea level, the climate, Summer and Winter, is salubrious and tonic. The bar
has a considerable elevation above the creek, and
is too heavy to invite the labors of the bar miner,
so that it is still smooth and grassy.

A mile north, up a tremendous hill, (1400 feet)
are the Empire mines, and the town of North Empire ; it and Georgetown and Elizabethtown, the
last two the same, located at the forks of the South
Fork, about five miles south of Empire, will be noticed with their mines. The most important mines
of the county are undoubtedly at Empire, or at
and above Georgetown, but our description will
perhaps be more intelligible if we begin at one end
of the county and go through it regularly.

THE IDAHO MINES.

Commencing, then, two or three miles below Idaho, we have half a dozen veins lying near together, the property of "The Federal Union Mining Company," at present represented by Gen. N. B. Buford of Rock Island, Ill. The General has erected some necessary buildings, a bridge over the creek, cut a race, and is building a wooden mill 50 by 70, into which he intends to put ten Mexican arastras. His power is water, used on a large turbine wheel. He is also mining, on the General Buford by adit, now fifty feet long ; on the Moline by incline, and on the Deerfield by shaft.

At Idaho there is much good mining property, but the greater part of it is idle. That of Womack and Seaton, comprising the Seaton and other lodes and a mill and water power in town, has been in the English market for a year or two ; what the prospects of closing the transaction are, we are uninformed.

The mill property of "The Lowe Mining Association" is in Idaho, and consists of a 12-stamp, water mill, running on the ores of the different companies for which Mr. T. H. Lowe, of Idaho, is agent. "The Lowe Mining Association" are taking excellent ore from the Seaton, No. 8, west. "The Kentucky and Colorado Mining Company" are getting out good ore from the Robinson, head of Virginia Kanyon, three miles north of Idaho. "The Louisville & Mill City Company" are developing the Rufus Snyder in Morris District, six miles above

Idaho.   Mr. Lowe is agent for these companies with head-quarters at Idaho.   They are confining themselves to developing their mines and getting out ores, a wise policy for the present.

"The Fulton Mining Company," represented by W. E. Sisty of Idaho, have their mine on the Crystal — crossing Virginia Kanyon a mile north of Idaho—well opened.   They have 361 contiguous feet including Discovery, upon which they have sunk 100 feet and drifted 100, the vein in the drift being from fifteen to thirty inches in width, ore worth $80 a ton by actual test, and 300 to 500 tons out.   They have taken some steps toward building a mill on Payne's Bar, and while they hesitate as to what they want, mining is suspended.

"The Star Gold Mining Company" own 1200 feet on the Crystal, west of Virginia Kanyon, from which they have run an adit west 200 feet, intersecting a shaft 153 feet deep, showing, said the agent to us, a fair crevice.   Three hundred feet west is another shaft 123 feet deep, in cap; and 300 feet further is another 65 feet deep, also in cap.   They have a water power 1500 feet long, 18 feet head, upper end of Payne's Bar, wooden mill building 55 by 100 feet, raised, and enclosed, machinery for forty stamps on the Missouri River.   They have besides a great deal of lode property from Idaho to Empire, and other valuable water powers.

SPANISH BAR.

Two miles above Idaho is Spanish Bar.   Famous in early times for its bar diggings, the deposit was too deep, the boulders too many and heavy, and the water too troublesome for bar mining to generally pay, and but little of the bed-rock was ever uncovered. Very rich quartz veins were early discovered on the abutting hills, and "The Silver Spring Mining Company" started a 20-stamp water mill in 1861 which ran pretty steadily for two years on surface material from the Whale, Lincoln, and other noted lodes in the vicinity. As much as $20,000 was taken from Discovery on the Whale.

Messrs. Thatch & Kinkead own a 12-stamp, water mill here, in good repair, and 3000 feet on the Cook, Anoka County, Phœnix, and Newcastle Lodes, all on the south side of the creek and coming down very near the mill, the Cook under it. On this an adit runs in, creek level, 180 feet, intersecting a shaft thirty feet deep near the entrance, and having one sunk thirty feet below, at its inner end. The vein shows a regular four-foot crevice of rich ore and quartz on and near the surface, but does not appear so well in the adit and deeper shaft. It is, however, considered one of the best lodes in the county. The Anoka County has a shaft forty feet deep, the other lodes are unimproved. Negotiations for the sale of the property East have been under way for a year or two.

"The Whale Mining Company" was organized in 1864 on the Whale and other lodes in the vicinity. The Whale comes down the face of the south mountain directly across the bar. An adit, starting 100 feet above the creek, has been driven in 277 feet, intersecting there a shaft 225 feet in depth.

The vein underlies at an angle of 30 to 40 degrees, and the shaft has a solid, smooth foot-wall all the way. The vein has been pinched and pockety both in the shaft and adit. Considerable ore was taken out of two levels and a shaft nearer the surface. The Company have a brick mill building on the bar the body of which is 75 by 139 feet, intended for 128 Bertola stamps, (weighing but about 300 lbs. each) an iron Chilian mill for each battery, tanks for catching the crushed ore, and tanks for treating it by Bertola process. Attached to the mill are two wings, each 50 by 75 feet, designed for fifty Bertola pans each, in which the ore is ground and amalgamated after its chemical steam bath. Six hundred feet above the mill a substantial dam has been put in, giving with the race a fall of 12 or 14 feet. There are two large turbine wheels, one at each end of the building. But a small part of the machinery has yet arrived, and only sixteen stamps, four Chilians, and ten pans have been set up. Mr. Thomas B. Moseley, Vice-President of the Company, has just arrived out, and means to see if *he* can make the Bertola process work. If successful, the rest of the machinery will be set up. The mill is a mammoth and substantial concern, the power ample, the mine believed to be good from its surface character, the Bertola process works satisfactorily in New York, and it is to be hoped the enterprise may prove a success.

" The South Clear Creek Gold and Silver Mining Company" are located a little way above Spanish Bar, on the north side of the creek and where the

Lincoln Lode is supposed to cross and become the Oro. An adit has been run in about on the creek level 135 feet, intersecting a shaft 65 feet deep; ore-vein from eight to ten inches in width throughout the adit, 50 to 60 tons of ore out. They have 900 feet of water power, substantial dam, flume-race 550 feet long giving fifteen feet fall, center-vent turbine wheel, 100-horse. Stone mill building on the lode 50 by 60, twenty stamps, two Freiberg pans, and Crosby & Thompson desulphurizer. Mr. D. B. Myres is the agent of the Company, and he has a nice, snug arrangement and a promising mine. He is mining and milling.

Mr. Myres is also opening the Summit Lode, head of Hukill Gulch—opposite Spanish Bar—for some parties in Chicago who will organize a stock company to work it if it shall prove good. Twenty feet down it shows a large quartz crevice which prospects at the rate of ten cents a pound.

"The United States Mining and Ore Decomposing Company" own a good deal of valuable property on Hukill Gulch. The Company's affairs are in a somewhat unsettled state, but before they became so they had done considerable work on the Edgar and Union, supposed extensions of the Hukill, developing on the Edgar, a vein of most beautiful ore fifteen inches in width.

"The Alden Tunnel Company" own sixteen full lodes lying parallel and near together on the face of the north mountain. They are driving a tunnel which in the course of 700 feet will cut them all, the last 700 feet deep; now in 138 feet at a cost of

$28 a foot. They have a water power, opposite the Whale Company's, 600 feet long, twelve feet fall, and are building a stone mill 40 by 90 feet, with wing 20 by 40 feet, designed for any process, including smelting, that careful tests of the ores may indicate as the best. They have other necessary buildings and are doing business with economy and energy.

"The Garden City Gold Mining Company" have started an adit on the Garden City Lode, which develops most encouragingly, just above the Alden Company's works, and designed to cut the same or a similar belt of lodes cropping out on the surface. They are in 85 feet, will go on 500 feet further, and then, being well under the mountain, break sharply to the left and cut their lodes, of which they have fourteen, at right angles. Mr. J. M. Dumont is attending to the business of the last two companies.

TRAIL RUN DISTRICT.

Trail Run comes in from the south-west, just above Spanish Bar. It rises very fast for about three miles, where it heads in a thick pine forest. A mile from its mouth, and high on the left mountain occur the Kelley and Champion Dirt Lodes.

"The Hale Gold Mining Company" have here a new mill, large alligator cracker, Kingsley's pulverizer (worthless,) and Keith shaking-table. The quartz is taken from an adit on the Kelley, and is run down to the mill on a wooden track 1400 feet long. The mill is to be supplied with a different pulverizer; the quartz is worth by actual test about $40 a ton in gold and silver.

A mile further up, the Freeland Lode crosses the run, opened, on both sides, for 4000 feet. For eighteen hundred feet of this distance there are two shafts on every claim, the deepest 285 feet. Some of the shafts and surface gouging have caved in; others are in good condition, a few being worked. The vein is one of the strongest in the county.

Just where the Freeland crosses the run is a cluster of mills, houses, &c., affectionately called "Bonito." Here is the primitive 6-stamp mill of Captain Anshutz, which Dr. E. F. Holland is running with reasonable success.

A little further up, "The Colvin Gold Mining Company" are making preparations to build a mill for the Keith process. They are also mining on No's 12, and 13 west on the Freeland, getting out some beautiful quartz. B. R. Colvin is the agent of this Company.

Next above is the mill of "The Baltic Gold Mining Company." It is intended for twenty stamps and ten Freiberg pans, which machinery is on the ground but not in place. This Company own No's 9 and 10, west, on the Freeland, and have sunk 150 feet, crevice pinched.

Three miles from Clear Creek is the mill of "The Noble Gold Mining Company," represented by J. Alden Smith. The mill has ten new 750-lb. stamps, short plates and shaking-table, also a Crosby & Thompson desulphurizer. The Company have mines on the Freeland, French, Jim Mulligan, and other lodes that prospect well.

Among other noted lodes of the District are the Tennel, Capital, Black-earth, Holman, Plutus, Coyote, Holland, Leavenworth; some of these have been largely developed. The District is easily accessible from Clear Creek, and is covered with a dense growth of pines.

FALL RIVER DISTRICT.

Fall River debouches into Clear Creek from the north-west, above the mouth of Trail Run, perhaps half a mile. It is seven or eight miles long, generally within an hour's ride of Central City, and its right bank, easily accessible and open to the sun, is almost as regularly pitted with prospect holes as a harvested potato patch. It is estimated that 1500 lodes have been discovered and pre-empted on the stream.* It carries enough water at all seasons, besides supplying the Consolidated Ditch, to run the largest reduction works, and has a heavy fall. Commencing at its mouth it has Iowa, Lower Fall River, Lincoln, Cumberland, and Upper Fall River Mining Districts.

A mile above its mouth, on the right, on the same hill that heads Russell Gulch, are the lodes of "The Equitable Gold Mining Company." They are run-

---

* It is a misnomer to call these *lodes;* for the most part they are nothing but potato patch holes, only they are in yellow dirt. If five, or one in each hundred claimed proves a valuable mine, the owners may feel well satisfied, for they will in that case have been fortunate.

ning an adit on the Calendar, and a tunnel 400 feet
above, designed to strike the Wilson, Chicago, Noye,
Red and New, which crop out on the surface. Also
building a dam, and preparing to build a mill ; have
600 feet of water power, abreast of their lodes, with
24 feet fall ; work carried on by J. M. Dumont.

Not far above these, Mr. Dumont is running a
tunnel into the right bank, calculated to strike the
following lodes, lying parallel on the face of the
mountain and running nearly east and west like
those at the head of Russell Gulch, of which they
are undoubtedly the extension, west; Jones, Cook
County, Advent, Briggs, Red, Cedar, and O K, all
struck on the surface. The hill is excessively steep
and 2000 feet high. A tunnel will gain more in
depth than in length.

A mile further up are the mines of "The Fall
River Gold Mining Company," organized in 1864.
They have run a tunnel 100 feet into the right bank,
designed to cut a belt of parallel lodes at great
depth ; also an adit 100 feet on the Pulaski, crevice
pinched. They have a dwelling-house but no mill
nor machinery. Sam Cushman of Central, is their
agent.

Next above is the property of "The Montrose
Gold Company of Colorado." They have sundry
feet on the Phillips, Almy, Buffalo, and twenty other
lodes. The Phillips paid largely in sluice and mill
on and near the surface. It has shaft more than
100 feet deep, vein pinched. The Almy has shaft
50 or 60 feet in depth ; walls smooth and perpendicular and 4 1-2 feet apart, crevice material pros-

pects moderately.   Have a mill on Fall River 40 by 94 feet, wheel-house 20 by 36, two-story dwelling-house 20 by 30 with a wing 13 by 23, well-finished, a boarding-house large enough to accommodate forty hands, barn, smith-shop, &c.   Water-power 1000 feet in length, 50 feet fall.   The mill contains eighteen stamps and four or five Dodge pans.   J. G. Mahany is the agent of the Company.

The most improved lodes of Upper Fall River are the Hardup, Ross, Sullivan, McClellan, Estelle. The Hardup has a shaft 127 feet deep, two feet of pure ore, assays $270 a ton.   The McClellan has two shafts, 45 and 60 feet deep, average 18-inch vein of ore, assays $300 a ton.   The Sullivan has four shafts from 25 to 50 feet deep, good dirt and quartz crevice, prospecting rich.   The Ross can be seen for 400 feet on the almost perpendicular side of a mountain, one edge of the ore crevice, forever covered with snow.   A good deal of work has been done on it.   Mary's Lode is another like the Ross, plunging for 200 yards down the face of the mountain into Mary's Lake, a sheet of water of five or six acres whence flows the right fork of the river. There are three Eastern and home companies in the District—"The Union," "The Black Eagle," and "The Fall River."   To the former belongs the deep shaft on the Hardup, much other improved and first-class lode property, and a 12-stamp, steam mill, 25-horse engine, and water power 500 feet long.   There is also an 8-stamp mill in the district, both of them in running order.   There is abundance of grass and timber in the vicinity ; six tons of hay

11

were made just below Mary's Lake in 1861. It is
the lower part of the basin whence issues the right
or east branch of Fall River, that it has been con-
templated to make into a great water reservoir, to
supply, through the Consolidated Ditch, the mines
of Gregory District with water. Referred to at
length under the head of Gilpin County.

MORRIS AND DOWNIEVILLE DISTRICTS.

These lie between Fall River and the forks of
the creek, and their business is so mingled that we
can better notice them under one head.

Half a mile above Fall River, Turkey Run comes
down from the south. On its bar are located the
works of "The Syracuse Gold and Silver Mining
Company," represented by George Copeland, a man
more experienced in mines and more original than
any other man in the whole world. They have 7000
to 8000 feet of mining property on both sides of
the creek and not very far from their mill, in condition to be worked for quartz when it shall be desirable. Have cut race and dug wheel-pit, and are
building dam and mill designed for a stone arastra
twenty-five feet in diameter, and to have twelve
heavy stone mullers. Mean to get in operation in
the Spring of 1867.

Between Fall River and Mill Creek comes in
Spring Gulch from the north. It is comparatively
a new district but has some noble veins, among
them the Golconda, very large crevice and very
rich quartz. "The Osceola Company" have a
10-stamp steam mill in the district, running occa-

sionally. From the Golconda they crushed for three months in 1865, the yield varying from $25 to $30 a ton. An arastra has taken as high as $45 a ton from a small lot. It is a pretty place, about two miles from Clear Creek, the hills smoothly-turfed and accessible by wagon, timber abundant, water rather scarce. The veins are numerous, strong, and rich, but not much developed.

A little way above the mouth of Spring Gulch is the mill of "The Adrian Gold Mining Company," stamps and pans, somewhat out of repair. The Company own property on the Hiawatha, north of the creek and just west of Spring Gulch, largely improved, and a great deal other in the vicinity, developed but little.

"The Boston & Chicago Company," represented by W. R. Hawkins of Mill City (mouth of Mill Creek, coming from the north-west, about four miles above the mouth of Fall River), are sinking a shaft, now down 140 feet, and running an adit and tunnel, now in 40 feet, on a supposed cross-lode called the Herring. In the course of 900 feet the adit will intersect the shaft 450 feet from the surface, crossing meanwhile half a dozen other lodes. The shaft is ten feet between walls, no well-defined vein of ore yet, but mixed through the crevice. Have built some necessary buildings and are pursuing a wise policy in developing their mines before erecting expensive reduction-works.

"The Piasaw Gold Mining Company," represented by G. B. Reed of Central, have run an adit 193 feet on the Piasaw, near the mouth of Mill

Creek, and are now sinking a shaft at the inner end of the adit. The indications are extremely encouraging.

"The Downieville Gold Mining Company" are mining on the Albro; have a shaft 132 feet deep intersecting an adit 200 feet long, two feet of good-looking ore; also mining on the Ohio and other lodes south of the creek. Have a 12-stamp water mill in operation. John Young, of Central City, agent.

"The Mill City Mining Company" own property on the Ulster County, Keystone, Washington, Richmond, etc., developed by shafts from 50 to 100 feet in depth. Frame mill near the mouth of Mill Creek, 50 by 90, intended for the Mason process of desulphurizing in a sort of lime-kiln furnace by superheated steam. The furnace is a cupola, seven feet in diameter by twelve high, and desulphurizes satisfactorily, thirty-five tons a day, using one and a half cords of wood. The difficulty is in amalgamating. The mill has two Dodge crackers, four pairs of burr-stones, let us say once and for all *worthless* for pulverizing raw ores, Dodge shaking-table and arastra.

"The Bullion Gold Mining Company" are mining on the Hiawatha in Downieville District, supposed to be an extension of the celebrated Hiawatha of Morris District. They have a Bertola mill on Clear Creek, incomplete, twenty-four stamps, twenty-four pans, power, turbine wheel, running occasionally as it can get quartz. They have 400 feet on the Hiawatha in Morris District, shaft 110 feet deep, lode considered one of the best in the county.

John Young of Central has a mill on Mill Creek, 35 by 42, power, overshot wheel; contains a Bullock crusher (Chilian principle) and stone arastra. Has 1300 feet on the Silver Star, considered as good as any lode in the district of the same development; average of a five-foot crevice assayed $73 a ton in gold and silver.

Jacob Snyder is mining for a Philadelphia company, driving an adit and sinking a shaft on the Albro, and running an arastra by water on surface quartz, manufacturing about a ton per day and getting $40 from it; vein averages fourteen inches in width.

UNION DISTRICT—EMPIRE MINES.

We have before located the town of Empire. It is at the mouth of Lyon's Gulch. Half a mile up, it forks, and between the forks, is Silver Mountain, rising very fast and soon to everlasting baldness and snow-banks. On its south-eastern exposure are the principal mines, and within a mile of the forks. Almost the entire of this face of the mountain has been sluiced off by water brought in a ditch four and one-half miles, from the head of Mill Creek. In places it seems to be quartz, *en masse*, and it is full of large and small mineral seams. The strongest veins are the Rosecrans and Atlantic; the Silver Mountain and Ben Franklin, the Tenth Legion, the Roland, the latter not yet defined, but underlying a mass of quartz 40 feet wide by 500 long, from which the dirt has been sluiced to a depth of 30 feet, and paying under stamps from $7 to $85 a ton. If these are not the strongest, richest veins, they are the most improved. Several Eastern companies have been formed on them, and they own property and have done work as follows:

"The Leibig Gold Mining and Mill Company" have 133 feet on Tenth Legion, shaft 115 feet deep, tunnel in to and under the shaft, striking it 225 feet from the surface; tunnel 350 feet long. Vein struck near the mouth of the tunnel called Leibig, drifted on 70 feet, shows a crevice of quartz and ore which pays well from one to three feet wide. Have 600 feet on the Northrup, above and running parallel with Tenth Legion; shaft 75 feet deep, good show; also 600 feet on the Winnebago, shaft 65 feet deep, adit 50 feet in length, good vein; much other undeveloped lode property. Frame mill on Clear Creek 45 by 102 feet, Keith furnace, calculated for 25 tons a day; Dodge cracker, ball-pulverizer, shaking tables, &c.; power, double-vent, turbine wheel, 26 feet head, all the water they can use. J. E. Leeper, of Empire, is the agent. Mining on Leibig and Tenth Legion and milling.

"The Bay State Gold Mining Company" have 350 feet on Tenth Legion, a tunnel intended to strike it, Silver Mountain and Livingston County, from 300 to 500 feet from the surface, now in 415 feet; gone through five lodes not known on the surface; shaft between the Holton and Boston, dipping together, intersects the tunnel 150 feet from its mouth, and is continued below 71 feet to the junction of the two crevices,—in all 160 feet from the surface; from 12 to 20 inches of ore at the bot-

tom of the shaft. Further down the hill, another
tunnel, designed to strike the same lodes at a greater
depth, has been driven 380 feet. Have much undeveloped lode property, own a steam 12-stamp mill
(Old Candee Mill) at the forks of Lyons' Creek,
to which they have added a Crosby & Thompson
desulphurizer, Collom separator, and Eaton amalgamator. Have a steam saw-mill at North Empire
in operation, and silver lodes on Douglas Mountain and Snake River acquired since the formation
of the Company. John Collom of Empire, an experienced Lake Superior miner, is the agent.

"The Star Gold Mining Company" have 780
feet on the Silver Mountain, one shaft 125 feet deep,
one 65, level at the bottom of the latter 160 feet
long, winze below level 25 feet, vein of first-class
ore two feet in width. Have 40-horse portable engine and 8-inch pump on the lode ready to put up.
Have property on the Rosecrans and Haskins, and
own a steam-mill (Old Tennessee) twenty-four
stamps, five pans, in running order, on west fork of
Lyon's Creek. Have very valuable mine and mill
property near Idaho, heretofore noticed. No agent
at present, property unproductive.

"The Knickerbocker Gold Mining Company"
have property on Tenth Legion, shaft 180 feet deep,
very strong vein of first-class gold ore, steam-hoisting works ; complete 24-stamp, water mill on Clear
Creek, one of the finest water powers and mills in
Colorado. Represented by George C. Munson.

"The Peck Gold Mining Company" have 500
feet on the Atlantic, high up on the mountain, from

which tne ore is run down by wooden rail 1500 feet to mill in North Empire. Shaft 225 feet deep, portable engine of 20 to 30-horse power, for hoisting, ten-foot crevice, half ore, coarse iron pyrites, the rest white quartz impregnated with iron pyrites, pays about $15 a ton; 1000 tons of ore out. Have 12-stamp, steam-mill in North Empire, to be repaired and enlarged in capacity. James Peck, of Empire, represents the Company.

"The Humboldt Gold Mining Company" have 250 feet on the Humboldt, shaft 115 feet deep; tunnel aiming to intersect this shaft 220 feet from the surface now in 380 feet and being pushed; struck four new veins, some of them valuable. Have 150 feet on the You Bet, shaft 60 feet deep, and much other undeveloped lode property. Frame mill on Clear Creek 50 by 100, driven by water, head of 33 feet, Dodge machinery throughout, not put up. H. W. Hill, of Empire, represents the Company.

"The Rosecrans Gold Mining Company" have 650 feet on the Rosecrans, high up on the east fork of Lyon's Creek; five shafts from 30 to 80 feet deep, crevice of seven feet, quartz and ore mixed; yield by stamps varies from $15 to $30 a ton. Frame mill on the lode 40 by 60, Little Giant engine, calculated to run the mill and mine, a Conkling crusher (Chilian principle) and twenty stamps, machinery not put up. Have much undeveloped lode property, and a water power on Clear Creek half a mile above Empire. N. G. Rounds represents the Company.

"The Eagle Gold Mining Company" have 650 feet on the Ben Franklin shaft 65 feet deep, very

strong vein of ore. In running a level 250 feet,
are thought to have missed their crevice and crossed
the Rosarico. Have 350 feet on the Knapp, undeveloped, and a one-third interest in the Argentine
silver mines of The Pine Silver Mining Company.
Have a stone mill low down on Lyon's Creek,
crushers on the Chilian principle, iron cylinder amalgamators, (worthless,) and a rude furnace for roasting ore in the rough. Organized in 1865 and paid
$35,000 the first year in salaries. Became embar-
rassed of course, turned over a new leaf, appointed
new officers in Colorado, and recommenced work.
Have a tunnel, starting at the Candee Mill, bearing
north under Silver Mountain, driven 147 feet.

"The Enterprise Gold Mining Company" have
650 feet on the Rosarico, and other lode property.
Building a stone mill above North Empire, dupli-
cating the Eagle Company's machinery except the
amalgamators. Running tunnel from their mill
west into Silver Mountain, in 50 feet. E. F.
Brothers and J. C. McElroy, superintendents.

"The Elk Gold Mining Company" have 1200
feet on the Roland, supposed to cross the south-
eastern face of Silver Mountain under the patch
diggings—spoken of before. Taking out the best
of what appears to be a 40-foot vein of quartz and
crushing it in Morris & Miller's 12-stamp mill
in North Empire. It may cost considerable to find
the true fissure, but it is claimed that for a width
of 40 feet it will pay for handling in a large mill.

GRIFFITH AND ARGENTINE DISTRICTS

Are so interwoven in their interests that they are

11*

easier noticed together than separate.   Griffith lies
at the forks of the south fork of South Clear Creek,
thirty-three miles from Golden City by the creek,
forty-six from Denver via the Mt. Vernon road, and
about fifteen south-west from Central City.   It has
two towns, half a mile apart—Georgetown, just
below the forks, and Elizabethtown, in a small park
just above them.   The divide between the forks is
called Leavenworth Mountain up to Huff Gulch
in Argentine, about six miles, when it becomes
McClellan Mountain, topping out five or six miles
further up in Gray's Peak.   Republican Mountain
rises abruptly to a hight of 1226 feet on the west,
soon becoming Sherman Mountain as it bends to
the west with the right fork, and in the other direction becoming Douglas Mountain beyond a certain
low notch through which a trail passes to Empire.
Alpine Mountain confronts Republican Mountain
on the east, and is tall enough to shade him until
a long while after the world first opens its eye in
the morning.   The surroundings are worthy the
pen of an Irving and we shall not desecrate by
attempting to describe them.   Suffice it that the
valley below is wide and smooth, slightly swelling,
and sprinkled with firs, pines, spruces, hemlocks,
alders and aspens.   The stream is generous in size,
clear as crystal, purity itself, and winds round and
round as if it imagined itself in a meadow instead
of in a deep gorge of the Rocky Mountains, and was
loath to leave its grand surroundings for the dreary
journey down over the arid plains to the sea.   It
seems to hug the banks of tiny islands of its own

creation, answering the kiss of the bending willows with a crying ripple as it glides past them and away forever. But it is with the eternal hills, rising boldly into the clouds, that we have to do.

Mines were discovered near the forks in 1859, and sluicing from the Griffith Lode paid very well. In 1863 there was a small stamp-mill at Georgetown, which had made a few good runs. It, with nearly all the known lodes of the district, passed into the hands of Eastern men during the succeeding Winter, and five Companies—the Georgetown, Washington, Mount Alpine, Wilson & Cass, and Express, were organized, and all but the last commenced work the next year.

"The Georgetown Company" put up a 40-stamp mill-building, brought on their machinery, did a good deal of work on the Western, Filmore, Express, and Lincoln Lodes, became embarrassed, and were sold out by the sheriff. In 1866 the property passed into other hands, and Mr. Biddle, of New York, is gradually getting it into shape to run again.

"The Mount Alpine Company" built a large, handsome mill, put up 24 stamps and started them, then stopped. They did a good deal of work on the Griffith, Corisannie, and other lodes. Subsequently the Company was reorganized and is now known as ".The What Cheer." Col. Wm. M. Hale, of Providence, represents it.

"The Wilson & Cass Company" confined their operations to mining, of which they did considerable on the Wilson and Cass County Lodes.

"The Washington Mining Association," represented by J. T. Harris, is developing the following property ; Douglas, by adit, 120 feet long, three-foot vein of galena and iron pyrites ; Burrell, by shaft, 50 feet deep, three-foot vein of cupriferous ore four tons of which gave by Bertola process $500, and by Keith process $415 ; Branch, by adit, 30 feet long ; Sweden, by adit, 25 feet long ; Panama, by shaft, 30 feet deep, ten inches of galena, has assayed as high as $2,200 a ton ; Morning Star, by shaft, five-inch ore-vein, has assayed as high as $1,978 a ton ; George M. Wilson, William Bennett, and S. F. Nuckolls, the latter having two feet of galena. They own 5000 feet on different veins and are now working on the Burrell and Panama, erecting a reverberatory furnace, fifteen tons a day capacity.

Early in September, 1864, Gov. R. W. Steele, James Huff, and Robert Layton, started out of Empire in search of silver, "which," says Gov. Steele, "we supposed to exist in and around the Range near the heads of the south-western branches of Clear Creek, where the same interlock with the heads of the Snakes." Two or three days found them in camp on Huff Gulch, where the Argentine cabins now stand. Next morning Huff went directly up the long eastern slope of McClellan Mountain, Steele and Layton going up Huff Gulch to the right, and all intending to meet on the summit somewhere, and if they should find nothing, seek a pass through on to the Snakes. It happened that Huff passed over the "cropping" of what was afterwards called the "Belmont Lode," which occurs well up on the ridge and is scattered over a considerable area. He picked some of it up, and upon exhibiting it to his comrades, they all agreed that it was silver ore or blossom, and that they need go no further. Opening the ground slightly they got a few pounds from the vein in place, took it to Central City and had it assayed, with results varying from $200 to $500 per ton. A few other men were let in on it, and an association formed, now known as "The Pine Silver Mining Company." During the ensuing Winter six accurate assays were made, one each by Prof. Hill of Providence, Behr & Keith of Black Hawk, F. T. Sherman of Nevada, George B. McClure of the Denver Branch Mint, and two by Prof. Dibben of New York, the average result being $827.48 per ton, gold and silver, chiefly the latter. The locality is about eight miles above Georgetown, and the discovery was made September 14, 1864.

Next year there was a rush to the spot. A district embracing the sources of the south fork of South Clear Creek and the north branch of North Platte was laid out and called "Argentine." The lodes generally assayed high in silver, and during the succeeding (last) Winter, several Eastern and some home companies were organized rather for the purpose of prospecting and acquiring property by discovery than for working the mines for their profits.

Among them is "The Argentine Silver Mining and Exploring Company," represented by C. S. Stowell. They have built a building in Elizabethtown containing a Scotch hearth, McKinsie blower,

Atwood's lead oxydizer, &c., all driven by a Little Giant engine of 16-horse-power. The intention is more particularly to experiment with the lead-oxydizing process, claimed as a cheap substitute for cupelling. A cast-iron cylinder three feet in diameter by eight in length, revolves slowly in a furnace fired to a red heat. Flanges on the inside of the cylinder lift and pour down the lead-riches, the lead oxydizing by the heat and passing out at one end of the cylinder into a chamber in the form of litharge. One machine is calculated to reduce the lead to a richness of 70 or 80 per cent. bullion, at the rate of 1000 lbs. in twelve hours. It has been in use for two years at Portland, Me., making litharge from English lead, giving the best of satisfaction. It is expected to greatly reduce the cost of cupelling. The jigger and Scotch hearth are such as are in use at Lyon's smelting works in Black Hawk.* They commenced work in September on ores from their mines on McClellan Mountain. Should everything work as expected and the lodes open well, similar but larger works are to be erected next season at Argentine on Huff Gulch.

"The Georgetown Silver Smelting Company," represented by J. T. Herrick, have put up a dam and cut a race on the right fork at Elizabethtown, and are erecting smelting works, of considerable capacity, costing $25,000. They have one of the best water-powers in Colorado, and though originally intending to confine their operations to smelting, have not been able to do so under the excitement

---

* See the chapter on Processes, under head of smelting.

caused by discoveries and extraordinary assays, but have themselves invested heavily in lodes. They think 1500 ounces of silver per ton a pretty nice thing, even if the veins are somewhat narrow on the surface.

"The Georgetown Silver Tunneling Company," represented by A. R. Wright, are sinking on the Elijah Hise, on Sherman Mountain, of which they own 700 feet. Sixteen feet down they have twelve inches of ore, an average of which, assayed by Mr. B. Hermann of Swansea, Wales, and Prof. N. P. Hill of Providence, R. I., gave at the rate of $1,339.20 a ton.

J. W. Watson is building a reverberatory furnace and small cupel at Elizabethtown, capacity three tons a day, to test the Baker, on Kelso Mountain, at the extreme head of the right fork. Half way up the mountain the lode crops out in seams for 30 feet in width, and there an adit is being run in for ore, of which there is a considerable quantity out. The indications are good for a very large vein of rich ore—seven feet it is expected—when these croppings shall have merged in the true fissure. It is fully believed by its friends that the Baker will prove one of the best mines in the world, and it is being energetically tested.

"The Bohema Smelting Company" have a reverberatory furnace, opposite Georgetown, the hearth five by seven feet, capacity three tons in twenty-four hours, such a furnace as is used in the lead mines. It works to the satisfaction of the owners. They have constructed a wagon road to the H. W.

Beecher, a very strong galena vein high on Republican Mountain, whence come their ores. The
Company was organized in Denver and is represented by Jno. W. Cree.

Besides these there are mining in Griffith and
Argentine, The Pine Silver Mining Company, The
Sonora Mining Company,* Hasbrouck & Co., and
many individuals. There are shafts from ten to
forty feet deep on the Argentine, Morse, Bowman,
Panama, Bond, Compass & Square, and others on
the eastern slope of Leavenworth Mountain; on
the Savage Extension, Black Hawk, Comstock,
Savage, Richmond, Belmont, Bob Morris, Animosa,
Wheeling, Great Bear, St. Lawrence, Bob Morris
No. 2 or Bullion, Mohawk or Paymaster, Fairview,
Monitor, Quincy, Ripley, Rockland, Christopher
Columbus, Premium, Ayres, Silver Wedge, Radius,
Debenion, etc., on McClellan Mountain; on the
Eugenia, South American, McClellan, Kalibagh,
Mammoth, Herkimer,† United States Coin, Brown,
and many others on Sherman Mountain; and on
the New Boston, R. E. Demmon, Cuckoo, Brook-
lyn, Wonder, Self, Knickerbocker, Wentworth, B.
Morrison, Partridge, G. W. Packard, DeGrant, Tal-
isman, and a great many others on Republican

---

*The Sonora Company, of which Mr. George Stille is agent, and
Mr. Rothpletz general director, or something of that sort, packed
in provisions late last Fall, no road having yet been constructed
more than two-thirds of the way from Georgetown, and have been
working a full force of hands all Winter—not less than 12,000 feet
above the sea.

† Behr & Keith certify that a fair average of this lode assayed
$1,158 a ton of 2000 pounds.

Mountain, and the one opposite, showing crevices from four to six feet in width, with veins of quartz rich in sulphuret and chloride of silver, and veins of argentiferous galena of from six to twelve, fifteen, twenty, and even thirty inches.

The lodes of the vicinity are not yet extensively exploited, but enough has been done to prove that some of them are true and rich silver veins, and the argentiferous galena is rich and can be worked cheap. A good deal is doing in the way of opening and testing them, and if they shall prove what assays indicate and of the usual size, the district must rival the best in the world ere many years. A wagon road is building from Elizabethtown up the right hand fork to the Baker Lode, about ten miles ; one will be built next season by the left fork to Huff Gulch, about six miles. The district has an immense water power. The fuel is ample now, but once mining were fully entered upon, would soon be exhausted, that is to say, in a few years. But the grade from the forks down the creek to the Valley is but eighty-six feet per mile, and when necessity arises, a railway can be built without any difficulty, making the inexhaustible coal-beds at the base of the Mountains available for mining purposes.

Four miles south-west from Mt. McClellan, one finds himself on waters running into the Pacific, and in a silver district, eight or ten miles long and two or three in width, equally as rich as that of Argentine or Griffith, known as " The Snake River Mines." A fold or elbow of the Range lies like a huge cap on this belt of lodes, which crops out for a greater or less width on each side, showing the same general characteristics, and preserving the true direction—north-east and south-west. Anywhere but in the very heart of the Continent, remote from all seas, rivers and railways, such a district would already have been made the basis of a new and flourishing State. However, railways are now rapidly stretching from either ocean toward Colorado, and when they shall have joined hands, with their accompanying columns of adventurers in these silver chambers above the clouds, Colorado, from her heaven-topped mountain throne, will hold forth a golden sceptre that shall enchant the world— perhaps !

Argentine, as we have said, is comparatively a new district, and we therefore add a little to the above, bringing our account nearer to date than last October. Fifty-seven dwellings, averaging in value $500, were erected in Elizabethtown and Georgetown* in 1866; one furnace building and furnaces costing $25,000, one costing $10,000, and a third about $7,500. Several new lodes have been found, among them the Bethany, Anglo-Saxon, Cherokee, and Summit. Of seven assays of ore from the Bethany, the highest was $22,137.30, the lowest $3,960.90, and the average, $10,912 per ton of 2000 pounds. The vein is very wide, the ore in small seams as yet, not more than six inches in width in the aggregate. At the depth of twenty feet the Anglo-Saxon has a vein of pure ore, sixteen inches in width, the

---

* These two towns, by late action of the inhabitants, are merged in one, and called Georgetown.

average assay of which is $1,600 a ton. The Cherokee is on the right hand fork, a few miles above the junction, is a galena lode, rich in silver. The Summit is on top of Alpine Mountain, the vein ten feet in width, streaked with numerous seams of ore which never has assayed less than 1500 ounces of silver to the ton. The writer from whom these statements are taken, and who is entirely to be trusted, claims that there is one lode near George-town seventy-five feet in width. "But saw-mills and smelters and 'big things' make a poor old Christmas," he writes, "after all. One would rather see a row of little stockings carefully arranged about the fire, than to hear of all these old matter-of-fact affairs. Big red apples, and red cheeks, and bright eyes will occur to a fellow in spite of himself on such occasions as this (Christmas Eve.) Don't you think we could raise an immigrant aid society for girls? Colorado needs a thousand to-day, and by New Year's a thousand more might find snug homes, warm hearts, and strong arms to keep them till death."

Later still, the shaft on the Elijah Hise had reached a depth of 35 feet, had one well-defined wall, vein of gangue and ore 5 1-2 feet wide; ore streak had varied in width from five to fourteen inches for the last 20 feet of the shaft; and its average value from daily tests had been $835 a ton. It comprised argentiferous galena, silver glance, brittle silver glance, cupreous sulphuret of silver, and a very little chloride of silver. The vein crops out 100 to 300 feet either way from Discovery, several feet in width, and shows many points of similarity to the great Comstock vein of Mt. Davidson. The Discovery shaft on the Belmont is twelve feet deep, shows a vein of white quartz about nine inches wide, carrying cubes of galena and specks of sulphuret of silver, the assay value of which is not far from $1000 a ton. A second shaft, some 400 feet east, discloses the same kind and three times as large a vein, the assay value of which is from $300 to $500 a ton. The Wheeling Lode, near the Belmont, and occurring in the same syenitic formation, has been opened in three places covering a lineal extent of 500 feet; Discovery shaft is fifteen feet deep, and contains on the surface three distinct veins of ore, varying in width from three to eight inches, and separated by four or five feet of gangue rock, or more properly, country rock; toward the bottom of the shaft these veins approach each other, and doubtless unite at a greater depth. The Baker Lode stands out on the eastern slope of Kelso Mountain,* like a great tree which has been stripped by the storms of all but three or four of its principal branches. Wm. Brückner, a mining and metallurgical expert, describes it as follows:

"The two principal ramifications, called the north and the south crevices, bear a course of S. 72° W., and S. 60° W., dipping 65° and 85° to the north. They are traced and disclosed by many prospecting pits, showing bodies of uncommonly

---

* Kelso Mountain is at the head of the right upper fork as Mount McClellan is at the head of the left.

rich ores, varying in width from twenty inches to twenty feet. The crevices consist of sulphuret and bromide of silver and argentiferous galena; all these ores being more or less interspersed within the vein matter of quartz and feldspar. Samples of ore, taken from these crevices, yielded by assay, as high as $800 to $2000 per ton. At the junction of the north and south crevices, a tunnel has been commenced, which shows a large body of ore, seven feet in width, consisting of sulphuret and bromide of silver and argentiferous galena, and a gangue, of quartz and feldspar. In order to ascertain the average value of this ore, samples of all the different classes of ore, more or less intermixed with gangue, were taken from all the different tunnels and surface pits, pulverized and equal weights of each mixed together. This average ore yielded by assay—gold, $6.11, silver, $69.00, $75.11 per ton of 2000 pounds. This is an *uncommonly* rich average yield for a lode of such enormous dimensions; from which, with a comparatively small amount of labor, hundreds of tons may be taken out every day; and in a locality, where good facilities for working the ore are very near."

Another account says :

"The ores which fill this vein are of varied character. The great body of them are chlorides, filling nearly two-thirds of the crevice, occupying a middle position in the vein nearly four feet wide. Next to the west side, along the underlying wall-rock, is a seam of bromide of silver about one foot in thickness, easily mined. To the side of the eastern wall-rock there is found a seam of galena, and closely united with it, brittle sulphuret of silver, and a small seam of fahlerz, in all from fifteen to eighteen inches in thickness."

It is believed that the most of the ore found in this vein is better adapted to treatment by amalgamation than by fire. Two tons of it, unselected, undressed, and without roasting, were smelted last Winter, yielding twenty-five pounds of silver—coin value $422.90—and 1500 pounds of lead, at ten cents a pound, $150. A piece weighing eighty pounds and assaying $532.12 per ton, was sent to the Paris Exposition. About three miles above the junction on the right fork and two thousand feet up from the creek, occur the John Brown, United States Coin, and Mammoth Lodes, parallel and within fifty feet of each other, standing above the surface, the Mammoth assaying sixty dollars a ton for thirty inches in width, the Coin $200 a ton for eighteen inches in width, and the Brown about $350 for sixteen inches. Some ore from the Brown has been smelted—they are all argentiferous galena—and the lead-riches, of which the yield is nearly one-half the weight of the dressed ore, assays about $1000 per ton. It will be seen that they constitute a somewhat remarkable group, possibly all coming together below. These items will give some definite idea of how the Georgetown and Argentine silver veins develop, and of their value. They are not the result of personal observation, but are derived from contemporary sources which are deemed trustworthy.

CHAPTER X.

UNLIKE Gilpin and Clear Creek Counties, which
are wholly within the Foot-hills, Boulder County
takes in a large slice of the best agricultural land
of the Valley—about eight townships. Long's
Peak is the north-west corner-stone, and the crest
of the Range the western boundary line. It adjoins Gilpin and Jefferson on the north, and is not
far from thirty miles square. Watered by the
Boulders, St. Vrain, Left-Hand, and Little Thompson Creeks, which divide it into so many all but
equal sections and flow through it from west to
east; occupying the end of the Great Mineral Belt
which approaches nearest and is most accessible to
the Plains; abounding in coal and deposits of valuable iron ore accompanied by all the materials used
in the construction and running of smelting furnaces; and having no less than two hundred and
fifty square miles of the finest agricultural land
admirably situated in every respect for irrigation,

Boulder may be not inaptly termed the gem of all the counties of Colorado.

Its numerous streams escape through the feather-edge of the Foot-hills by the abjectest kanyons, worthless but as avenues of access; but above these the surface has been fretted by thousand rivulets making down from the Range until it is one vast park, chiefly covered with forest, but still presenting sunniest openings on the banks of clearest and most musical waters.   It affords a pleasing and beautiful landscape from any elevated point on its circular enclosure.   It was early invaded by the adventurous gold-hunter.   Seven years ago, the Boulder Diggings at Gold Hill made quite as much noise as those of Gregory.   Gold Hill is not properly on either of the Boulders, however; it is between Four-Mile and Left-Hand Creeks, say 1200 feet above them and eight or ten miles from the Valley. There used to be half a dozen mining districts in the county, each the size of a township, the precise boundaries of most of which either never were recorded or the record has been lost.   Now-a-days, only Sugar Loaf, Gold Hill, Central, Ward, and Phœnix are ever heard of.

Ward District lies at the Head and on the North side of Left-Hand, extends east and west eight miles, and north from the creek, five.   Gold Lake District adjoins Ward on the north, and is as much noted to date for containing a lake of 160 acres—Dr. Parry's "Osborne's Lake"—as for its gold mines, which, although they prospect well in a pan, do not seem to have interested anybody much in their development.   Central District lies east of Ward, between Left-Hand and St Vrain's, and contains the James Creek mines, just now attracting attention and engaging effort.   This was Utilla District in olden times.   South of this comes Gold Hill, south of Gold Hill, Sugar Loaf, and west of Sugar Loaf, Phœnix District.

Among the most noted lodes of Gold Hill are the Horsefall, Williams, and Hope.   In 1860 there were a dozen quartz mills, small and rude of course compared with the mills of the present, running in the district, besides quite a number of arastras. All but three or four drew out in the Fall of the year mentioned and moved to Gregory or elsewhere. The mills were incomplete, most of their owners had no mines in their own right ; they were new to the business of quartz-milling ; and the quartz and dirt of the surface were soon exhausted, leaving the miners on cap or in sulphurets.   Two or three mills persevered through another year or so, but they gradually failed and quit   In 1863 the owners of the Horsefall, to the number of twenty or more, formed an association called "The Union Company," fitted up a 6-stamp mill and ran it till they wore it out.   Since that nothing has been done there, probably because there are so many to be consulted.   For a year the district has been deserted.   It has at least three or four lodes of the first class which might easily be made productive.

In the other districts of the county little has yet been done beyond prospecting and recording, with the single exception of Ward District.   Indiana

12

Gulch cuts it from north-west to south-east, and on this the principal known lodes occur. The most considerable and the most improved is the Columbia, opened or struck under that name for between 2,000 and 3,000 feet, and continued as much further east of Indiana Gulch under different names. The Niwot Mining Company own 1,300 feet of the vein, 650 feet of it contiguous, a portion of which—No's 9, 10, and 11, west—has been developed by four shafts from 70 to 80 feet deep, and a level 40 or 50 feet from the surface the entire length of No. 10. The crevice is from six to ten feet wide. In the Fall of 1861 Davidson & Breath took a 6-stamp, steam mill in on to Indiana Gulch, which was run, off and on, up to the Fall of 1865. The district was wild at that time and the mill was intended merely for a prospector   In the course of a few months it took $40,000 from the property now owned and worked by the Niwot Company, the yield varying from $40 to $65 a ton, the cost of taking out $3.75 a ton. The little mill was sold to Gen. Joseph Hayes in the beginning of 1866, and is now being run by Mr. Bixby, of Central City.   While Colorado mines were selling in the East the Niwot Mining Company was organized on this and 35,000 feet on other lodes in the district, and a 50-stamp mill purchased and sent out. It arrived in October, 1865, four months on the road from Grinnell, Iowa, and was immediately set up. The mill-building is a frame, 44 by 84 feet, engine-room 24 by 30, situate on the lode, No. 10, west. From the top of this mill is presented one of the finest views in Colorado.

Audubon's Peak looms grandly up in the west, but a few miles distant ; to the south, the park of Left-Hand, the Boulders, and North and South Clear Creeks, spreads away as far as the " Old Chief," " Squaw," and " Papoose," and the "cloud-compelling summits," among which the last-named stream takes its rise ; east, the Foot-hills, except here and there a gigantic crag, assume an almost level appearance, over and beyond which the eye sweeps the Plains from the head of Cherry Creek to the Platte far below its great eastward bend. The Plains seem to bank up like the ocean to meet the sky, and the division is lost in the dreamy distance. To return : The engine is 125-horse power, and runs as smooth as oil on water. It belts directly on to a counter shaft driving the cam shafts, the latter thrown in and out of gear by clutch-coupling. The stamps are set up in two sections along one side of the mill, five batteries of five stamps each in a section. The crushed ore passes over long, stationary, copper-plates, then over blankets into small tanks intended to catch escaping quicksilver, then away. Each battery has 65 square feet of copper-plate. The stamps weigh 650 pounds each. The mill is a plain, substantial, old-fashioned stamp-mill, without any foolishness, well located and put up. Water is brought from a noble spring a half-mile distant, giving head enough to throw it all over the mill if desired. Half the stamps were started about August 1st, and the others were to start a month later. The first twenty days' run with 25-stamps, on a mixture of quartz,

ore, and stuff that was thrown aside while using the
old mill, averaged something more than twenty
ounces of gold a day. The Company also have a
steam saw-mill on Left-Hand, half a mile from the
mill, with which they have cut all their lumber.
The battery timbers were found in the immediate
vicinity, although timber-line is not more than
five miles back and but little higher. They have a
wagon-road from the district down Left-Hand to
the Valley—about eighteen miles. It is considered
the best as it is the shortest route from the agricultural districts into any paying mines except those
at Gold Hill which are on this road, six or seven
miles below; it has a water grade except in one case.
The timber in the district is quite thick and of the
common size for the Mountains, the hills only moderately steep, the whole region furnishing unequaled pasturage and frequently small parks where
hay can be profitably made and the hardier vegetables grown. The Niwot Company have a good
boarding-house, lodging forty men; a wood-shed
holding 500 cords, and are building shaft-houses on
No's 9, 10, and 11, hoisting to be done by a line of
shafting belting directly on the engine. Wm. A.
Davidson is the Company's agent, and the present
improvements in Ward District are largely due to
him.*

* After the above was written the Niwot mill caught fire and
burned to the ground, but slightly injuring the machinery however.
By the end of January last a new mill was ready to raise. At the
same time Crosby & Thompson had got a new 24-stamp mill running on the Stoughton Lode, paying handsomely. The stamps are
a part of those torn out of the Excelsior Company's mill last Fall.

Another mining company called "The Long's Peak Gold Mining Company," are at work in the district. They have 200 feet on the Columbia, shaft 100 feet deep, vein of mixed ore, quartz, and country rock, six feet wide. Putting up a whim preparatory to sinking. Also 600 feet on the Comet (extension east of the Columbia) two shafts, just started, showing very wide quartz vein and prospecting rich. Also 600 feet on the Manhattan, shaft 45 feet deep, average vein, prospects well. Have besides a very large amount of unimproved property on the best lodes in the district. Have built a frame mill on Indiana Gulch, where the Columbia crosses and becomes the Comet. It is set like stairs against the east bank, a peculiarity of construction quite common and intended to facilitate the manipulation of ores. It has a 35-horse Little Giant engine, Dodge crusher in the quartz room, upper story; two ball-pulverizers on the second story, also an improved dolly-tub for amalgamating ; and directly under this story, a room for drying or other manipulating of the concentrated tailings from the amalgamator. The last is intended to realize an idea of J. V. Pomeroy's, the agent of the Company, it being to prevent the float-gold from passing off in the water by cribbing it, and to sink

---

Bixby was still successfully working with the little old Niwot mill, and Cushman, Cressey & Co. were about ready to start a new stamp mill. Ward District has become an attractive spot since the new Niwot mill went into so successful operation, thus calling attention to the great richness and size of its lodes. It seems that the Winter is just the season to carry on work there, too, if it is 10,000 feet above the sea.

the coarse but rusty particles into the concentrated tailings, which it is designed to dry and re-grind. The tub is of copper and has a triple, funnel-shaped bottom, a paddle stirrer, and a faucet underneath whereby to draw out the tailings, the slimes having gone off in the water through the vent, which is high up but under or outside of the first bottom. As the water is drawn off to clean up, the float-gold is expected to adhere to the funnel-shaped coppers, one after the other, the very last of it to be caught in a pan the same as the concentrated ore and coarse gold. Mr. Pomeroy expects to dipense with desulphurizing. He believes that all that is required is, to free the gold and brighten it by perfect pulverization when plain stirring will amalgamate it. The Company's mill and other buildings were commenced in May, and are now nearly ready to run, the entire cost being $25,000.* This is the result of strict personal attention to business.

These companies are the only parties doing much of consequence in the district. There are a great many lodes, among them the Ward, Nelson, Crœsus, Niwot, Banner, California, Stoughton, Norman, Rothschild, Susie, Larned, developed from 20 to 120 feet deep, and drifted out more or less ; some of them having gossan that pays moderately for sluicing ; some of them with large piles of quartz out awaiting the arrival of mills ; all of them wide and open, prospecting rich. The mines are forty-five

* In February last Pomeroy was replacing his crushing machinery with twenty stamps, which he expected soon to be ready to run.

miles north-west from Denver and twenty-five north from Central City, and are accessible by fair wagon roads from either place.

It has transpired quite recently that Central District, between Ward and the Valley, has some of the strongest, richest gold, silver, and copper lodes in the country. About one hundred have been discovered and pre-empted within three months. They do not differ greatly in their general features from the lodes common to the Belt, and are not more than ten miles from the Valley, nor than 1500 feet above it in altitude. Present indications are that these are but the beginning of discoveries in that region. The advantages it has in contiguity to the Valley and consequent ease of access, must secure its rapid development.*

---

* From 200 to 300 prospectors have wintered in the district and a great many lodes have been discovered. The mines are on James Creek, a tributary of Left-Hand, and the town is called Jamestown. It already boasts from 100 to 200 houses. Three saw-mills and a smelting furnace were in process of erection between January and February. As an illustration of miners' life, the subjoined extract from a late Jamestown letter is not bad:

"There is great excitement about town lots just now. All the front lots, or lots near the gulch, are pre-empted for about three miles along the stream; also, all mill-sites. And now as there are some coming in and threatening to jump the lots not built on, it creates some excitement. Miners' meetings are in vogue, and we are having a good many. I attended one not long ago, which was conducted after this fashion: When the crowd had gathered, the business was introduced by the singing of 'Sweet Betsey from Pike.' The Chairman then took his seat and the object of the meeting was stated to be, 'the opening of the lots held by speculators to actual settlers,' &c. Discussion followed. The floor was soon claimed by three or four—half a dozen were speaking at once, and I could gather only a few words, such as 'Open 'em,' 'Pioneers,' 'Broke

Boulder Valley is perhaps the best farming district in the nothern portion of the Territory. The indigenous grasses are thrifty and rich, vegetables grow to enormous size, and wheat yields twenty-five bushels per acre. There are two considerable towns in it, Boulder City, the county seat, twenty-five miles from Denver and twenty-five from Central City by an excellent wagon road just completed; and Valmont, four or five miles below, where the South Boulder and Left-Hand Creeks form a junction with the North Boulder. The latter is hardly a year old, but has a population, including the valley around it, of five hundred, supports a small weekly newspaper, has a good hotel, two churches, several stores, a flouring-mill, many residences, and a thriving trade with the magnificent farming country which forms its setting. Boulder City is one of the oldest

---

the ice,' 'No right,' &c., &c. During the confusion the Chairman was *seen* to wave his hand and speak, but was not heard. At last a man with a stentorian voice reached the ears of the Chairman and crowd, and 'moved that we all *keep still.*' Motion obtained. A motion was then made to appoint a Committee to inquire into, and find out, if a lot had actually been sold for a keg of beer. Before the motion could be put, it was stated by one of the best men we have that no doubt a lot had been sold for a keg of beer, but the beer was drunk, and drunk or sober the title was just as good as if the consideration had been money. After a great many other 'motions,' and 'resolutions,' which were all as clear as mud, a Town Committee was appointed to survey lots and see to their impartial distribution. But to-day a man went to work on a lot; another man warned him off; they had a fight, and the one that drew the 'first blood' held the lot. Now the talk is to call another miners' meeting and make it a law that 'first blood' shall hold against all other titles. We want your candid opinion—*Is first blood a good title?*"

towns in the Territory, is the entrepot of the mines of Boulder County and also has a large trade with the farmers and rancheros of the Boulder Valley which it overlooks for a long distance. It has the features of any town, and the present year has witnessed quite an influx of population, and consequent energy in building and other improvements. With the revival of mining in the county and the construction of a direct wagon road to the Gregory mines, the town must prosper.

In Boulder County occur very considerable outcroppings of coal, and the only deposit of iron ore that has been improved. The coal measures which along the eastern base of the Mountains throughout the most of their extent were brought edgewise to the surface by an upheaval of the latter subsequent to the deposit of the former, are peculiar in that they occur in the Tertiary formation, having no connection with the carboniferous coals in geological position, if they have any in character. From some improvement in Boulder and Jefferson counties, they would seem to be from three thousand to five thousand feet thick, the whole series, particularly in the latter county, deposited unconformably on the Silurian, being ten thousand feet thick. In the contact of two series of rocks, so widely different in age and lithological character, is presented large scope for investigation. It is as yet an almost untrodden field. Geologists say that at the time of this Tertiary deposit, what now forms the base of the Mountains was a low range of hills, the shore of an ocean extending from the Arctic region into

12*

Mexico, and the Parks of the Range, inland seas.
A high temperature and consequent energetic metamorphic action existed in both the older and newer
series.   This is inferred from the absence of fossils
below the coal measures, and from the fact that in
places the gneiss has been changed to syenite and
granite a mile or two back from the Tertiary sandstones.   The latter also exhibit the intensity of the
metamorphic action in their extreme hardness, enabling them to form a series of marginal ridges,
fronting the main Mountains and from one to four
miles distant, occasionally broken down to the
common level of the plain by the mountain streams,
or cut and worn away by denuding agencies proceeding from the Range, outward; but generally
preserving an elevation of five hundred to ten
hundred feet, and forming a striking feature in the
topography of the section.   They appear to have
once formed a continuous line, the western summit
offering a bold escarpment, the base of which is
covered by the debris fallen from above.   The
eastern slope is that of the strata, and the surface
is frequently in great part that of the rock itself
scantily overgrown with bushes, cactus, and grass,
springing from the crevices.   In some localities
there are one, in others two, and again three or four
of these sandstone ridges, called "hog-backs" by
the natives, separated by the space of a mile perhaps, and gradually sinking away in the prairie
toward the east.   Outside of these, fronting Golden
City and standing guard on the banks of Clear
Creek at the royal gate of the Rocky Mountains,

there is another group, or rather block, of basaltic formation.   If they once constituted a single block, ten miles long by three in width and eight hundred feet high, their summit a *mesa* of large area upheld round the edges by vertical walls of rudely-columnar greenstone or hornblende from one hundred to two hundred feet in hight, they do not now, for the creek has cut them in two, although not otherwise altering their characteristics.   They are called "The Table Mountains."   The soil near their base is fertile, and is cultivated some distance up their very steep slopes.

It is between these *mesas* and the Mountains, among the sandstone ridges, that the coal outcrops. At Golden City, and extending north and south for twenty miles, occur two all but vertical veins of coal, each from six to nine feet thick, accompanied by heavy beds of fire-clay of fine quality, and separated by a fifty-foot stratum of sandstone, standing high above the face of the plain.   A large establishment at Golden City manufactures fire-brick, roofing, tile, window and door-sills and caps, and assay crucibles from this clay.   A shaft has been excavated to a depth of one hundred and thirty feet on one of the coal veins.   One wall is the solid sandstone, the other a dirty, rotten shale or slate, and the underlie to the east is about five feet to the hundred in depth.   On Coal and Boulder Creeks, fifteen to twenty miles north from Golden City, several veins of coal have been opened, varying in thickness from three to twelve feet.   They are three times as far from the edge of the Foot-hills as those at Golden City, and while one of them is almost vertical, the others dip from the horizon at angles between two and forty-five degrees. For instance, one vein, which has been penetrated for one hundred feet, is six feet thick, and inclines two or three degrees toward the north. Another bed near this is in two positions, the upper seven feet thickness of coal, separated from the lower, which is four and a half feet thick, by an eighteen-inch stratum of dark blue fire-clay. It has been opened for one hundred feet, and dips about 18° toward the east. A third bed twelve feet thick, has been worked one hundred feet, down a slope of some 10° toward the east, for the Denver market. Half a mile east, it has again been struck. A vertical vein, seven feet thick, has been sunk upon fifty feet. In none of these shafts or tunnels is there yet experienced any trouble from water, and the veins are usually free from any intermixture of stony, earthy, or slaty matter. Ten or twelve miles east of this locality, a coal bed was opened in 1866, at the base of a considerable hill, nearly horizontal in position, accompanied by fire-clay and fifteen feet thick, not greatly different from those already described in anything. At Canon City and other places on the waters of the Arkansas River, the coal measures crop out the same as above.

An analysis of this coal by Dr. Torrey showed it to contain about sixty per cent. of fixed carbon. He pronounced it a *lignite*, and not a *coal*, remarkably free from sulphur as compared with most bituminous coals, and in calorific power, between dry-wood and bituminous coal. "There is no reason," says Torrey, "why it may not be used for the smelting of iron and other ores." In point of fact, it has no superior as a grate or steam coal. In the Arkansas Valley it is applied in blacksmithing, but on the Platte it is either unfit or how to use it has not been discovered. In the reverberatory furnace it works well. In the blast furnace its use has not been seriously attempted. It constitutes the chief fuel of the Valley towns, brings five dollars a ton at the mines, and twice or three times that in Denver and Golden City. It contains seven thousand to eight thousand cubic feet of gas to the ton, which it yields at a low red heat. As to its extent, it is co-equal with that of the Mountains themselves. The veins which are on edge near the Mountains are found in horizontal strata on the Plains, and along the ridge between the Platte and Arkansas extend eastward two hundred miles. East of Denver there is hardly a stream that does not disclose workable veins of coal.

On the South Boulder, in the midst of the outcrops of coal above described, and of an extensive deposit of iron ore, Langford & Co., of Black Hawk, erected a small blast-furnace in 1865, and ran out one hundred and fifty tons of white iron of fair quality. The ore is a compact hematite, nearly pure peroxide of iron, scattered over the surface of thousands of acres, but unconnected with the strata of the hills, in pieces of all sizes up to those weighing half a ton. It is in excellent condition for the furnace from its long exposure to the elements, and is not deteriorated by the intermixture of foreign stony material. It yields about thirty per cent. of iron, and for that used, was reduced by charcoal brought from the neighboring hills, at a cost of seventy-five dollars per ton. Prices at the time ranged much higher than previously, or than they ever can after the advent of railways in that region. By the enlargement of the works, and the use of *mineral* fuel and the *hot*-blast, the cost of production may no doubt be brought within a compass that will leave fair profits. The enterprise was only an experiment, but it was so satisfactory that it would have been pursued had not *old* iron become cheaper than *new*, through the shipment to Colorado of so much worthless quartz machinery. The materials for constructing and supplying blast-furnaces exist in abundance on the ground. The making of iron in Colorado is worthy the attention of capitalists, in view of the wants of railways, a system of which is to be built in the Rocky Mountains on their own grand scale, and of the perpetual demand for iron in quartz-mining, which must ever be the staple business of Colorado and her sister mountain communities. It is greatly to their interest, having the raw material, that they make their own iron, since they always *must* import many of the necessaries of life. There is no safer nor more promising enterprise in the yet infantile but vigorous and growing West. Connected with the Bellemonte iron and coal mines and furnace and owned by the same firm, are a foundery and machine shop at Black Hawk, in the heart of the Gregory mines, which turns out three to five tons of castings a week, makes mine-pumps, engines, quartz-pulverizers, and all quartz-mill and mining machinery. With additional facilities, much of the machinery heretofore brought from the States at such great cost in time and money, might be made from the ore on the ground, and better satisfaction in every respect given.

CHAPTER XI.

PARK COUNTY is nearly identical with the South
Park, its boundaries generally coinciding with the
crests of the surrounding ranges and spurs. In
the upheaval of this portion of the Mountains it
appears there were two or perhaps three great centers of eruptive force. Two of these are Mt. Lincoln and Pike's Peak. Their relative positions to
each other and to the Park have been elsewhere
noticed. They stand one hundred miles from each
other, and are connected by semi-circular spurs, as
the towers in the walls of ancient cities were by the
walls. Between these spurs and upon their shoulders
is upraised and upheld the plateau of the South
Park, about thirty by sixty miles in extent, foot-hills
forming a separate system between the Park proper
and Pike's Peak, making its total area perhaps three
thousand square miles. Of the great parks it is
the third in size. Mt. Lincoln rises at its head to

an altitude of 17,300 feet,* overlooking its entire
extent and the solid, banked-up billows within the
limits of vision on every hand, any of which would
be a wonderful mountain elsewhere—yet is Lincoln
as Saul among his brethren.   From his sides the
waters flow to the East and the West.   Hence de-
part the Grand for the Pacific, and the Arkansas
and South Platte for the Atlantic.   The Park slopes
away gently to the south-east, and on its bosom are
gathered a multitude of brooks, which, uniting
twenty to thirty miles from their extreme sources
in the eternal snow-banks and morasses of the
Range and the Montgomery Spur, form the south
branch of South Platte, break through the eastern
wall and bear away across the great Plains on their
journey to the sea.   Let us be a little more precise :

At the base of Mt. Lincoln is situate the mining
town of Montgomery, enjoying or enduring an
elevation above the sea of 10,000 feet.   Here *the*
South Platte debouches from the Range, four or
five miles from its extreme source, a cluster of
mountain pools, fed by the ever-during snows.
Eight miles east of Montgomery, if you cross the
root of a huge spur running down into the Park ten
or twelve miles to Fairplay, or twenty miles if you
round the point of said spur, is Hamilton, situate
on Tarryall Creek, where that stream escapes from
the Range.   Six or seven miles south from Montgomery, a tributary stream escapes from the Montgomery Spur, and here is the county seat of Park
County, the original "Buckskin Jo," still called

* Calculation of Prof. Alfred Du Bois.

"Buckskin." Two miles further south, at the mouth of a similar gorge and on a like stream, is Sterling City, originally called "Musquito." These towns are each in the midst of a cluster of rich quartz veins. The forks unite six or seven miles south-east of Montgomery, and between their junction and Fairplay, perhaps three miles further down the main stream, occur immense bar diggings, the bar being very wide and from sixty to one hundred feet in depth and prospecting everywhere and all through. This bar has always been wrought with fair success, and preparation is making to aggregate the "claims" in which it has been held into a large tract, so as to justify the expense of putting in a bed-rock flume and working by steam machinery. A steam dredge will do the work of fifty men with shovels.

About ten miles west of Fairplay and five south of Musquito, another affluent of the main stream escapes from a vast horseshoe in the Range as from the mouth of a jug. In this horseshoe about sixty lodes have been discovered, one-third of which are strong veins, containing more than the usual proportion of silver. The surface formation is trap, and there is considerable galena which will doubtless disappear at a greater depth. Four of the lodes have been sunk upon from thirty to sixty feet and are considered first-class. The district is called "Horseshoe," and the stream "Horseshoe Creek." From Fairplay, which seems the natural entrepot of these mines, the stream glides smoothly down through the Park with a descent of one hundred feet per mile, and receiving a few miles further down considerable tributaries from the north and from the south, its banks spread out into an arable plain, which, though 9000 feet above the sea level, has sufficient strength and warmth to mature vegetables and the small grains. This Park has salt springs, beds of gypsum, coal shales, veins of chalcedony, carnelian, and other curious stones and minerals. It has not been thoroughly explored and no one fully knows its resources or curiosities. Silicified wood abounds in its lower portion, and at one point, about thirty miles west of Pike's Peak, there is a small patch of petrified stumps still standing, one of which is fifteen feet in diameter.

Some twenty miles below Fairplay, extensive salt works were erected in 1866, by Rollins, Hall & Lane. The brine is rich and boils up all over an acre of ground, flowing off quite a stream. There is practically no limit to it, and consequently no limit to the amount of salt that may be furnished by these, the appropriately named, "Colorado Salt Works." They now furnish all of the article used in the Territory. Nothing, we fancy, could more delight or surprise a stranger, traveling over the virginal and somewhat lonesome Park, than to come suddenly upon these capacious and well built kettle-houses, drying and store-houses, saw-mill, barns, dwelling-houses, &c., nestled away in one of those secluded nooks with which the Park abounds. Toward the Park nothing can be seen from the Salt Works, it being shut out by a low ridge, but a little way to the south-west lies the miniature Sierra, low, dark, and

completely forest-crowned, which divides the Park
from the kanyon of the Arkansas ; and over and
beyond that immense kanyon can be seen, in a clear
day, the sharp peaks of the main Range, rising to
awe-inspiring hights in the deep blue of heaven,
and lifting their quite terrible desolation into an atmosphere whose perfect purity we love to associate
with something prettier. Colorado affords many
beautiful, many grand, not to say, awful views, but
this is a rare one.

In the Summer months the scenery of the Park
is one kaleidoscopic picture. In its upper portion
the great and unchanging mountains rise abruptly
from its bosom, collecting the snows and distilling
the waters. Here, as we have said, are the mines
and the towns. Lower down the immense spurs or
wings of the Range become low, wood-crowned
ridges, the plateaus between smooth and level as a
floor and covered with a strong, rich turf, in places
along the streams yielding from a ton to two tons of
hay per acre. Everywhere the lawn continues up
the sides of the hills and ridges, searching its way
among the low, scattered evergreen trees, suggesting all of loveliness it does not present. In the
lower portion, except on the stream banks, the Park
is dry, like the Plains, roughly carpeted with a puny
sage and stubbed crisp turf of wiry grass.

On the whole it is well watered and timbered and
the streams are full of trout ; it is covered with indigenous grasses, the richest in the world, and is
equal in its native state to the production of two
thousand tons of hay per annum. It is easily ap-

proached from the Plains through gradually ascending parks or valleys only second to itself in beauty
and utility.   Communication all over and through
it is perfect, since a smooth, hard road can be made
across it in almost any direction without labor—
just by wearing off the grass.   Hay seldom brings
more than thirty dollars a ton, and the Arkansas
with its numerous valley affluents, accompanied by
rich alluvial bottoms, enjoying a climate adapted to
all cereal productions common to the temperate
zone, is less than one hundred miles distant over
an easy and delightful road.   Entering the Mountains at the base of Pike's Peak, this road follows
the banks of willow-lined streams or winds through
charming little parks with a rise of but four thousand feet in seventy-five miles.*   When the Park
mines shall be known and worked, Canon City will
be no contemptible rival of Denver.   It is the
natural entrepot of the mines of Park, Lake, and
Summit counties, the extent and richness of which
are as yet hardly suspected.   These counties all
lie at a great elevation, consequently timber is
somewhat sparse and small.   But they exhibit
good signs of coal, and are no doubt underlaid to
a great extent with an excellent combustible coal,
such as that found along the eastern base of the
Mountains.†   There need be no uneasiness on the

---

* In 1862 a train with the accustomed load—about 1000 pounds
to a yoke of oxen—made the trip from Kansas City to Buckskin in
twenty-seven days, never reshipping or at all lightening the load.

† Prof. Wm. Denton found true carboniferous coal in the Middle
Park, the only place in the Territory it is yet known to exist.

score of timber and fuel for a great many years at least.

At the base of the north-western wall of the Park, the various strata of the most modern rocks are together bent upward as one might bend the leaves of a book, and on these leaves of rock is plainly written the history of this portion of the world. To the geological student it is a book of unusual interest, showing, as it does, the regular gradation from the most recent to the metamorphic rocks. Traversing the Park, similar phenomena are apparent, but in less degree, as the upheaval was not so abrupt nor so great in extent. Rocks containing recent marine shells and reptiles are found at the north-eastern and northern limits, and going westward, each successive layer, to the schists and mica slates, occurs. The great central axis of the mountain chains alone exposes the oldest of the metamorphosed rocks ; the newer are folded in regular succession upon the slopes. And in accordance with the views of Murchison and Whitney the auriferous districts occur where these rocks are thus exposed. In this vicinity it is generally true that the older metamorphic are the auriferous rocks. There are, however, marked exceptions, and the investigations of the past three years indicate a much wider distribution of gold than has hitherto been recorded. In small quantity indeed it has been known to exist in various rocks, but here are some new and old containing the metal in notable quantity, even as much as the rich ores of other gold-mining countries. This accounts for the wide and abundant distribution of stream or placer gold in this region. The Park is one vast placer. The deep and extensive deposits of gravel and boulders are rich in fine gold. At some time, more or less remote, an ocean current swept through the passes from the north-north-west with great and constant force, and through the abrasion of centuries the superficial rocks have been transported to the broad, still basin below, and of course the gold liberated by their pulverization. Veins were certainly abraded as well as the country-rock, but large and numerous as they are, they could have supplied but an insignificant proportion of the gold in this vast field. There is no ancient diluvium like that of the Sierra Nevada in this region from which store of gold could be drawn and newly distributed; all appearances indicate that this deposit originated wholly *ab ovo*, from the beginning.

These rich placers in 1860-61 formed the great attraction for the adventurers then flocking into the country. It was then that Buckskin, Fairplay, Tarryall or Hamilton, and Montgomery rose like mushrooms in the night, and were the centers of that intense life peculiar to new mining regions. Many gulches and patches were wrought with success, and had such a population contained in itself any of the elements of permanence, the north-western portion of the Park would now be densely peopled. But the gold-hunter is of all adventurers the most restless. The history of California in the matter of stampedes has been repeated in Colorado, and with even more ruinous effect. The multitude which rushed from all parts of the world to California in 1849, which followed in succession the "Gold Lake," "Gold Bluff," "Kern River," "Colville," and "Frazier River" humbugs in that country, flocked to Pike's Peak in 1859, and was equally as feverish in one place as in the other. Few tarried long in one place. "Ounce diggings" were abandoned for others reported to yield *two* ounces. These were deserted in turn for diggings of said-to-be greater richness. It was in good degree Salmon River and Bannock, which soon became Idaho and Montana Territories, that made the crowded hamlet in the South Park of 1861 the deserted village of to-day. Some remained, however, and their well-wrought placers attest their industry and success. Tarryall, Fairplay, and one or two minor gulches have been uninterruptedly worked, and with a fair profit. The first of these is estimated to have yielded since 1859 $1,250,000; the second $150,000; Sacramento, not wrought the last three years, $75,000. At present large amounts are annually washed in the above-named and other localities of less note.

During the year 1866 keen men acquired title in one way or another to large tracts of land, supposed, indeed *known* to be gold-bearing, in this, Lake, and Summit counties. Two or more individuals would take out a certificate of incorporation under the General Territorial Incorporation Law, designating in such certificate their "claim." Or they would buy off old claimants and hire men to pre-empt by the hundred feet (under the miners' district laws) and deed over.   In this way nine companies were formed for the purpose of placer mining in the Park, which each acquired title as above to sufficient territory to justify the expense of *acequias* to bring water, the putting in of extensive bed-rock sluices or flumes, and the purchase of hydraulic machinery or steam dredges for moving dirt.   The country may generally be regarded as rich enough in gold to pay well for washing in this way ; and too poor to pay for washing in small claims or patches as heretofore attempted.

Beaver Creek or Gulch empties into the Platte just below Fairplay.   It is about one hundred yards wide in its lower course, twenty to thirty feet deep, and pays from the grass-roots.   "The Beaver Creek Mining Company" have been at work here four years getting a bed-rock ditch and flume in to the richer portion of the gulch.   The flume is twenty by twenty-four inches in size, three-fourths of a mile long, and its upper end has just touched the bed-rock, which will give some idea of the fall of the gulch.   This Company have sold a three-fifths interest in their property to "The Pennsylvania Gold and Silver Mining Company," organized in Philadelphia in 1866, through Gov. A. Cummings, and owning the gulch above as high as water can be brought into it—three miles.   Their nominal capital is $250,000 ; available for immediate use, $30,000.   About one hundred and fifty inches of water runs in the gulch, but that is not enough. A ditch ten miles long bringing water from the Platte at Montgomery and designed to carry five

13

hundred inches, has been surveyed and will be constructed at once. Then the Company will have three miles of a rich gulch to work out, estimated to contain, from numerous prospects, $500,000. This is an illustration of what other parties are doing in Buckskin and Sacramento Gulches, at Fairplay and at Tarryall. To give an idea of the extent of these placers, let us notice the latter more particularly.

Hamilton is situate near the head and in the western edge of the Park, on Tarryall Creek where it breaks away from the Range. It is at the entrance to one of the best passes through the Range, and in 1859 was crowded with people. All the affluents of the creek were staked and claimed to their extreme sources. A plot was made of the town of Hamilton, which may be seen at the Hamilton post-office, and is a right pretty map. A huge gambler's booth, running twenty tables, occupied the roomy *plaza*, and five hundred people walked the streets seeking whom or what they might devour. All this has departed, the town is dead to the waist, its seeming early promise having been broken to the hope. But above and below, and under and along by and around it, the entire soil will pay for washing, and with the amount of water available, cannot be exhausted in a great many years ; so that Hamilton ought to live again, and doubtless will.

A mile above this town a few men have worked for seven years, Summer and Winter, sinking and drifting out and washing the "pay-streak." Abreast of Hamilton the gulch is very wide with little fall. Below is one of the prettiest sections of the Park, (it is called by the inhabitants "The Park," *par excellence*) smooth as a floor, strongly turfed, and descending evenly and regularly perhaps one hundred feet per mile for fifteen miles. Two or three companies mined within three miles below town the past season, with hydraulics. One of them worked into the bank four hundred feet, the pay increasing the further they went, the last week of their operations realizing an ounce and a half per hand to the twenty-four hours. The soil is about twelve feet thick, a dry gravel, very hard but easily knocked down and dissolved by water. A mile south-west is Park Gulch, which has also been very successfully wrought by hydraulics the past Summer. Tarryall Creek and Park Gulch come together ten miles below Hamilton, and here parties have regularly mined since 1860. They are $4-diggings. Four miles further down is Nelson's Bar, which has been worked to some extent, though not paying very well. The creek banks are nearly level and there seems no good reason why the whole "wash" on either side to where the bed-rock shall pitch toward other streams, will not pay for handling. This deposit of gold-bearing gravel is duplicated at Fairplay, if not at many other places in Park, Lake, and Summit counties. Indeed the South Park, for ten or fifteen miles down from its north-western wall, pans out the color ; and with five, ten or a dozen companies operating to advantage, the annual production of gold of the county should exceed what it has been in the aggregate since it was settled. Meanwhile the prettiest portion of the Park will have been torn to pieces, and rendered of all landscapes the most unsightly. It may well be asked whether it be not worth more for pastoral or agricultural purposes, or even to look at, than the paltry amount of gold there is in it.

From the town of Hamilton goes the route north-north-west through what is called "Breckenridge Pass," to the mines of the Blue, on the Pacific slope. It was through this pass, that John S. Jones of Empire took a train of seven wagons loaded with twenty thousand pounds of freight in the dead of the Winter of 1865–6. He was aiming to open a ranch on Bear River, west of the Middle Park, but owing to the loss of his stock, was obliged to locate temporarily on the Grand in the Middle Park. Perhaps a sketch of his trip would convey the best idea of the climate, fall of snow, etc., of this Range of the Rocky Mountains of anything we could give. The train started from Denver, December 8th, 1865, and on the 15th had arrived at Slaght's Ranch on the north branch of the South Platte, the mercury having ranged since the 12th from 9° to 22° below zero. On the 17th they were at Hamilton, mercury at zero, deep snow in the Pass above, more falling, and high wind. By the 25th they had reached the summit of the Pass, eight miles above Hamilton, seven men constantly shoveling snow. Of the last eight days, on the 18th the mercury stood at 16° above zero, on the 19th 8° below, on the 20th at zero, 21st ditto, 22d 10° below, 23d and 24th about at zero, 25th 20° below. The snow averaged thirty inches in depth, while some of the drifts were twenty-five feet deep and three hundred long. Hay was brought from Hamilton and there was little difficulty in keeping the track open. The next five days, the mercury standing about at zero, were consumed in getting the train one-half mile down from the summit on the western slope. On the last day of the year the mercury marked 18° below zero and the men were completely discouraged. A huge "slide" was made, the "camp and garrison equipage" put aboard (the wagons and freight left to be brought on afterward) and at 10 o'clock it started out, Jones and one other man having broken and shoveled some sort of a track. Two and a half miles were made before stopping, the last one in thick timber where the snow was not drifted. Next day the camp reached Breckenridge, eight miles from the summit, through two feet of snow. That night the mercury sank to 20° below zero. The extra stock was sent forward fifteen miles, where the snow was less than a foot deep and the sunny sides of the hills were bare, sleds were made for the mules, and by the 27th of January the wagons and freight had been brought from the summit down to Breckenridge. It had been snowing almost continuously since New Year's. On the 21st and 22d a warm rain fell, settling the snow about a foot. The loose stock had been driven five or six miles ahead and arrangements made for some one to come up from the Park and get them. But from a misunderstanding no one came, and there being a stiff crust on the snow, rendering it difficult for cattle to get around, they stood still and starved and froze to death. There was no wagon road down the Blue, so the freight was packed on mules and ponies which proceeded on the ice to the Grand. The sequel of the expedition is of no particular interest in this connection, but it is soon told. Jones opened a ranch low down on the Grand in the Middle Park, but he had not time to fence or watch it, and so, although the wild flag grass and grain grow there so rank as to almost hide a horse, he got no crop. But the main Range of the Continent had been crossed with a train of merchandise in mid-Winter, and it is believed that were business carried on, both sides of the Range, so that considerable travel would be unavoidable during the Winter, there would be no more trouble in keeping open a good sleigh-path than in many sections of the Northern and Eastern States.

In the mountains bordering the north-western portion of the Park are found the conditions favorable to the occurrence of auriferous veins, and it is here that the first and most recent discoveries have been made. Late in 1861, while pay-dirt was still profitable in Gregory, the Phillips Lode was struck. The out-crop for several hundred feet in length was ore decomposed by the elements, the "pay-dirt" or "top-quartz" of Colorado, the "gossan" of Cornwall. Washing with sluices resulted so well that a Mr. Farrand soon brought in and erected a stamp mill for the quartz. Other stamp mills and rude Mexican arastras soon followed, and quartz-mining

was inaugurated in the South Park. Most satisfactory were the first results. Gold came in at
every turn of the wheel, and would doubtless have
continued to do so had the skill and prudence of
miners been among the qualities of the operators.
But the lode was wrought by an open cut and all
from above, so that what was made was in spite of
every disadvantage. When they reached a harder
rock, about forty feet from the surface, and the big
bunch of ore—thirty to forty feet in width—nar-
rowed, and scattered into "strings," the natural
roasting also having penetrated no further the earth,
they struck cap—that cap which has been discovered in every lode in Colorado which has from any
reason ceased to yield a profit under stamps, and
which cap means, a narrow or pinched place in the
vein, or a change from paying to barren ground.
Such was the success and the end of the working
of the Phillips of Buckskin, the most remarkable
lode in the Park.

The excavation on the lode is estimated at
300,000 cubic feet, and the amount of gold taken
from it at $310,000. Other lodes were discovered
in rapid succession and many of them worked, with
varying success. Of these the mention of the
names of a few and their estimated yield, must
suffice. In Buckskin and Musquito Districts, Orphan Boy, stamps, $170,000; Excelsior, arastras,
$45,000; Honeycomb, arastras, $20,000; Bates,
stamps and arastras, $30,000; Evening Star, stamps
and arastras, $30,000. In Montgomery District,
Allen, stamps, $180,000; Pendleton, stamps and

arastras, $60,000; Parsonage, stamps, $90,000; North Star, $47,000.

The limited scale and generally wasteful mode of mining and milling which prevailed at that time, moves us to regard these results as wonderful, and a most flattering augury for the future of the mines of this section. If the production of a few lodes so unskillfully managed reached so considerable a sum, what will it be when the hundreds of equally as good lodes in the Park region shall have been made productive?

The mineral veins in the Montgomery Spur strike nearly north and south, and crop out plainest on the edges of the gorges where the affluents of the Platte break into the Park. They extend without apparent intermission from Horseshoe District to Montgomery and beyond. Indeed the Montgomery Spur continues northward into the Middle Park, twenty to thirty miles, between two forks of the Blue, and quartz veins show themselves from Montgomery to its northern point. On the heads of the main Blue the promise of a rich silver region is almost as favorable as on the heads of the Snake, a tributary of the Blue rising considerably further north-east than the main stream. Silver was often found in nuggets in McNulty's Gulch in the days of placer mining.

At the extreme head of the Blue, just where the water begins to run west, lie Pollock and Silver Lake Districts. The most noted lode of Pollock is the "Virginia." It has been described as a ledge of whitish rock, fifty feet wide and one-fourth of a

mile long, streaked with veins of dark ore, about-
equally rich in gold and silver, and yielding to the
rude mill of early times twenty dollars a ton. A
company has been organized and is sinking on one
of the thickest of these strings of ore.

The most noted lode of Silver Lake is the "Ver-
mont." It shows in the face of a mountain for a
thousand feet, and is partially hidden by a pepetual
snowbank. It has a vein of well-burnt quartz six
feet in width, then horse or key-rock, whitish and
bearing gold and silver in small quantities, then
another three foot vein, of quartz. Considerable
of this material was crushed at Montgomery in
1862, paying about eighteen dollars a ton, silver and
gold. The top of it is 13,000 feet above sea. It is
believed by those best acquainted with this region
that the rich silver belt of Argentine and the Snakes,
after having disappeared for a season, again crops
out on the extreme head of the Blue. As early as
1861 the silver outcroppings of the head of Blue
attracted attention, and companies were formed and
commenced developing some of them, the Brooks
Silver Lode, head of McNulty's Gulch, for one.
Quandary Mountain, covered with bits of silver
ore, was staked off and claimed in patches, and what
was called "The Quandary Lode," was hunted for
with all the enthusiasm, but little of the persever-
ance that has characterized the search for the
philosopher's stone. Colorado has always been afflicted with periodic silver excitements, but has not
yet been able to realize anything from her undoubted
silver treasures. Work ceased on the Brooks

13*

Lode from the "impecuniosity" of the numerous owners.

Among the famous lodes of Montgomery District are the Parsonage, Harrington, Washington, Pendleton, Putnam, Eldorado, North Star, and Allen & Ogden. They all paid well on the surface, and are opened by shafts 100 to 270 feet deep, from 400 to 800 and 1200 feet in length. A company was organized in Pittsburgh in 1864 by Lewis Jones on a portion of the Harrington. They purchased and sent out a 30-stamp mill, with engine, pumps, &c., but have not attempted to do anything further. Another company, called "The Pioneer," was organized in Philadelphia about the same time on scattered lode property, the great bulk of which had none but an imaginary existence. After some pretty costly bungling, including the original purchase and the erection of a mill-building where they did not want it, this Company got to work *right* about the beginning of 1866. Capt. Daniel Plummer, a miner of twenty years' experience in Superior is their agent. He is mining on the Parsonage, and by adit, and late in 1866 started his new mill. The latter is 60 by 80 feet in dimensions, exclusive of boiler-house, has six batteries of five stamps each, two 20-foot arastras and a set of six Tyrolean amalgamators. When the mill was started Capt. Plummer had out, at the mouth of his main adit and in the mill, 500 tons of quartz and ore which he was satisfied was worth $100 a ton clear through.

Among the noted veins of Buckskin and Musquito are the Phillips, Prospect, Excelsior, Bates,

Colorado, Sublette, Union-Four, and Dodge-Union-Four, Orphan Boy, De Mary, Evening Star, Jenny, Platte, Doucer, Lulu, Payson.   Two or three Eastern companies have been organized for the purpose of working some of them. "The Sterling City Gold Mining Company" built a stone mill-building in Musquito in 1865, designed for thirty stamps. It has not been started nor much mining done by the Company, of which J. W. Smith, of Denver, is the agent. At Buckskin there are two companies operating — "The Colorado Gold Mining Company of Philadelphia," and "The South Park Gold Mining & Exploring Company." Prof. Alfred Du Bois is agent for both, and also for "The American Exploring Company," another Philadelphia organization, whose purpose is sufficiently indicated by its name. The South Park Company have done little of consequence as yet. The past season they were excavating two shafts on the Orphan Boy, the object being to determine whether that and the Kitty Clyde are the same or separate veins, or whether the latter is a spur of the former.* But the Colorado Company have gone in on their nerve, built a large mill which was gradually getting under way at the end of last year, taken thousands of tons of quartz and ore from the Excelsior Lode, and made other improvements. The Excelsior Lode crops out along the edge of the gorge north and 1000 feet above the town. Company own 1000 feet on it, only 200 of which are they working. The

---

* Would'nt it be cruel to divorce the Orphan Boy from his (sweet) Kitty Clyde?

vein is seventeen feet wide, quartz and dirt, and averages, without counting in a small but regular formation of silver of $5,000 a ton richness, $79 a ton. Very rich copper ore begins to appear 130 feet from the surface. The ore is conveyed down to the mill through a chute and by self-acting cars. About 400 feet below the outcrop, a tunnel has been started in by which it is expected to work the lode when it shall be finished. At the base of the hill, another tunnel has been commenced, which is expected to reach the lode by the time the back of the upper adit shall have been exhausted. The mill contains a Hodge & Christie cracker, two sets of Cornish rollers, and six stone arastras, twenty feet in diameter, the whole having a capacity of one hunderd tons a day. It is of wood, the lumber and timber cut out by the Company's saw-mill. It is so arranged that the ore moves as desired by its own gravity.

Although in latitude 39° north and having an elevation above the sea at its head of nearly two miles, the climate of the South Park is not more inhospitable than that of New York or New England. The average temperature, though not lower in Winter is a good deal lower in Summer, and it is also much more equable. The following mean of the thermometer and barometer for the year 1866, is kindly furnished us by Prof. DuBois, it having been determined under his auspices. He writes:

"My barometrical observations were not *all* made with a *reliable* instrument, and therefore only give approximate results. Taking these, and computing the hight of Buckskin above tide-water, we have 10,488 feet. Observations made the same months in Denver and in Buckskin, fix the difference of elevation at 5,124 feet. These differ so little, as Denver has an elevation, well ascertained, of 5,317 feet, that we may consider the figure nearly right. This, with 7,000 feet as the elevation of Mount Lincoln above Buckskin, will give, I do not doubt, quite a low figure as to the hight of that mountain—under the truth. I think it may be safely stated at 17,500 feet. The observations enclosed are not perfect, because their number was unequal at different periods and taken only at morning and evening."

SUMMARY.

	DAYS OBSERVED.	THERMOMETER.	BAROMETER.
January, - - - - -	15	22.66	20.198
February, - - - - -	28	18.51	20.196
March, - - - - - -	31	22.79	20.145
April, - - - - - -	30	28.53	20.193
May, - - - - - -	30	33.42	20.222
June, - - - - - -	30	42.77	20.297
July, - - - - - -	9	51.75	20.399
August, - - - - -	28	48.42	20.381
September, - - - -	30	38.66	20.295
October, - - - - -	31	30.22	20.265
November, - - - -	30	24.10	20.157
December, - - - -	31	18.75	20.048
Average for the year, -		32.55	20.233

Among the romantic incidents which have marked the brief history of the South Park, are the murderous campaign of the Espinosas, and the Reynolds guerrilla raid. The Espinosas are supposed to have been outlaws from Chihuahua, two cousins; one was a large, dish-faced, iron-looking, beau-ideal of a villain, the other, a little fellow of no particular type. They diversified their journey northward from Mexico by the murder of two merchants in Santa Fe, and of a soldier at Conejos. Arriving in the vicinity of Canon City in March, 1863, they signalized a three weeks' lurking in the bush between there and the South Park by the murder of nine men. The inhabitants were prostrated, blockaded in their houses at last, by consternation. No one knew the character of this mysterious dispensation of Providence, no one knew from what concealment the messenger of death which had never missed its mark might reach him. After a while Jno. McCannon of Lake County raised twenty volunteers who elected him their Captain, and, at the expense of Lake County, started to hunt down the assassins. He first settled with a lot of thieves then infesting the county. One of them was captured, taken from his men by the soldiers at Fairplay, and hanged. The rest fled to Montana and were hanged in due time. Finding a trail in the lower part of the Park leading toward Canon City, McCannon with eight men followed it into one of the deepest kanyons of that rough region, where he found two horses feeding. Quietly concealing themselves, the Espinosas soon appeared and the big one was felled by a shot through the right side. Rising on his elbow he kept firing with his revolver, the men having to drop to escape his yet unerring shot, until a ball was sent through his head by a brother of one of his victims. The little devil clambered up the rocks, hid away, and finally escaped. The blood-stained wearing apparel of twelve murdered men, some money and personal trinkets, a knife and memorandum book were found on the body of the dead fiend, who was left where he fell, and in their camp. The little one picked up another cousin, a mere boy, and hiding in the Sangre de Christo Pass, carried on the business of the old firm, although in a rude, apprentice-like way, until late in the Summer, when, ravens rising from the offal of a butchered ox they had stolen disclosing their retreat, they were set upon by a party of soldiers from Fort Garland and both killed. Some papers addressed to Gov. Evans concerning an alleged despoliation of the Espinosa family by Government officers, together with a book of prayers and some insane religious raphsodies, were found on their persons. One of the latter ended— " the Virgin Mary will be sitting on my head until I die in her arms, amen Jesus!" *The* Espinosa was without doubt one of the worst bandits of Mexico, and his career in Colorado is one of those events which give rise to the trite remark that " truth is stranger than fiction." In a paper addressed to Gov. Evans, he claimed to have killed twenty-two men, and *on that account* demanded the restoration of his property.

Sometime in April, 1864, James Reynolds picked up a party of skulkers and deserters from the Confederate service numbering twenty-two, in the vicinity of Fort Arbuckle, Texas, and started for Colorado, steering as near as he could for the Spanish Peaks. Driven to eating their pack animals on the way, they struck the roads from the States to Santa Fe, hungry. With the first train they intersected, they traded a horse for something to eat. The next one, not showing fight, they captured. Another captured train gave them ample subsistence and transportation, arms and ammunition, five thousand dollars in drafts, a large sum in greenbacks, and two thousand dollars in coin. Upon this they quarreled and thirteen of the party turned back. The rest *cached* their plunder and went on through the settlements of Colorado, quite civilly, until they got into the South Park, where Reynolds had formerly lived and borne a good character. Here they broke loose, captured the coach from Buckskin to Denver, robbed the mail and safe, and chopped up the coach wheels. For several days thereafter they infested the road between the South Park and Denver, living at the ranches, stealing, trading, doing foolish rather than smart things. The people soon got after them, parties of soldiers and bands of citizens from the Park and from Denver. One night a dozen miners under Jack Sparks crossed the Range eastward from Summit County, ran into them on the north fork of Platte, and fired on them, killing one, named Singleterry, and wounding Reynolds in the arm. The band was effectually dispersed, and every individual member "lit out" for himself, the general direction being toward Texas, whence they came. Pursuit was made by the inhabitants, and one, named Holliman, was captured. He turned State's evidence. This did not amount to much, however, the robbers easily managing to elude the pursuit of large bodies. But they had nothing to eat, and five of them were caught by lying in wait for them at the ranches below Canon City. The other two escaped. They were first brought before a military commission, and then ordered to Fort Lyon in custody of Capt. Cree, Third Colorado Cavalry. At the old Russell-ville town-site, thirty miles out of Denver, the wagon in which they rode and their guard fell behind the command a little while watering the mules. Here "the prisoners," says the *Rocky Mountain News*, of that date, "made a concerted attempt to escape, were fired upon by the guard, and all instantly killed." In such tragic style ended this unique performance in the invasion or guerrilla line.

CHAPTER XII.

MOUNT LINCOLN is the north-east corner-stone of
Lake County. Thence the boundary runs west on
the 39th parallel to the western limit of the Territory, one hundred and fifty miles ; thence south to
the summit of the Uncompagre Mountains, one
hundred and ten miles ; thence east-north-east
along the summit to the main Range ; following
that until it curves northward, it jumps across it
and the Arkansas River to the crest of the Montgomery Spur, along which it proceeds to the top of
Mount Lincoln, the place of beginning. Its area is
about sixteen thousand square miles. It embraces
the sources of the Arkansas River, and the course
and tributaries of that stream for about fifty miles.
It also includes the Gunnison Fork of the Rio Colorado. It is with the former section we have chiefly
to do, however, as in that are the principal settlements. On the western slope of the Montgomery
Spur, opposite Buckskin, heads California Gulch,
worked more or less in former times for about five

miles in length. The settlement here is called Oro City. The upper Arkansas Valley is so wide, including its foot-hills, that it seems, from the summit of the Montgomery Spur, where the trail from Buckskin to Oro City crosses, like a not unworthy sister of the South or Middle Park. Bayard Taylor, who crossed here in 1866, says of it:

" Our elevation above the sea-level could not have been much less than thirteen thousand feet. The timber line was far below us; near at hand we were surrounded by a desolation of snow and naked rock. Mount Lincoln, on the north, gathered together the white folds of the separating mountain-ranges, and set his supreme pyramids over them ; while far to the south-east, where the sage-plains of the South Park stretch for a hundred miles, all features are lost in a hot purple mist. Before us, however, lay the crowning grandeur. The ridge on which we stood slid down, like the roof of a house, to the valley of the Upper Arkansas, which we could trace to the very fountain-head of the river, its pine groves and long meandering lines of cotton-wood drawn upon a field pearly gray-green. Starting from Mount Lincoln, the eye follows the central chain — the backbone of the Continent—in a wide semi-circle around the head of the valley until it faced us on the opposite side, and then kept on its course southward, on and ever on, slowly fading into air—a hundred miles of eternal snow! Beyond the Arkansas Valley (where there is a pass considerably below the timber line), glimmered as if out of blue air, the rosy snow of other and farther ranges.

Westward, seventy miles distant, stood the lonely Sopris Peak, higher than Mont Blanc.

"New landscapes are often best described by comparison with others that are known; but I know not where to turn for any mountain view at all resembling this in wondrous breadth and extent—in the singular combination of subdued coloring with great variety of form.* It is at once simple, sublime and wondrous. With a very clear atmosphere, the effect might be different; as we saw it, the farthest peaks and ranges melted insensibly out of the line of vision, suggesting almost incredible distances. There were no glaciers, thrusting down their wedges between the forests; no great upper plateaus of impacted snow, pouring their cataracts from rocky walls, as in the Alps. The snow-line, though broken by ravines, was quite uniform, but the snows were flushed with such exquisite color, and cut the sky with such endless variety of outline, that they substituted a beauty of another and rarer kind. This and the view of the Blue River Valley, in the Middle Park, are representative landscapes, and they alone are worth a journey across the Plains."

Across this park of the Upper Arkansas, to the south-west from Mount Lincoln, Lake Creek comes down from the main Range beyond, after escaping from which, it spreads out into two dark sheets of

---

*Gilpin, speaking of the Sierra Madre, says: "I am unable to illustrate it by comparison, because it stands supreme and alone, the standard to which all other mountain masses must be submitted." In this case the Doctors do not disagree.

water, together about two miles wide by five long, and separated by a belt of land one-fourth of a mile wide, covered with pines. They are called the Twin Lakes, constitute the most considerable body of water in Colorado, and give name to the county. Dayton, the county-seat, is located under the Range, at their head.

Up the extreme left considerable fork of the Arkansas River is one of the easiest passes through the Range, opening out on Piney Creek or Eagle River, which puts into the Grand below the Middle Park. This pass is said to be three thousand feet lower than the Berthond Pass. Nearly opposite California Gulch, comes in Colorado Gulch from the west, more recently discovered than California, and worked from year to year with considerable success. Just below California, on the same side, is Iowa Gulch, also worked at the present time. It is twelve miles thence down to the mouth of Lake Creek, coming from the west, immediately below which is Cache Creek and Diggings. Then the mountains seem to crowd the river; the stupendous chasm through which it makes its way becomes gorged; the dividing ridges between the tributary streams, Clear, Pine, Chalk, Cottonwood, which come out of the Range at intervals of seven or eight miles, continue down to the very brink of the river, probably at one time damming it completely. On these tributaries, the valley becomes wider, and below the mouth of Cottonwood, which is forty miles from the sources of the river, down to the mouth of the South Arkansas, a distance of

twenty miles, farms line the banks of the stream.
They have an altitude of six thousand to eight
thousand feet, are in latitude thirty-eight, are sheltered by high ranges of mountains on either side,
accessible only from the South Park, sustain stock
without feeding during the Winter, with irrigation
produce fair crops of vegetables, oats, barley, and
by a diligent use of the entire season, Spring wheat.
The road from the South to the San Luis Parks, *via*
Trout Creek, the Arkansas, the South Arkansas,
and Poncho Pass, goes through this part of the valley. The soil resembles that of the Parks or the
Plains. From the head of the river to Canon
City, it is an alternation of bar and kanyon, the
bars masses of boulders and gravel more or less
overlaid with a light alluvial soil, and occasionally
belted with pinon orchards which are very pretty
viewed from a distance ; the kanyons dark, rough
and deep passages of the stream through the roots
of the mountain masses. The course of the Arkansas River, in the mountains, is probably not far
from one hundred miles long. Immediately below
the mouth of the South Arkansas commences the
kanyon, *par excellence.* It is called fifty miles long
and is not impracticable for a wagon road, a considerable portion of it being an open valley like
those above.

Gold is found in the stream and on its south-
western tributaries from the Cottonwood to its extreme sources. A mining district was organized
on the heads of Cottonwood in 1866, called, "West-
phalian." About thirty lodes have been discovered

here, none of them more than fairly struck, the ore, coarse iron and copper pyrites and sulphurets with some galena and zinc, coming to the surface, not decomposed in the least.

On Pine Creek, twelve miles above Cottonwood, is another mining district, called "Pine Creek," not now worked nor inhabited, and about which little is known.

A short distance above Pine we have Clear Creek, upon which is a mining district called "La Plata." Eight miles up the stream about thirty lodes have been discovered. Nothing of consequence has been done on them, but it is known that they possess the same general characteristics as those of the rest of the Range. At the mouth of the creek is Georgia Bar, formerly worked considerably in Winter with hand rockers, and paying from three to five dollars a day. This bar, Kelly's Bar, and the Arkansas River for thirty miles below Lake Creek, have always been the Winter's resort for grub of many of the miners of Lake County. Seventy-five thousand dollars is estimated to have been thus taken from them. In 1861 a company built a dam on Lake Creek and flumed the Arkansas River at Georgia Bar for one thousand feet, at a cost of ten thousand dollars. They were nearly ready to commence sluicing the bed of the stream, which is very rich, when their dam gave way and carried off their flume. The men immediately enlisted in the First Colorado Volunteers, and no attempt has since been made to flume the Arkansas, although the sand for a hundred miles from its source, taken up on a shovel and panned down, gives a fine color. This company had obtained as high as $1.50 to the pan of dirt from the bed of the river.

About three miles above Clear, is Cache Creek, a creek only by courtesy, or rather by virtue of a ditch bringing five hundred inches of water during the rainy season, from the precipitous southern rim of the Twin Lakes, its whole length, nine miles, cost of construction, $20,000. Cache Creek is at the lower end of a park, or bar, three miles up and down the river in length, and two from the river west to the mountain in width. A party who were prospecting the Arkansas River, cached their provisions here, and in that way gold was discovered. In this park are Cache Creek Gulch, discovered by Campbell and Shoewalter, estimated production to date, $30,000 ; Bertschey's Gulch, discovered by G. Bertschey & Co., estimated production to date, $25,000; worked out ; Gold Run Gulch, discovered by Long, West, & Co., has produced $22,000, now worked out ; Gibson Gulch, discovered by one Gibson in 1861, has paid to date, $30,000, now worked by D. Houghton & Co., by bed-rock flume 500 feet long ; Oregon Gulch, discovered and worked out in 1860, by Thomas & Co., paid $11,000 ; Ritchey's Patch, discovered by J. Ritchey in 1864, now worked by him and others, production to date, $17,000 ; and Lake Creek Diggings, at the northeast corner of the park, discovered in 1860, now chiefly owned and worked by H. M. Severs & Co., who are erecting a saw-mill to facilitate operations, estimated yield to date, $55,000.

Cache Creek Gulch is very deep and has but a slight fall, so that it could not be worked to advantage in 100-feet claims, as all the gulch was originally taken up. It soon passed into the hands of Ramage Brothers & Co., who commenced a bed-rock flume in 1862. The property has since been transferred to "The Gaff Mining Company," J. W. Gaff of Cincinnati, Wm. F. Bailey and Joseph Hutchinson, of Aurora, Ind., and Geo. W. Lane of Denver. Their flume is four feet square and now some three-fourths of a mile long. They work about thirty feet in depth by one hundred and fifty in width. Side-sluices, leading into the main one, are used when necessary. Mr. Hutchinson lives at Cache Creek and attends to the business.

There are patch diggings in the points of the hills bordering Cache Gulch, from which has been taken to date, estimated, $86,000. It is thought the whole park would pay for washing, could it be got at on a large scale, but a scarcity of water is complained of.

West of this park the range rises abruptly to an altitude of 3,000 or 4,000 feet, and near its summit on the eastern slope is Lost Kanyon Gulch, discovered in 1860 by a party of prospectors returning from the park of the Gunnison River, west of the Range, and who here became convinced that they were *lost*. Of course they prospected—a *lost* prospector will always *find* himself when he can get a fair color,—and as good luck would have it they struck a rich spot. About $60,000 was taken out in 1861. Next year the pay streak was lost, and

14

although hunted for diligently ever since, has not again been found. So that the spot is doubly *lost*. All this section we have last described belongs in "Hope Mining District."

On the opposite side of the river a very rich lode was discovered in 1866, upon which a mining district was organized and called "Lake Falls." A load of quartz from the said lode, which is called "Hattie Jane," treated by Bertola Process, in Clear Creek County, is stated to have yielded at the rate of $200 a ton. We have no figures as to the width of crevice from which the quartz was taken.

Lake Creek empties into the Arkansas at the upper end of Cache Creek Park. It is five miles from its mouth to the head of the Twin Lakes, which we have referred to before. They are beautiful sheets of water and full of trout. South of them the Range rises abruptly from their very edge; on the west there is a large bottom and here is Dayton, the county-seat. Hence to the Red Mountain at the extreme sources of the creek is about fifteen miles, in a west-south-west direction. Red Mountain seems to be in a belt of lodes, some three miles in width, which here crosses the Range in the true course — north-east and south-west. From the top of the Red Mountain at the head of the left fork of Lake Creek, other red mountains can be seen both to the east and west. Eight miles west in an air-line a Boston Company did some work in 1866, finding similar ore to that found here. This point is about one hundred miles west of Pike's Peak. The crest of the mountains crossing the belt is mostly a gneissoid rock, sometimes a syenite. That has been broken and worn off in places, exposing an iron conglomerate of unknown thickness, with veins of purer pyrites bursting up through it without much regard to the proprieties. The pebbles of which the conglomerate is composed are quartz, and carry as much iron as the cement quartz which holds them together. Where the cap has crumbled or been washed off from this conglomerate, exposing it to the elements, the iron has become an oxide, giving the outside of the quartz a brilliant red color. This is noticeable as far as the belt can be seen, and the width so exposed is not less than a mile. In the streams and where the creek escapes from the mountains, numerous well-defined lodes have been discovered, not greatly different in width, lineal extent, and character of ores, from those of other parts of the Territory. Like them, too, they vary in richness. Some of them are absolutely barren and some contain $100, gold, to the ton, as tests of which we were personally cognizant, have indicated.* It is believed the requisite capital has been secured to establish at once one or two mills in this, called " Red Mountain District." There is not now a quartz-mill in the county nor a shaft more than thirty feet in depth, although the Berry tunnel near the head of California Gulch, has been driven one hundred feet. In this a pay-vein six feet in width

---

*Ex-Secretary Elbert, of Colorado, had forty-six samples of ore from forty-three of these lodes assayed by Behr & Keith of Black Hawk. They varied from $59 to $441 per ton, averaging $138.25. One sample yielded seventy per cent. of copper.

is claimed. The ore assays seventy or eighty dollars a ton in gold and silver, and is very rich in copper. But nothing very definite with reference to the quartz mines of the county is known.

Since up Lake Creek goes the old Ute Pass from the Arkansas to the Gunnison River, we may as well note here that both quartz and placer mines are known to exist throughout the immense park which pours into one channel the waters of the Gunnison. Among the paying gulches discovered and worked are Taylor's, Kent's, Union, Washington, and German. Ores were found there quite recently like those which occur elsewhere in the Territory. But it is out of the world as it were, and there has been no surplus energy to spare for the improvement of this vast wilderness, or even for its exploration.

About twelve miles above Dayton is California Gulch, divided into three mining districts—"Arkansas Independent," "California," and "Sacramento." It stands second if not first among all the gulches ever worked in Colorado for extent and yield of gold. It was discovered by Slater & Co., late in 1859, but its richness was not developed until the next April. Adventurers poured in at once and it was soon pre-empted in 100-feet claims for seven miles in length. Discovery claim produced $60,000 that season. No's 5 and 6, above, yielded $65,000. No. 1, below, has paid to date $55,000. A large quartz vein runs through Discovery and No. 1 below, from which $216 was sluiced by three men in 1863 in a half day. No. 4, below, prospected from one to ten dollars to the pan on the pay-streak, and has produced to date $75,000. No. 5, below, has paid $55,000. No's 11 and 12 below, paid $26,000. From 13 to 25 the average yield was $10 a day to the hand. No's 26 and 27 paid $50,000. No's 28 to 35 paid $15, and 36 to 41, $25 per day to the man. From 42 to 45 there was no pay, but thence to 56 the average was $18 a day per hand. No. 57 never paid anything, nor did any ground below that, which was but little more than a mile from Discovery. These figures are given to show the spotted character of the best gold-producing ravines. No's 14 to 18 above, paid $20,000 each. No's 19 to 20 yielded $80,000 in three months. No. 21 paid $15,000. No's 22 to 28, as well as the other claims above Discovery not here specified, paid from $3,000 to $5,000 each. From 28 to 36 the yield gradually fell off. No. 25 paid $15,000 ; 30, $6,000 ; 31 to 35 inclusive did not pay wages ; 36 paid $3,500. From No. 22 to the head of the gulch occurs a black cement, one to twelve feet thick, too loose to blast to advantage, too hard to be decomposed by water, hydraulics with 100-feet head having no effect on it. For the first three years mining was carried on by sluices, long toms, Georgia and hand rockers, and pans. Since that time, the claims have been largely consolidated, and mining done by ground sluicing and hydraulics. Thus W. H. Jones now owns and works 1, 2, and 3, below ; Leahry & Co., 26 and 27 below ; and White, Burroughs & Co., 14 to 30 above. The pay streak in these claims yields from $10 to $15 a day per man. Not more than half the gulch is considered worked out. Rich quartz veins traverse it in four or five different places, though these have never received any attention beyond pre-empting and sluicing out their dirt crevices, some of which paid extraordinarily. A tunnel called the "Berry Tunnel," at the head of the gulch, discovers, a short distance from its mouth, a strong vein of excellent ore. Although a few parties still make enough to support them through the Winter by working in this gulch during the Summer, its future prosperity, and this is true of the entire county, must depend on the development of its quartz mines. Nothing, indeed, can be more deceiving or ephemeral than the feverish prosperity of a placer mining country. California Gulch, which six years ago was infested by 5,000 to 6,000 people, is now almost deserted. The relics of former life and business—old boots and clothes, cooking utensils, rude house furniture, tin cans, gold pans, worn-out shovels and picks and the remains of toms, half buried sluices and rifle boxes, dirt-roofed log cabins tumbling down and the country turned inside out and disguised with rubbish of every description, are most disagreeably abundant and suggestive. May a new and better and more permanent life be founded upon these ruins, through the extent and excellence of the quartz deposits, thus fulfilling that Scripture which says "the last shall be first."

Colorado Gulch puts into the Arkansas opposite the mouth of California Gulch. It is five miles long and worked more or less its entire length, employing during the Summer from fifty to a hundred hands. It is chiefly owned by McCannon & Co., De Mary & Co., Long & Co., and Breece & Co. Each of them now have in bed-rock flumes, sixteen inches square, and from 600 to 1500 feet in length. It is worked from sixty to one hundred feet in width, and is from twelve to fifteen feet deep, the pay being confined to within a foot of the bed-rock. Gold was first discovered in the gulch 4th July, 1863, and since that time, much of the work having necessarily been of a preparatory nature, about two thousand ounces have been taken out.

There are other less important and far less work-ed gulches in the valley or park of the Upper Arkansas—among them Iowa (Adams District) just below and on the same side of the river as California; and Frying-pan, a tributary of Colorado Gulch. From Sacramento Flats, three miles above the mouth of California Gulch, nearly $200,000 has been taken first and last. The Arkansas River for seventy miles from its sources, with its tributaries and bars, is gold-bearing; and when placer mining shall come to be conducted on a larger scale and with more appropriate means, it may and probably will become, in Lake County, a business of consid-erable importance.

The approaches to the county are all through the South Park, and with proper care in laying out and working the roads, might be made very easy. From Fairplay to Dayton, crossing the Montgomery Spur north of the Buffalo Peaks, is about forty miles. The route goes up a tributary of the Platte by an easy grade, across a low notch between snow-banks, and follows down an affluent of the Arkansas, also, by an easy grade. The true route into the county, however, is via Canon City and the Colorado Salt Works, crossing the Montgomery Spur south of the Buffalo Peaks, where it has not an altitude of more than five hundred feet above the South Park, striking the Arkansas at Mayol's Ranch, twenty miles below Dayton, thence up or down the river. There is besides a trail from Buckskin over the Spur into California Gulch, and it may be said in favor of the climate at so great an altitude that the mail is carried over on this trail, weekly, the year round, by a man sixty years of age.

CHAPTER XIII.

SUMMIT COUNTY occupies all that portion of Colorado lying west of the crest of The Range and north of the 39th parallel. It may be entered by numerous passes from the South Park, from the Arkansas Park, from the Gregory or Boulder mines, the most noted of which are the Berthoud, head of Clear Creek, Boulder, head of Boulder Creek, and the Breckenridge, head of Tarryall Creek. Through the latter only, however, is there as yet a passable wagon road. The Middle Park is the most notable natural feature of the county. It is perhaps fifty miles in extent east and west, and seventy north and south. But at the ends proper the enclosing ranges shoot in spurs so far and numerous as to make it seem largest east and west. From the Boulder Pass, precisely at its head or east end, flows down Ranch Creek; from the Berthoud, Moses Creek; from the Vasquez, Dennis Creek, the last-

14*

mentioned passes being twelve or fifteen miles south of Boulder Pass, and leading from Clear Creek into the open head of the Park, about twelve miles due north.   A little west of Vasquez Pass is another called Packard, not much known, from which flows down St. Louis Creek.   These Creeks unite near the head of the Park and become Frasier River. Twelve or fifteen miles down, the Grand, formed by the junction of three considerable streams which rise in the range between the Middle and North Parks, bursts into the Park and receives the Frasier. Lower down, it breaks through a low range of mountains flung directly across the Park, and receiving numerous tributaries from the mountains on either hand, among them the Blue, which rises near Montgomery and is itself sixty miles long, it breaks away from the Park to the south-west through a deep kanyon, and goes out in search of the Pacific Ocean.

For three-fourths of its course through the Park the Grand has no first bottom, the fall being too great for soil to accumulate.   But the kanyon dams the stream to some extent, and for the lower ten miles it has a rich alluvial bottom perhaps a mile wide, from side to side of which it winds almost regularly, itself from two to six feet deep and fifty yards wide, the water clear, rapid, smooth and cold, as seen from the neighboring hills, one of the most beautiful landscapes in the world.   The larger tributaries of the Grand—William's Fork and the Blue, Troublesome and the Muddy—also have considerable arable valleys, extending five to ten miles up from the Grand. The second bottom is perhaps a hundred feet above the stream beds, is nearly level, covered alternately with a thrifty growth of sage brush, and the most nutritious grasses, among which grow native the white and red clover, timothy and red-top, and the genuine Kentucky blue-grass. We have ridden ten miles in one direction across this table-land. It constitutes the bulk of the open country in the Middle Park, and is estimated at twenty thousand acres, unsurpassed by any in the world for pastoral purposes. Among the flowers Bayard Taylor mentions the columbine, sedum, saxifrage, flame-colored euchroma, pink geranium streaked with purple, orchid, almost identical with the cyclamen of Italy and Greece, violets, rose-colored *pogonias*, blue larkspur, scarlet wort, crimson and violet lupins, white and scarlet star flower, &c. In one of his Middle Park letters, Taylor says:

"The sun came out, the clouds lifted and rolled away, and one of the most remarkable landscapes of the earth was revealed to our view. The valley of the Blue, which for a length of thirty miles, with a breadth varying from five to ten, lay under our eyes, wore a tint of pearly silver-gray, upon which the ripe green of the timber along the river, and the scattered gleams of water seemed to be enamelled. Opposite to us, above this sage color, rose huge mountain foundations, where the grassy openings were pale, the forests dark, the glens and gorges filled with shadow, the rocks touched with lines of light making a checkered effect that suggested cultivation and settlement.   Beyond these were wild ridges, all forests ; then bare masses of rock streaked with snow and highest bleak snow pyramids piercing the sky.   From the north to south stretched the sublime wall—the western boundary of the Middle Park—and where it fell away toward the kanyon by which Grand River goes forth to seek the Colorado, there was a vision of dim, rosy peaks, a hundred miles distant.   In breadth of effect—in airy depth and expansion—in simple yet most majestic outline, and in originality yet exquisite harmony of color, this landscape is unlike anything I have ever seen.   I feel how inadequate are my words to suggest such new combinations of tints and forms.   There is great vertical grandeur among the Alps ; here it is the vast literal extent which impresses you, together with atmospheric effect occasioned by great elevation above the sea. You stand on the plains of the Alpine glaciers ; a new vegetation surrounds you ; a darker sky is over your head ; yet the grand picture on which you look is complete in all its parts, or, if any element is wanting, its absence is swallowed up in the majesty that is present."

The geology of the park is the same as that of the Plains.   Rocks of the most recent Tertiary occur, although at an elevation of three thousand feet above the highest Plains on the eastern slope.   A fragment of rock belonging to the Tertiary was found on the top of Long's Peak, fourteen thousand feet above the sea.   In the Middle Park proper, no minerals in paying quantities except coal have been found. The out-croppings of coal are observable from the head of the Park westward to Utah. Petroleum in enormous quantity in the form of a coal similar to the Albertine coal of New Brunswick occurs on the White River near its confluence with the Green, the veins vertical and traceable for miles and having a thickness of three to four feet. The soil in the vicinity of these veins is saturated with petroleum. The hot sulphur spring on the Grand, ten or twelve miles above the foot of the Park, if not a mineral production is one of the chief attractions of the Park. A large stream of water, strongly impregnated with sulphur and about as hot as can be borne by the hand* issues from a rock formed by its own sediment and falls ten feet into a big bathtub, also its handiwork. During the Summer season this spring and the adjacent fishing and hunting grounds are the favorite resort of people of leisure. Antelope, deer, elk, and bear abound in the Park and the forests of the surrounding ridges, and the streams are alive with mountain trout which grow

---

* Dr. Parry says of this: "The temperature of the water at its several issues is 112° Fahr., and at the point where it falls into the basin 110°. A smaller spring, less exposed to the external air, shows a temperature as high as 115°. The water is clear, has an agreeable softness to the touch, and a distinct saline odor. Along the course of its several streams floats a slimy growth of feathery *confervæ*, exhibiting a great variety of colors, including pure white, red, green and blue. Animal life is also exhibited in these tepid waters in a small mollusk of the genus *Lymnæa*. The sulphurous odor is not very perceptible, and to the taste, though disagreeably tepid, there is sufficient sparkle to render it not unpleasant. There is no doubt that the springs possess valuable medicinal properties, which will be in due time appreciated."

to a weight of three or four pounds. The inside of the mountain walls of the Park, especially of the main Range, is heavily timbered, pine below nine thousand feet elevation, spruce and fir above that and below twelve thousand where all aborescence ceases. Grass and flowers grow on the tops of the highest mountains, except where they so peak up that there is no place for soil to stick on. The climate is the same as that of the Plains so far as extremes are concerned, but more rain falls in Summer and more snow in Winter, and the mean temperature of the year is much lower. At the hot spring the elevation of the Grand is eight thousand feet, and of course that portion of the Park above is too high for successful cultivation. It is valuable only for pastoral purposes. Below the hot spring and in the valleys of the Bear, Grand, and White, are large bodies of fine arable land. The valley of the Green River on the western line of Colorado is also susceptible of cultivation, its elevation at the mouth of the White being but four thousand five hundred feet—about the same as that of Salt Lake. A tolerable wagon road was con-structed from Empire to the mouth of the Grand via Clear Creek and William's Fork, during the Summer of 1866, making with the efforts of the season before on the part of the Overland Stage Company, a passable road for wagons at least going eastward from Salt Lake to Denver, one hundred, some say two hundred miles shorter than the stage route now traveled. The completion of this road will open to white encroachment the Middle Park

and all the country of the Grand, Bear, White and
Green rivers, which together constitute a basin,
similar to that of the Great Salt Lake, although
generally much higher and more mountainous.

Away in the extreme south end of the Park,
under the immediate Winter shadow of Mount Lincoln rises the Blue River. For the upper twenty
or twenty-five miles of its course its tributaries are
numerous, reaching from twelve to twenty miles
into the encroaching mountains not unlike the ribs
of an open fan. Among these are the Snake,
Swan and French on the left and Ten-Mile on the
right. The latter and the Snake empty into the
Blue opposite each other, twenty-four miles from its
extreme source, and ten miles below Breckenridge,
the county-seat. Ten-Mile Creek has a heavy fall
and sufficient volume to furnish unlimited power
for mills. Ten-Mile Mining District is very large,
taking in all the sections drained by the stream,
which is twenty miles in length. The principal
known mines are twelve to fifteen miles west of
Breckenridge, and easily approached from that
place over good natural roads. At the head of
Ten-Mile, opening south via the east fork of the
Arkansas River, occurs also the lowest pass through
the Range of any known. Here the waters of the
Atlantic might easily be conducted into the Pacific
or *vice versa*. This is the way wagons came into
McNulty's Gulch in 1861. Besides the latter, upon
which the silver lodes drew attention as early as
1861, Ten-Mile has for tributaries Clinton and Gilpin gulches, parallel and three miles apart, four or

five in length each, and described as "wide, accessible, with an abundance of water, timber and grass, containing also ledges of slate, sandstone, limestone, marble and indubitable evidences of coal. Magnetic and bog iron ore also occur. The mountains are steep and high, offering great advantages for mining by tunnels. The lodes, crossing them from north-east to south-west, assume the pitch of the stratified rock on the surface, and become more vertical as they pass down into the eruptive granite until in the valleys they are quite perpendicular. The ores are chiefly argentiferous galena, sometimes associated with pyrites of iron, or with antimony in a gangue of heavy spar or quartz. Some of the veins yield true silver ores, among them the ruby and gray. They are generally strong and well-marked, often cropping out above the surface for a long distance or lining the bold faces of the mountains.* In width they are described (this is the only portion of Colorado we have not personally examined) as ranging from eight inches to twenty and even forty feet. The veins of ore probably vary in width from two and three to four

---

*The Justice Lode, discovered in 1861 and re-discovered and pre-empted every year since, on the mountain between Gilpin and McNulty gulches, is one of these. It crops out on the southern exposure and well up on the hill for six hundred feet in length and seemingly one hundred and fifty in width. It is supposed to be what is called "a blow-out," which laps over the walls, and the lower edge having been worn down by the elements, that wall, against which some slight excavations have been made, was easy found. The ore is not rich on the surface but grows better very fast as it comes from a greater depth. It is "claimed" four or five deep, and recorded as high as No. 100—two miles!—each way.

and five feet. Among the best known lodes of
Clinton, and Gilpin gulches are the Ino, Incas,
Atlas, Oro Fino, Augustine, Boulder, Olympic
No. 2, Blackstone, Balahoo, Uno, Curious, Colorado, Esmeralda, Sublunar, Detroit, Utah, Whit-
tier, Watson, Young, Polygon, Noyes, Newark,
Pomona, Siberian, Saint Regis, Tribune, Merrimac,
Keyes, Hard Cash, Florentine, &c. They have not
generally been much developed. The Merrimac
has a shaft eighty feet deep, and the crevice is
twelve feet between walls—galena and quartz.
The Polygon has a shaft of the same depth and a
crevice three feet wide. We can only judge of the
richness of these ores by assays, and although that
is commonly a most unsatisfactory test; yet we
have such numbers of them in this instance that
they may safely be taken as a fair indication.
One thousand assays have been made, the results
ranging from $30 to $27,000 a ton, the average being $100, and these from surface ores.

A. A. Hayes, M. D., State Assayer of Massachusetts, gives the following returns:

Pyramid	Lode, silver, per ton of ore, coin value,					$106.17
Merrimac	"	"	"	"	"	89.17
Polygon	"	"	"	"	"	346.14
Hard Cash	"	"	"	"	"	140.57
Blackstone	"	"	"	"	"	111.67
Young	"	"	"	"	"	84.50
Tinsley	"	"	"	"	"	231.40
Siberian	"	"	"	"	"	138.44
Augustine	"	"	"	"	"	287.53

Fred. Eckfeldt, melter and refiner of the Branch
Mint, Denver, certifies that the average result of

assays made by him of thirty samples of ore from the Snake River mines was at the rate of $130.80 per ton. Albert Reichenecker, a mining and metallurgical expert of great experience in the mines of Germany, now of Central City, Colorado, certifies that of seventy-six assays of average ores from the Snake River mines the aggregate was $9,245, or $121.64 per ton. The ores of Ten-Mile and the Snake are the same in character. The working returns may undoubtedly be put at from $50 to $100 a ton.

Galena is one of the most economical of silver ores, especially where the proportion of silver is so large, as all of the latter may be obtained by smelting; or by smelting this ore which contains a large amount of lead with the pyritous gold ores, the gold and silver may be obtained from both at a comparatively small cost. In England galena ores are smelted for about three dollars a ton. In Colorado it can scarcely cost more than four times as much, which would still leave a large margin for profit.

At the head of Ten-Mile and on the Blue is where nuggets of metallic silver used to be found in the days of gulch mining, weighing from an ounce to a pound. Nuggets of gold weighing fifty pennyweights were also found, and it was not unusual in McNulty's Gulch for a pit twenty feet square to yield from $10,000 to $20,000.

The only company at work in the district is that of Whitney & Whiting, under the able superintendence of A. A. Sawyer, Esq. A party of their men are engaged driving a tunnel under Fletcher Mountain to the Capitol Lode, intended to strike it 1200 feet from the entrance and 1000 from the surface.* Tunnels gain nearly a foot in depth for one in length throughout this region.   In addition to the silver and gold, copper, iron, coal, and especially lead and salt, must be taken into account in calculating the resources of the section.   With a railroad giving access to the markets of the world, all these will become available as sources of wealth.   Below Breckenridge on the Blue are found strong saline springs, and within twenty miles of that town occur extensive beds of excellent fire-clay.   The latter, the coal, and the salt, will be of immense value to the future of silver mining.

Snake River rises on the western slope of the Range, opposite the southernmost sources of Clear Creek, and its mines, which line the upper ten miles of its course for a width of perhaps two miles, are only separated from those of Argentine of which they are undoubtedly the continuation, by the crown of the mountain, four or five miles over. Two trails connect the two sections, and this year will witness the construction of at least one wagon road between Georgetown on the eastern slope, already connected by wagon road eighteen miles long with Central City, and Peru and Montezuma, the silver towns of the Snake on the western slope, connected with the outer world via the Snake, Blue,

---

* On the 1st of January last this tunnel had reached a depth of 160 feet, and was to be driven all Winter and forever by 8-hour shifts.   The progress was two feet in twenty-four hours.

and Hamilton or Ute passes. A good team readily hauls a ton at once from Denver to Montezuma, on the South Snake, by this route. Peru is on the main Snake and about twenty miles via the wagon road route from Georgetown. A railroad is quite feasible so far into the Mountains as Georgetown, and hence that town will probably come to be the base of supplies for the Snake River mines in due time. Peru and Montezuma each gives name to a mining district. As remarked before, the mines of the Snakes and Ten-Mile are identical in character, as are also the general features of the districts. During the last season considerable progress was made in the development of some of the lodes. An experimental furnace was erected near Montezuma by J. T. Lynch for the purpose of testing the Suky, a lode remarkable for its strength and the richness of its ore. His operations were successful as far as they went and are to be continued, and extended in the future.* The most noted lodes of Montezuma are the Suky, Cooley, Cooley Extension, Cooper, Harrisburg, George Washington, Pink, Broadway, Tiger, City of Philadelphia, City of Newark, Lone Star, Ben Franklin, Colfax, and El Domingo. None of them is developed to any very considerable extent.

In Peru District the Colorado Prospecting & Mining Company, W. N. Byers, agent, the Nonpariel Company, Sanderson & Company, and the Summit County Prospecting & Mining Company,

---

* Mr. Lynch is now excavating a tunnel to the Suky Lode, and had reached a depth exceeding one hundred feet in February last.

Stephen Decatur, agent, are busily improving by tunnel and shaft various lodes, among them the Anglo-Norman, Butterfield, Emperor, Aurora, Malabar, Gould & Curry, Elephant, Great Western, Bouncer, National Treasury, A. McCune, and Rocky Mountain News. This season will doubtless witness the erection of smelting furnaces, and a more satisfactory demonstration of the character of these veins, which have only been known for two years and for that reason are not much developed. It is expected that some of them will prove permanently silver-bearing. Whether they do or not may be regarded as of little consequence beyond its bearing on the reduction works to be erected, as they will no doubt prove profitable gold, if not silver mines.

It was in 1859 that the first explorers of the South Park crossed the Range from Tarryall via the Georgia Pass on to the Swan, a stream fifteen to twenty miles long, and emptying into the Blue a few miles above the mouth of the Snake. The first party consisted of one hundred men, and they were sorrowfully prospecting the numerous dry and wet tributaries of the Swan when reports came of murders by the Utes on the western tributaries of the Arkansas. Not having found the fabled "pound-diggings," the prospectors were glad of a pretext for a general stampede back. But later in the season more persevering prospectors discovered gold dust in paying quantity at Gold Run, Galena, American, and Humbug Gulches, and Delaware Flats. French Gulch empties into the Blue a few miles above the

Swan. It is twelve miles long, heads in what is called French Pass, and among its tributaries are Gibson, Negro and Corkscrew Gulches, and Stetson's Patch. Further up, the Blue receives Illinois Gulch, and still above, a sort of upper and last fork, Hoosier Gulch. These gulches were all worked more or less from 1860 two or three years, and at Gold Run and one or two other localities, extensive gold-washing operations are still carried on.

It is said that the Weaver Brothers, the discoverers of Gold Run, went home from their first season's work with ninety-six pounds of gold. The gulch is four miles long, on the south side and near the mouth of the Swan. Early in the Spring a thousand inches of water flow through it, decreasing as the Summer wanes to almost nothing. The season lasts from the 1st of May to the 1st of November. In 1860 a ditch was constructed, bringing water from the Blue, six miles. Two years afterward another ditch, nine miles long and carrying five hundred inches of water, was constructed, also bringing water from the Blue. A bed-rock flume was commenced in 1863 by the Gold Run Ditch Company, and in that and the succeeding year they took out $70,000 in gold dust, valuing it at $18 an ounce. The flume is two by three feet in size, 1650 feet long, and cost to build and keep in repair for four years, $6,800. In 1865 the Gold Run Flume Extension and Quartz Prospecting Company was organized. At the end of last season they had built a new flume 1550 feet long at a cost of $6,500 in dust and $5,000 in water. In the last two years they took out $30,000 in dust. A creek claim in Gold Run embraces one hundred feet of the stream and extends seventy-five either way. A bank claim is one hundred feet square. Anybody is entitled to hold one creek claim and a bank claim in each tier of claims on either or both sides of the creek. Claims hold good without representation from the 1st of November to the 1st of July. There are more than eight hundred claims in the district. Most of the pay has been taken from the west side of the stream, that bank having been washed off a thousand feet in width.

Buffalo Flats is in the same district (Union) as Gold Run; its production of gold is larger. Water is brought by two ditches from French Gulch. In the mining season about two hundred people find employment in the district. Their attention has been so entirely turned to gulch mining that only twenty lodes have as yet been recorded, and these were discovered in gulch mining. They are immense, however; for instance, the Discovery, 44 feet wide, Adelia 43 feet, Inferno, 30 feet, auriferous and argentiferous quartz, seamed and mixed with galenous and pyritous ores. The flume last spoken of crosses these lodes, and being sunk eight feet in the bed-rock, there can be no mistake in their stated width. It may be doubted however, whether such extraordinary width of vein is an advantage. It certainly is not if only the same amount of the precious metals be distributed through it as in those more confined. In French Gulch strong, rich lodes occur, on some of which a good deal of work has been done—shafts and tunnels excavated, &c. In 1865 a stamp mill was set up in the gulch, the only one by the way west of the Range, but it merely started and has since been idle.

The above description of mining in Gold Run applies to the business wherever it is carried on in Summit County, Gold Run and Buffalo Flats being the most important gulch mining localities.

The basin of the upper Blue, which is twenty to thirty miles in diameter, is one of the richest mineral sections in Colorado. Generally its minerals consist of silver, gold, copper, lead, iron, coal, salt, sulphur, and indications are not wanting of platinum and quicksilver. There are slates and shales, marbles and limestones, sandstones, and fire clay. Timber and water and pasturage are in the greatest abundance.

Communication with the eastern slope is possible through numerous passes from Georgetown round to the Arkansas River, and with the western via Gore's Pass, or the North Park under the Rabbit-Ears. Of course the fall of snow is deep in the Winter, not less on the average than one hundred and fifty inches, and the whole basin suffers an elevation above sea of nine thousand feet and over ; but the Range, though a terrible is not an impassible barrier, even in Winter ; (loaded trains have twice passed it at the coldest season) and the climate is not half so disagreeable if it is a very little colder than the climate of Chicago.

Beyond the Middle Park and this basin of the upper Blue, little is certainly known of the vast mountain wilderness included in Summit County. In July, 1860, a party numbering one hundred left Breckenridge for the purpose of exploring the White and its tributaries for mineral deposits. They went up Ten-Mile ten miles, crossed over south-west on to Piney, down that to its kanyon, then over on to Roaring Fork, as large as the Grand, which they followed to its junction with the latter. Here occur immense hot and cold saline springs, acid and thermal springs. The party "claimed" them, crossed the river and struck for the head of the south fork of White River, which they followed down to its junction with the Green. They found no gold in the undisturbed stratified rocks. Turning to the south-east, they traveled three hundred miles (estimated) over ashy and sandy deserts and flat rocks to the sources of the Animas and Del Norte in the San Juan Mountains. Down the latter and via Fort Garland to Denver finished this grand exploring tour, and since that the greater part of the region within the bounds of Summit County has been regarded as destitute of minerals.

15

CHAPTER XIV.

OF the methods in use for getting gold, silver, and copper out of their gangue or matrix, the stamp-mill is the general favorite in all countries. A minute description of the process can hardly be necessary at this day. The ore is crushed fine by the percussion of heavy iron stamps, and in case of gold, escapes from the stamp batteries through screens of any desired fineness, and is carried evenly over amalgamated copper plates by a gentle sheet of water, constantly running through the batteries. The gold unites with mercury, which is put in the batteries and on the copper plates, and the ore, being lighter and having no affinity for mercury, runs away. When the mercury becomes loaded with gold, it is taken up, strained through buckskin to as small bulk as possible, and then driven off the gold in the form of vapor by the application of heat, when, the vapor having been condensed into mercury again in the same operation, it is ready to be used over.

In Australia this operation has been so perfected, and mining at the same time so systematized, that, in large ledges in which the gangue is not combined with sulphur nor full of substances deleterious to the action of quicksilver on gold, rock which yields but two pennyweights ($1.60) per ton, is made to pay a handsome profit. The mine from which this is done consists of the principal portion of the Black Hill, on the Yandrie—about fifty acres. Tunnels have been run into it at different levels, and connected with the open workings, or shafts. The average width of the lode is ninety feet, and it has numerous leaders and feeders. The cost of mining per ton is two shillings, (English) and of crushing, two shillings, sixpence. Ninety men and four horses are employed, 150 tons of fire-wood per week used, and 1000 tons of quartz, or 1500 of soft casings, crushed in the same time. The material is conveyed into the mill on dump-cars, the mill containing six batteries of ten 770-lb. stamps each, and driven by a 100-horse engine. One man, assisted by a self-feeding apparatus, supplies the batteries with quartz. The screens have one hundred and twenty holes to the square inch, and the crushed material is conveyed by gentle water currents through sluice-boxes with quicksilver rifles, and then over blanket surfaces twenty-four feet long. The blankets are washed every eight hours in tanks, which move on wheels, and the rinsings thus collected amalgamated in revolving barrels containing hot water and a weight of mercury equal to that of half the ore. The Company have a small foundery of their own for renewing their stamp-heads, the average wear of iron in stamps being one ton a week. "Surely," says the English engineer from whose report this is condensed, "what has been done here can be elsewhere, now it has been shown how to do it. It is a great feat that quartz averaging less than three pennyweights per ton can be made to pay thirty per cent. per annum on a large capital."

The following conclusions are the result of twenty-five years' experience in the Lake Superior copper mines. The figures of cost are below what they would be in Colorado, probably one hundred per cent.; but the method of mining, the estimates, facts, and suggestions, modified to suit different conditions, apply to the business, everywhere. The first cost of opening a mine, including sinking the shafts and winzes, excavating levels, cutting plats for windlasses, etc., should be counted in *openings*, and the openings should be in proportion to the stoping ground. For each shaft or winze at least 240 feet of levels ought to be excavated, to-wit: A shaft 70 feet deep opens one lift of ten fathoms,* at $175 a fathom, $1,750; giving 240 lineal feet or 40 fathoms of levels, at $48 a fathom, $1,920; cut-

---

*"Fathom," six feet; cubic fathom, 216 cubic feet. Eighteen cubic feet of broken Lake Superior rock weigh a ton, a fathom weighs 12 tons; 12 feet of *un*broken Lake Superior rock weigh a ton, a fathom weighs 18 tons. The sulphurets of Colorado are probably 30 to 40 per cent. heavier, and the gossan as much lighter.

ting plat for windlass and stulling up with eighty stull-timbers, $255 ; total cost of opening 400 fathoms ready for stoping, $4,000, an average of $10 a fathom. Allow for stoping 400 fathoms at $15 a fathom, $6,000 ; for mills or chutes and sundries, $400, and we have a total of $10,400, $26 a fathom, for mining, including openings ; counting a fathom as ten tons of *mineral*, a cost of $2.60 per ton.

This supposes the whole of the ground opened to be productive, which is not usual. It also allows a shaft for every 240 feet of length of vein, which is more than is necessary. Working shafts, with a winze between, may be 400 feet apart ; and when a vein is unproductive it should be avoided as much as possible and left as a support to the mine. The cost of sinking a shaft or winze is out of all proportion to that of the excavation of levels, and the latter again to the cost of simple stoping. Usually, while a mine is being opened, the main surface improvements are making. Two lifts of 70 feet each are as much as can easily be excavated in a year. It is possible to sink a shaft three lifts, or 210 feet in a year, but it is very seldom done. Stockholders in mines should be patient during this process, because the average cost per fathom of opening a mine compared with that of taking out the ore by stoping after the mine has been opened, is as five to one, and it is quite possible for it to overrun the value of the ore obtained by many per cent. Practical men should avoid more excavating of shafts and winzes than the proportion here stated. Every fathom of ground *opened* should give seven of stop-

ing. To produce one hundred tons of ore per day,
a mine should be opened one thousand feet in
length, and to work to the best advantage, two
levels in advance. To produce fifty tons a day, the
ground worked may be proportionately less. If
the two lifts are kept excavated ahead, two working shafts, with a winze between and one outside
of each shaft, are sufficient. Winzes are made to
accommodate the ground. A shaft is properly
from six by ten to eight by fourteen feet in size ;
where timber is plenty, curbed with timbers twelve
to sixteen inches square ; where it is not plenty, a
set put in once in three or four feet and the space
between lagged up. Winzes are the width of the
vein when it is as much as four feet wide, and five
or six feet long.

A skip is used for hoisting the ore, guided by
ribbons if the shaft be vertical, running on ways if
it underlie very much. They vary in size with
the power and scale of working, but usually hold
about twenty-two cubic feet, 2,240 lbs., which, considering that the skip is not quite filled and that the
rock is sorted upon its arrival at the surface, about
makes a ton of mineral. From a stull the ore is
filled into the skip through a mill ; from a level it
is dumped on a platform and shoveled in, the latter
because the car cannot be filled with sufficient
regularity to connect with the hoisting machinery.
With the top of the skip on the level of the platform, two men shovel in one hundred tons per day.
It ascends from twelve to eighteen feet in a second.
Sometimes the *car* is hoisted out, as in the coal

mines. Wood is used for these railways and cars,
indeed, economy is studied in everything. Wire
rope, a half or three-quarter-inch in size, is found
to be the cheapest for hoisting. The drum round
which this winds should be forty inches in diameter.
Two skips may be used in the same shaft, but if
two shafts can be run by the same engine it is better to have a skip in each, and have the descending
aid the ascending one by its weight. The skip
should dump itself and find its way back down the
shaft without help.* A forty-horse engine, using
four cords of wood, will hoist one hundred tons a
day from a depth of less than five hundred feet. In
the Pennsylvania coal mines that amount of power
hoists from the depth mentioned five hundred tons
a day. With a wet mine a separate engine for the
pump is desirable.

Having our mine opened and the requisite machinery and power for hoisting, the next step is to
get out the mineral. To do this at the rate of one
hundred tons a day requires a force as follows :
For getting the ore down from the stopes, tramming
and filling, which should belong to one contract,
twelve men at $2 a day, $24 ; for hoisting, landing,
and pumping, one engineer and assistant and one
lander by day, and one engineer by night to run
the pump, $9.00 for labor, $4.00 for fuel, and $1.00
for lights, oil, wear and tear, &c. ; for breaking, pick-
ing, and sorting the rock, five men, each handling

---

*This is perfectly accomplished by the Williams Elevator, a Col-
orado invention, of which A. J. Williams of Denver is the Western
agent.

twenty tons a day, $10 ; conveying to the stamps four men, $8; for crushing and dressing the ores allow $1.25 a ton, and for barrels, cooperage, and hauling to the harbor, dockage, and shipping, eight cents a ton. The latter item may be put against cleaning plates and retorting in Colorado. Allow that a miner can break three fathoms in a month at $15 a fathom, $45, 26 tons of selected mineral, it will require one hundred miners, *stoping*, to produce 2,600 tons per month, cost of stoping per ton $1.42 1-3. To produce 100 tons mineral per day, we have then :

For mining (opening),	per ton,	$2 60	per day,		$260 00
Tramming and filling,	"	24	"		24 00
Landing, hoisting,	"	14	"		14 00
Breaking and sorting,	"	10	"		10 00
Tramming to stamps,	"	8	"		8 00
Stamping and dressing,	"	1 25	"		125 00
Barrels, teaming and shipping	"	8	"		8 00
Repairs, wear and tear, &c.,	"	40	"		40 00
Agency, office, sundries,	"	9	"		9 00
Stoping,	"	1 42 1-3	"		142 33
Whole expense per ton,		$6 40 1-3	Per day,	$640 33	

These estimates have been worked to in the Lake Superior mines, so that they are no fancy sketches, but deserve study. The number of men required, the cost of which is included in the above estimate, supposing the mine *opened*, is one hundred to stope, twelve to wheel and fill, five to hoist and land, five to break, four to tram, twenty in stamp mill, fifteen for surface work—together, one hundred and sixty men to get out, crush, dress, barrel, and ship, 100 tons of mineral per day in the Lake Superior mines. A mine producing at this rate will use 50,000 feet of lumber and timber, and 6,000 cords of wood annually, allowing one-fifth of the latter for family use. Which is equal to clearing sixty acres of Lake Superior, and from four to five times as much of Colorado wood-land.

For crushing the ore, a 100-ton mill requires forty head of 1,000-lb., or fifty head of 800-lb. stamps, and a 100-horse engine, using twelve cords of wood every twenty-four hours, one horse-power being equal to reducing one ton to the fineness of a 16-to-the-inch mesh in that time. The stamps in use generally weigh 1,000 lbs. each, and drop sixteen inches sixty times a minute, each crushing two and a half tons of trap-rock to the above fineness in twenty-four hours. It has been found that Franklinite iron, mixed with Juniata or Lake Superior iron, or white chilled iron, or the white waste around blast furnaces, makes the best stamp-heads. Of these, which weigh 100 lbs., the average service each before wearing out is 300 tons. The best quality will stand sixty or seventy per cent. more than that, however. Hodge & Christie, of Detroit, have got the manufacture of quartz-crushing and mining machinery down to a dot. They make a horizontal quartz-crusher, worked by an eccentric, which we do not hesitate to recommend for Colorado as superior to any possible arrangement of stamps. The capacity depends on the size of the machine and the power applied. That is to say, it is unlimited. They also make another, a cylinder crusher, something on the principle of a corn-sheller,

15*

equal to crushing 250 tons of sulphurets a day. Both of these machines are followed by Cornish Rollers, the capacity of which also depends on the size and power applied. In amalgamation, the rollers are followed by arastras. Where the ore is to be smelted, the rollers will pulverize it sufficient- The Blake Rock Breaker, with a 20-horse engine, is equal to crushing ten tons an hour. Those who have used both say that Hodge & Christie's is a better economizer of power than Blake's.

In California, in 1861, there were thirty-eight quartz mills in operation, producing six millions in gold. The average cost per ton of mining was $5.47, of treatment, $2.65, aggregate, $8.12. The average yield was $22.87, leaving a profit of $14.75 per ton. Five years later, the number of mills had doubled, and were producing eight millions per annum, with no change in cost. The expense of mining varies greatly with different mines, and of milling it is higher or lower according as steam or hydraulic power is used. "When both mine and mill are favorably situated," says Prof. Ashburner, "it requires quartz yielding eight dollars per ton to cover the expense of mining and milling. Therefore, when the vein is of moderate size, say five or six feet in width, and water power can be employed, quartz yielding ten dollars per ton may be regarded as valuable, and affording a certain profit." The veins generally dip and strike with the rock strata which encore them, and which are slate, granite, and greenstone, equally prolific, and in workable width vary from a few inches to thirty or forty feet, though it invariably happens that the wider the vein the poorer it is. The history of the working of these veins, all and singly, shows great unevenness in the yield of gold from month to month, or perhaps from year to year, and it is not yet proved that, in the more permanent veins of California, the percentage yield of the quartz is less down deep than on the back or surface.

In Nevada, according to statistics officially published within the two or three years last past, the average cost of quarrying, crushing, and treatment per ton of rock, is $30, coin, which is about eighty per cent. of the gross yield of the rock. The great mine is the Comstock, a fissure vein of extraordinary width and productiveness, two miles in length, generally worked out five hundred feet in depth, that space having yielded in five years ore worth sixty millions of dollars, sixty per cent. of which has been extracted and thrown upon the markets of the world. The rich bonanzas of the surface having been nearly exhausted, the yield has latterly fallen off considerably, and most all the companies have been extensively exploring for new deposits. In the opinion of eminent mining experts, they will be found within the limits of profitable working, which Prof. Ashburner puts, with the ore yielding thirty-five dollars per ton, at ten hundred to twelve hundred feet.

In Colorado the cost of milling and mining per ton used to be five, six, or seven dollars. Since about the close of 1863, when the backs of the veins had been exhausted and war prices began to

prevail, it has been about twelve, coin, and the
average yield not far from twenty-five.* This as
ordinarily worked with stamps. The Keith process
has realized from 100 to 200 per cent. more than
that on considerable quantities of ore, and so has
careful running through stamps, while smelting de-
tects from $100 to $300 value per ton in the best
ores. The common yield under stamps is no criterion of the value, not only because of the refractory nature of the matrix of the gold, whatever it
is, and it may well be doubted if anybody, even
Hermann, yet knows ; but because at least an equal
quantity of nearly barren rock is always run through
the stamps with the ore, under the impression that
more value is obtained by slow running. The
veins average about five feet between walls ; half
of which is pay-rock or ore. They are irregular in
size and richness, as are all other gold veins. It is
believed that some of them extend for miles, but
none is worked to profit more than a half-mile, and
most not near so far—perhaps 1,200 feet. In Australia, California, and Nevada, the precious metals
are held in the vise of a perfectly untractable
matrix to some extent, while in Colorado they are
only found *not* so held to some extent. Still there
are spots on the Burroughs, Gunnell, Gregory, Bobtail, and Bates, which pay something above expenses under stamps. For instance, The Smith &
Parmelee Company got out 5,529 ounces during
the six months ending March 1, 1867, of which the

---

* Only a careful estimate—there are no statistics on the subject,
nor does it seem likely there will be any soon.

Superintendent insists 66 per cent. is profit. Other companies are selling their best ore to the smelters, and realizing from $20 to $40 a ton by stamps from second-quality. But the larger moiety of the really fine stamp-mills of the Territory are either idle or unfinished, from the well-founded belief that it is a waste all around to try to manipulate the deep ores with stamps. Mr. Hermann, of Swansea, confessedly standing at the head of metallurgists, pronounces them "the most wasteful expenditure," and the greatest of all Colorado's obstacles to success. Still the fact remains that we *have* these mills, on the ground and in running order, and it must be confessed not yet badly beaten by any of the so-called improvements. Perhaps for the backs of veins and for the deeper ores and rock of second quality, considering that the first cost is already incurred and that running them is not expensive especially in skill, they may be the best treatment. As used in Colorado they are susceptible of improvement. It has been suggested that a mistake was made in getting so heavy stamps and gearing them so slow, and that perhaps a stamp weighing 450 pounds and dropping very rapidly would do more work and make the same ore yield more per ton. The suggestion is not of much weight, because if percussion is necessary to amalgamation, it would be better to have separate batteries, with light, quick-dropping stamps, for that purpose, than to lose two-thirds of the pulverizing power as proposed. Power is best economized in crushing by stamps to have them 800 or 1,000 pounds in weight, dropping sixteen inches once a second. The use of some good rock-breaker on the ore before it is fed into the batteries would be of advantage, because it would increase their capacity and save wear and tear. The use of long blanketed surfaces, and of hot water and the barrel amalgamator, as in Australia, might be introduced with little expense and no doubt with profit.

Within the last few years, different parties have been endeavoring to improve on stamp-mill amalgamating by first calcining the ores. Others have thrown aside the idea of amalgamating, and sought some practicable method of directly attacking the ores by fire, as in making an assay. Some account of both follows. It is a subject the writer approaches cautiously because of its importance, and because of the difficulty of determining the truth. He will confine himself to a statement in popular language of what the friends of the processes *claim* for them, their method of operation in brief, and what has been done and is doing in each, endorsing by the way Mr. J. W. Taylor's suggestion, that the subject is worthy of investigation by a scientific commission at the expense of the Government.

"The Keith Process" was patented by Keith, Behr & Keith, in September, 1862. It consists in bringing the finely-pulverized ore in contact with the flame of a furnace rapidly and economically, thus driving off the volatile substances, melting and aggregating the fine gold into larger and spherical particles upon which quicksilver readily acts. The advantages claimed for it are, complete oxydation and calcination at one operation ; economy of labor and fuel ; delivery of the ore in a finely-powdered state ; all the gold left in particles of a globular shape and free from combination with other metals or minerals. The ore is pulverized, *dry*, by stone-breakers and ball-crushers. The furnace is made of brick, the fire-chamber lined with fire-brick, and consumes one cord of pine wood in roasting thirty tons, which is the capacity per twenty-four hours of those furnaces now in use. The cost of the furnace is not above that of any other roasting furnace of equal capacity. After calcination the ore is scoured by being passed through a ball-pulverizer, when it is amalgamated by simple stirring or shaking. The cost of treatment is five dollars per ton. It saves from sixty to eighty per cent. of the gold in ores free from galena. The latter it does not attempt to treat. It has been in more or less successful operation at the Mammoth Company's mill in Black Hawk for three years, and in 1866, four other mills adopted it, which we believe are all now running. The right to use it is sold for $5,000.

"The Crosby & Thompson Process" claims to do all that Keith's does, by the use of iron cylinders ; and by the addition of a large condensing chamber, to catch a great deal of gold so fine as to be impalpable that would otherwise pass out of the chimney. It was introduced in Colorado early in 1865 and a good many companies adopted it. Of thirty of these, about one-half set up the machinery, but none of them has succeeded in making it work, practically. The difficulty has been in amalgamating, and within the past Winter they think they have discovered the hitch and how to overcome it.

The idea is, that soon after its chemical union with mercury, the gold commences oxydizing and escaping in the form of a brown powder. The remedy proposed is, to change the mercury before the oxydation of the gold has time to begin, and then to promote such oxydation by the use of water and stirring, as a means of separating the gold from the mercury. It remains to be shown on a working scale and in Colorado that this is more than an ingenious and plausible theory. And we think it remains to be shown, practically, that the iron cylinders constitute the best method of roasting the ores. The friends of the process are very confident, however, of speedy and full success, and are entitled to credit for uncommon tenacity of purpose. The whole thing is covered by letters patent.

"The Mason Process" has been tried to some extent in Colorado, but so far with no generally appreciable success. It consists in the use of superheated steam in connection with the flame of a furnace, applied moderately at first and increased by degrees, to the ore before pulverizing, in a furnace not unlike a lime-kiln. A cupola seven feet in diameter by twelve in hight holds thirty tons, and using one and a half cords of wood, this charge is treated in twenty-four hours. In California and Nevada better success has attended the process than in Colorado. It roasted $9-rock at a cost of $1.12 1-2 per ton, making it yield $25. Chemists say that the principle is sound.   The cheapness of its application is a recommendation, if it will only answer the purpose.   There is a controversy pending in the courts with regard to the right, between Mason and Hagan.   Mason is now further testing it in North Carolina.

"The Monnier Metallurgical Process," but recently introduced in Colorado, and not yet fairly and fully tested, consists in roasting in the presence of sulphates of soda, iron, or other similar salts, in a long furnace or muffle.   The flame passes under and heats the sole of the furnace, on which the ore, mixed with one-tenth its weight of sulphate of soda, is worked from one to the other end, the heat being gradually increased as it approaches the point of discharge.   Almost all the sulphur is expelled, and the copper and silver salts left in a soluble condition.   The after process consists in the leaching and precipitation of the copper and silver, and the amalgamation of the gold.   The advantages claimed are, improved roasting furnace, economizing the heat produced by combustion of the sulphur in a long chamber ; using a powerful promoter of oxydation in the sulphate of soda, an auxiliary in eliminating sulphur, and also in preventing in a measure insoluble forms of the copper and silver so liable to occur when the ore is roasted alone.   It proposes to save all the metals of value, even to the sulphur, if desired, in the ore.   Counting labor and material three times as high as in the East, a set of works for treating 350 tons a week by this process would be and cost as follows :

1 steam engine and boiler, and house,	-				$15,000		
1 rock breaker,	-	-	-	-	2,000		
1 double Cornish crusher,		-	-	-	4,000		
5 arastras, $500 each,	-	-	-	-	7,500		
48 Tyrolean amalgamators,		-	-	-	4,800		
Sundries,	-	-	-	-	-	1,700	$35,000
6 calcining furnaces,		-	-	-	$75,000		
6 evaporating furnaces,	-		-	-	54,000		
60 tanks and house,		-	-	-	30,000		
Stack and culvert,	-	-	-	-	4,000		
Sundries,	-	-	-	-	-	2,000	$165,000
Total,	-	-	-	-	-		$200,000

The cost per ton of treating the ore at Colorado
prices, when it contains five per cent. of copper, is
$30.58; when it contains only one and one-half per
cent. of copper, $22.15; and when it contains no
copper $18.31. This is a very liberal estimate of the
cost in Colorado, since it allows it to be three times
as high as in Virginia, where the process has long
been worked. And that cost is constantly diminishing, too. A company called "The Monnier
Metallurgical Company of Colorado," has been organized in Philadelphia with a capital of $250,000,
for the purpose of introducing and using the process in Colorado, and they have commenced operations.

A patent desulphurizing furnace, which makes
fuel of the sulphur in the ore and uses no other
after getting started, has been introduced at Black
Hawk by James E. Lyon & Co. It is a large chimney, perhaps twenty feet high, down through which,
by means of a self-feeding hopper and an arrangement in the flue of successive courses of fire-tile,
the ore is continuously and slowly sifted. It must

contain 18 per cent. of sulphur, far less than most Colorado ores. At Swansea they have eight of these furnaces, requiring three men to attend them, and roasting thirty-two tons a day. It seems to us that this furnace must eventually supersede all others for ores containing the requisite per centage of sulphur.

We come at last to an important enterprise—the introduction of smelting, in other words, assaying by fire on a working scale. The attempt is due to James E. Lyon, the head of a wealthy co-partnership, prominent in Colorado for many years. In 1864 he took some selected Gregory ore to the furnaces near New York city, and finding the yield to be from $214 to $250 per ton in gold, silver, and copper, eight-fold the average yield of such ore by stamps, he thenceforth devoted his whole attention and energy to the introduction of smelting in Colorado. During the year 1865, he erected several furnaces, with the requisite crushing and dressing machinery in Black Hawk, which were run with partial success for nearly a year. Under the advice of Mr. Hermann, the plan that had been adopted— fusing and amalgamating by lead and cupelling— was then abandoned for the simple concentration by fusing of the ores into regulus, or a matt, weighing one-tenth to one-fifth the original heft of the ore, and containing of course all the valuable metal of whatever kind. It can hardly be necessary for us to describe the operation, since it is older than the hills and is in every cyclopedia ever printed. The rock as commonly taken from the mines, is sorted, crushed by rock-breakers, and Cornish rollers, dressed and washed to nearly pure mineral by various ingenious contrivances, losing in weight and bulk in sorting, washing and dressing perhaps 60 per cent., roasted, and fused, the matt containing the metals precipitated from the fused mass and the slag allowed to run off. The calculation has been to transport this matt to Swansea for separation of its metals, but an effort is to be made the present year, backed by ample means and having command of the best skill in the world, to establish complete works in Colorado. This will be under the personal supervision of Prof. N. P. Hill of Providence. An early day will without doubt see the great range of furnaces at Swansea duplicated on Clear Creek below Golden City, with a railway winding thence to the mines of Gilpin and Clear Creek counties through the profound kanyon of that stream. Competition will ensure equitable division of the profits between the miner and smelter, who will each have and pursue his branch of the business, independent of the other. By the end of October, 1866, the necessary alterations in the furnace of Lyon & Co., had been made. There were then three roasting and three smelting furnaces, each set having a capacity of twenty to twenty-five tons a day. Besides these they had the patent roaster noticed before, three American hearths for lead ores, and one cupel furnace. They used steam power, and were all the time improving their arrangement, including crushing and dressing machinery. Later in the Fall the works were sold by Lyon & Co., to the Consolidated Gregory Company, with whose great Gregory mine, now in the best of shape, they were consolidated. They have from 100 to 200 tons of matt on hand, valued at $800 to $1,000 a ton, half of which is claimed to be profit. James E. Lyon is general director of the Company, and M. B. Hayes, of Central, the agent in Colorado, while Dr. Johnson, formerly of the Staten Island furnaces, immediately superintends the smelting works.

Perhaps we cannot more appropriately close our account of these efforts at improving the gold-saving art, than by urging the necessity of employing a more competent class of men to superintend heavy and expensive mining operations. Of the manifold requirements of a good mine-captain, the first is a thorough business education and experience, the next a most rigid habit of personally attending to duty, *faithfulness*. To these should be added sufficient acquaintance with mechanical affairs to know when wood, stone, and iron work are properly constructed and done; and a knowledge of mining in all its branches, geology, mineralogy, chemistry, &c. It may well be that there are few such men, quartz-mining being a new business, and hence the great importance of the mining schools, springing up in different parts of the country. Successful gold mining depends as often on the qualities of the operator as on those of the mine. A California paper remarks: "We have many successful mines, it is true, but in almost every instance, the mine is either extraordinarily rich, or the operator is peculiarly qualified for his position.

It is not an unfrequent occurrence to see an abandoned mine sold for a nominal figure, reopened by the purchaser, and made a splendid success. This is no chance; the mine had its merits which the ignorant pretender who was operating it failed to discern, through a lack of knowledge." Let mining companies to whom success is an object bear this ever in mind.

CHAPTER XV.

Important Mining Legislation—Gregory District Miners' Laws, Adopted February, 1860—Mining Legislation of Colorado Territory—Act of Congress Opening the Mineral Lands to Preemption.

DURING the first Winter in the mines of Gregory District, the then existing miners' laws were codified and somewhat amplified. The following is an act of the sovereign people in person, approved and adopted February 18, 1860, "defining claims and regulating title thereto:"

SECTION 1. *Be it enacted by the Citizens of Gregory District in Convention assembled*, That all mining lodes of gold, or any other precious or useful metals, and all mining and other claims, shall be held under and defined by the provisions of this act.

SEC. 2. That the term CLAIM as used in this district shall be construed to mean when applied to a lode, one hundred feet running the length of the same and fifty feet in width; when applied to a gulch, one hundred feet following its meanderings and extending from bank to bank; when applied to patch or placer diggings, one hundred feet square; when applied to tunneling claims, the entire distance intended to run the same for discovery purposes as shown by record and the stake at the mouth of the tunnel; when applied to a quartz-mill claim, the distance of two hundred and fifty feet square; when applied to a ditch claim, the entire distance staked out which they intend to run the same, or (as) shown by the survey and stakes; when applied to a water-claim, the exclusive right to use water for mining purposes upon any ditch or stream not exceeding in distance two hundred and fifty feet ; when applied to a farming or ranch claim one hundred and sixty acres ; when applied to a building claim, forty feet front and one hundred feet deep.

SEC. 3. That no person shall have more than one lode, gulch, patch or placer claim in this district except by purchase or discovery.

SEC. 4. That no person shall hold more than one water, building, farming or ranch claim except by purchase.

SEC. 5. That each discovery claim shall be marked as such, and all purchased claims shall be recorded, and in either case they shall be safely held whether worked or not.

SEC. 6. That any claim or claims now held, either by purchase or discovery, if abandoned for ten consecutive days after being staked off, shall be forfeited to any person or persons who may take up the same and work them and not abandon them as aforesaid.

SEC. 7. That no claim shall be regarded as good and valid unless staked off with the owner's name, giving the direction, length, width, and date when the same was made ; and when held by a company the name of each member thereof shall conspicuously appear.

SEC. 8. That when members of a company consisting of two or more shall work one claim of the company, the rest shall he considered as worked by putting a notice of the same thereon.

SEC. 9. That all mining claims which have been or may be taken up before the 1st of June next need not be worked until that date ; provided however, that the person who so has or shall take up a claim as aforesaid shall file with the Recorder for record a statement thereof, wherein he shall describe the claim and aver that it cannot be worked profitably for the want of either water or the proper machinery until the first day of June next, at which time he believes the said water·or machinery can be procured.

SEC. 10. That in all cases when parties shall have complied with the law as far as possible, priority of claim, when honestly carried out, shall be respected.

SEC. 11. That all contracts of partnerships or agreements whereby an interest in claims or lands are concerned, and all contracts relating thereto, hereafter made, shall be in writing and give the name and interest of each of the parties, and when a partnership the firm name also ; and the same shall be recorded before the first day of April next, or the said contracts shall not be regarded as binding upon or affecting any but the original parties in any transaction whatever.

SEC. 12.   That all deeds, bonds, contracts, bills of sale, or instruments of any kind relating to the conveyance [of] claims and bonds shall be witnessed by at least two disinterested witnesses and recorded.

SEC. 13.   That when any miner shall hold both a gulch and lode claim, if one be worked the other may be held without working by recording the same.

SEC. 14.   That any person owning a quartz-mill claim upon which he has a mill or is preparing to place one, may claim the right to cut a race or ditch from any stream to bring water to said mill, not interfering with vested rights.

SEC. 15.   That all claims held by laws heretofore in force, shall be regarded as vested property, and no person shall be disturbed in the possession thereof.

SEC. 16.   That when water is claimed for gulch or quartz-mining purposes on the same stream, neither shall have the right to more than one-half, unless there shall be insufficient for both, when priority of claim shall determine.

SEC. 17.   That if two or more parties wish to use water on the same stream or ravine for quartz-mining purposes, no person shall be entitled to use more than his proportionate share of water; but in case there shall not be water sufficient for all, priority of claim shall determine the right to such water.

SEC. 18.   That when water companies are engaged in bringing water into any portion of the mines, they shall have the right of way secured to them, and may pass over any claim, road, or ditch, provided the water shall be so guarded as not to interfere with any vested rights.

SEC. 19.   That in other questions not settled by the provisions of this act arising out of the rights of riparian proprietors, shall be divided [division shall be made] according to the common law.

SEC. 20.   That claims of every kind, except discovery mining claims, must be recorded unless the same are continuously worked or used according to law.

SEC. 21.   That the rules and regulations observed in mining regions within the United States, relating to digging for gold under building lots, upon ranch, farming, and other claims, shall be observed in this district.

SEC. 22.   That if any person shall locate a tunnel in this district

16

for the purpose of discovery, he shall first file a specification of the same with the Recorder, whose duty it shall be to record the same upon payment of his fees. The said specification shall state the place of commencement and the termination of said tunnel, together with the names of the parties interested therein. A four-square stake shall be placed at its mouth, having written thereon the same things hereby made necessary to record.

SEC. 23. That any person or persons engaged in working a tunnel, provided he or they shall comply with the requirements of the law, shall be entitled to two hundred and fifty feet on all lodes discovered in consequence of the same ; and such parts of the lodes as they are entitled to in consequence of said discovery shall be held as discovery claims ; provided, however, they do not interfere with any vested rights ; and if it shall appear that lodes are staked off on the line of said tunnel so that the required number of feet cannot be taken near to the same, they may be taken upon any part thereof wherever the same may be found vacant.

SEC. 24. That if the person or persons locating a tunnel shall fail to work the same for twenty consecutive days after the 1st of July next, they shall forfeit their claims to said tunnel, but not to the claims they have discovered and held by virtue of discovery before the time of forfeiture.

SEC. 25. That the person or persons working a tunnel, shall, after the same is legally located, have the priority of right to all lodes discovered on the line of the tunnel from the recorded line of its mouth to its terminus ; and shall have the right of way through all lodes which may lie in the course said tunnel is recorded, staked out, and worked.

An act of the sovereigns, approved and adopted February 20, 1860, exempts from levy and sale upon execution, all tools for mining, bedding, clothing, cooking utensils, and necessary provisions for three months ; and in case of a man residing with his family, a dwelling-house not exceeding $500 in value, and such articles of household furniture as are strictly necessary, together with a Bible, family pictures, and relics. Another act, adopted and approved at the same time, declares that the laws passed on the 18th and 20th of February, inst., shall take effect fifteen days from date, and thenceforth all conflicting laws shall be null and void except as to suits already commenced and pending at that time.

Upon the organization of the Territory of Colorado, its Legislative Assembly hastened to reassure the miners against fears of molestation of their rights by the passage of the following act "concerning lode claims," which was approved November 7, 1861:

Be it enacted by the Council and House of Representatives of Colorado Territory:

SECTION 1. That the term CLAIM, as used in the mining portions of this Territory, when applied to a lode, shall be construed to mean one hundred feet of the length of such lode, surface measurement of the entire width of such lode or crevice; Provided, That in no [any] case where the regulations of any mining district have heretofore defined the term claim to mean other than as above defined, nothing in this act shall be so construed as to impair the rights of any person or persons holding claims under such regulations as may have been heretofore established by the people of the district in which such claim or claims are situate.

SEC. 2. That whenever any person or persons are engaged in bringing water into any portion of the mines, they shall have the right of way secured to them, and may pass over any claim, road, ditch, or other structure; *Provided,* The water be guarded [so] as not to interfere with prior rights.

SEC. 3. That no person shall have the right to mine under any building or other improvement, unless he shall first secure the parties owning the same against all damages, except by priority of right.

SEC. 4. That if any person or persons shall locate a tunnel claim, for the purpose of discovery, he shall record the same, specifying the place of commencement and termination thereof, with the names of the parties interested therein.

SEC. 5. That any person or persons engaged in working a tunnel, within the provisions of this act, shall be entitled to two hun-

dred and fifty feet each way from said tunnel, on each lode so discovered ; *Provided*, That they do not interfere with any vested
rights. If it shall appear that claims have been staked off and
recorded, prior to the record of said tunnel on the line thereof, so
that the required number of feet cannot be taken near said tunnel,
they may be taken upon any part thereof where the same may be
found vacant ; and persons working said tunnel, shall have the
right of way through all lodes which may lie in its course.

Sec. 6. That when it shall appear that one lode crosses, runs
into, or unites with any other lode, the priority of record shall determine the rights of claimants ; *Provided*, That in no case where
it appears that two lodes have crossed one another, shall the priority of record give any person the privilege of turning off from the
crevice or lode which continues in the same direction of the main
lode upon which he or they may have recorded their claim or
claims, but shall at all times follow the crevice running nearest in
the general direction of the main lode upon which he or they may
have recorded their claim or claims.

Sec. 7. That where two crevices are discovered at a distance
from each other and known by different names, and it shall appear
that the two are one and the same lode, the persons having recorded
on the first discovered lode shall be the legal owners.

Sec. 8. That to determine when the two lodes are one and the
same, it shall be necessary for the person claiming that the two are
the same lode, to sink shafts at no greater distance than fifty feet
apart, and finding a crevice in each shaft, and forming a continuous
line of shafts from one lode to the other, shall be conclusive evidence that the two are one and the same lode.

Sec. 9. That in no case shall any person or persons be allowed
to flood the property of another person with water, or wash down
the tailings of his or their sluice upon the claim or property of
other persons ; but it shall be the duty of every miner to take care
of his own tailings, upon his own property, or become responsible
for all damages that may arise therefrom.

Sec. 10. That every miner shall have the right of way across any
and all claims for the purpose of hauling quartz from his claim.

Sec. 11. That all claims taken up and recorded by persons who
have, since the recording of the same, enlisted in the army of the
United States, or the volunteer force of this Territory, shall be
deemed and held as real estate for a period of nine months from
the expiration of their term of enlistment or discharge from service ;

after which time, if not represented by the said soldier or soldiers, all such claims shall be forfeited to any person who (may) take up the same.

SEC. 12. That a copy of all the records, laws, and proceedings of each mining district, so far as they relate to lode claims, shall be filed in the office of the County Clerk of the county in which the district is situated, with the boundaries of the district attached to the same, which shall be taken as evidence in any court having jurisdiction in the matters concerned in such record or proceeding.

This act shall take effect from and after its passage—*Laws First Session, p.* 166.

A Territorial act, "declaratory of the rights of occupants of the public domain, except as against the United States," approved November 7, 1861, declares that the right to possess and occupy any portion of the public domain, as the same may exist under the local laws, shall be represented in law and equity in all the courts and tribunals of the Territory, as real estate ; transferable and therefore a sufficient consideration to sustain a promise ; to be ascertained and determined by the local law, or in the absence of law, *custom* of the district where situate ; to be expressed and described in a declaration of prescribed form in case of original occupation, and by a deed in case of purchase ; such paper to be acknowledged by the proper officer and recorded in the County Recorder's office ; this record to be taken as presumptive evidence of the regularity and legality of the paper itself in all legal or equitable proceedings ; the burden of proving the contrary to rest on the challenger. This act was to regulate the claiming and holding particularly of *ranches*, and the last section provided that gold or silver lodes or diggings should be excepted from its provisions, wherever found; that they should be subject to occupation and enjoyment under the *miners' laws* of the district where situate, or if there were none, then those of the nearest mining district.

A Territorial act "to protect the mining claims and property of soldiers," approved November 6, 1861, declares that all claims and property of soldiers shall be exempt from levy or sale by virtue of any of the miners' laws or the judgments of their courts, until the soldier shall have been legally free from service one year; provided, a list of such claims and property, signed with his name, shall have been left with the Recorder of the district by the soldier.

A Territorial act, approved March 5, 1864, provides that the citizen-soldiers of the Territory while in service and for one year thereafter, may acquire the same as citizens of the Territory not in service, agricultural, mining, or other claims, either in person or by agent, the agent to first make affidavit before some proper officer that it is a *bona fide* piece of work.

A Territorial act "to confirm and legalize certain acts of the people of Colorado Territory," approved August 15, 1862, declares "that all judgments and decisions rendered by any of the so-called Miners' Courts, Miners' Clubs, or Claim Clubs, or People's Courts, or Kansas Courts, according to the rules and regulations adopted by any neighborhood or mining district within what are now the limits of Colorado Territory, when both parties made an appearance, or had notice according to such rules, and all the executions, writs, processes, sales or proceedings growing out of or resulting from the same, are hereby confirmed and legalized."

An act supplementary to this provides that it shall apply only to such proceedings as were had prior to the passage of the act, and that it shall not be construed to prevent the filing of bills in chancery to test the equity of cases involving sums of $250 or more, if filed within one year from the passage of the act.

A Territorial act, approved August 15, 1862, provides for the reviving, by *scire facias*, of any unsatisfied judgments of the Miners', People's, or other Courts, confirmed by the above acts, directing magistrates with whom properly certified copies of such judgments may be filed, where the amount claimed shall not exceed $100, to enter judgment thereon for the amount due, subject to limitations and appeal as in other cases.

A Territorial act "concerning arbitrations and awards," approved November 7, 1861, makes the adjudications, decisions or judgments of the Judges of the People's or Miners' Courts in all controversies in which the party proceeded against has been duly notified, except when the action was founded on a written contract to pay money, of the same force and effect as adjudications under legal arbitration, as provided for in this act.

A Territorial act "relative to Notaries Public," approved October 24, 1861, confirms all acknowledgments and official acts of Notaries Public holding their commissions under the Territory of Kansas, and also of all Judges or Justices of any organized Courts.

A Territorial act, passed and approved at the First Session, authorizes any person holding lots, lands, or mining claims, either by pre-emption, gift, purchase of the original claimants, or under decrees of execution of the People's, Miners', or Provisional Government Courts, to maintain actions for injuries done the possession thereof, except as against the United States ; provided, "*it shall be lawful for the citizens of mining districts to declare an abandonment of any creek, river, gulch, bank, or mining claim, and a forfeiture of the rights of the claimants thereto ;*" in which case, the parties claimant shall not be entitled to maintain such action for trespass or injury.

A Territorial act, approved August 15, 1862, provides that on all lodes to be discovered, claim No. Three, in one or the other direction from Discovery, shall be set apart for the benefit of schools, the County Superintendents of Schools to hold the certificates and to annually report to the Territorial Superintendent, who shall recommend to the Territorial Legislature what he thinks proper regarding their leasing or working.

An act supplemental to this, passed and approved during the Fifth Session, declares the jumping of the school claims, or the failure to relinquish upon the county records the title acquired by such jumping prior to June, 1866, a misdemeanor, rendering the parties guilty of it liable to a civil action for damages, and subject to a fine of from fifty to ten thousand dollars. Requires the County Superintendents of Schools to bring civil suits for damages against all trespassers on the school claims, and when damages are assessed by juries, the courts to render judgments for three times the amount of damages so assessed. Makes it the duty of the County Superintendents to annually present schedules of the school claims to the several Boards of County Commissioners, who shall, upon the recommendation of the Superintendents, fix the price for which each claim may be sold or leased; fixes the term of such lease, without renewal, at six years, and requires ample security of the lessees; their payments to be made semi-annually; and authorizes said Superintendents to make good and valid title. Provides that the Superintendents shall give bond, the penalty of which shall be fixed by the County Commissioners; provides for the employment of necessary counsel and its pay out of moneys accruing under the act; also fixes the pay of Superintendents at ten per cent. of the sum so accruing up to $3,000 a year, the surplus going to the general school fund. Provides a penalty for neglect on the part of Recorders to record school claims, also for recording them for jumpers, of from $500 to $5,000; and declares any sale or conveyance of school claims except as in this act provided for, null and void.

An act supplemental to this, provides for the use and disposal of all moneys accruing to the Territory under its operation.

A Territorial act, approved March 11, 1864, fixes

16*

the legal length of all lodes to be thereafter discovered, at 800 feet either way from Discovery shaft
on the line of the lode.

A Territorial act, "concerning mines and minerals," approved February 9, 1866, gives to every
discoverer of a lode thereafter, 1,400 feet, lineal
measure, to be called "The Discovery Claim."
Requires him to mark the point of discovery with
a substantial monument inscribed with his name
and that of the lode, and the date of the discovery,
and to sink a shaft to a well-defined crevice before
recording.   Provides a penalty for the malicious
removal or defacement of such monument.   Gives
him in virtue of discovery all spurs, off-shoots, dips,
angles, feeders, cross or parallel veins occurring
within twenty-five feet, either way, from the center
of his lode.   Extends this last provision to prior
discoverers, except where it would infringe on existing rights.   Provides for the location of 100 feet on
each end of the Discovery claim, to be known as
"No. 1, East," or "No. 1, West," one for the benefit
of schools, and the other for a "Miners' Relief and
Territorial Poor Fund."   Provides that Recorders
shall have four dollars for recording and issuing a
certificate of pre-emption, two dollars for entering
the same on any abstract of title, and twenty-five
cents for each transfer thereafter entered on the
abstract, and that the School and Poor Fund claims
shall be recorded free.   Directs as to the selling or
leasing of the latter claims, and the disposal of their
proceeds for the benefit of schools, disabled miners
and the poor of the Territory.

In the Territorial Incorporation Law, approved March 11, 1864, it is provided that the certificate of incorporation of tunnel companies shall specify where the proposed tunnel is to be run, where to begin, course, termination, and the minerals designed to be excavated. Such companies to have and hold 250 feet on each side of their tunnel on all lodes discovered by them while excavating it; 100 feet on all lodes discovered by others crossing said tunnel after the commencement of the same; and through all lodes discovered previous to such commencement, the right of way.

A Territorial act, approved February 8, 1866, commonly called "The Abandonment Act," declares all pre-emptions of water-powers, mill-sites, tunnels, and mining claims, and all rights acquired under them, void, where the pre-emptor shall have been absent from the Territory three years and shall not have had any agent in the Territory to represent him, and shall not either appear himself or by proxy and occupy and work said claims within one year from the passage of the act. Not to apply to persons absent from the Territory in the United States' service.

Such is the more important of the mining legislation of the Territory. It remains to give the great Act of Congress opening the mineral lands to pre-emption. It is modestly entitled, "An act granting the right of way to ditch and canal owners over the public lands, and for other purposes," and is as follows:

Be it enacted by the Senate and House of Representatives of the United States of America in Congress Assembled, That the mineral lands of the public domain, both surveyed and unsurveyed, are hereby declared to be free and open to exploration and occupation by all citizens of the United States, and those who have declared their intention to become citizens, subject to such regulations as may be prescribed by law, and subject also to the local customs or rules of miners in the several mining districts, so far as the same may not be in conflict with the laws of the United States.

SEC. 2. *And be it further enacted,* That whenever any person or association of persons claim a vein or lode of quartz, or other rock in place, bearing gold, silver, cinnabar, or copper, having previously occupied and improved the same according to the local custom or rules of miners in the district where the same is situate, and having expended in actual labor and improvements thereon an amount of not less than one thousand dollars, and in regard to whose possession there is no controversy or opposing claim, it shall and may be lawful for said claimant or association of claimants to file in the local land office a diagram of the same, so extended laterally or otherwise as to conform to the local laws, customs, and rules of miners, and to enter such tract and receive a patent therefor, granting such mine, together with the right to follow such vein or lode with its dips, angles, and variations to any depth, although it may enter the land adjoining, which land adjoining shall be sold subject to this condition.

SEC. 3. *And be it further enacted,* That upon the filing of the diagram as provided in the second section of this act, and posting the same in a conspicuous place on the claim, together with a notice of intention to apply for a patent, the Register of the land office shall publish a notice of the same in a newspaper published nearest to the location of said claim, and shall also post such notice in his office for the period of ninety days ; and after the expiration of said period, if no adverse claim shall have been filed, it shall be the duty of the Surveyor-General, upon application of the party, to survey the premises and make a plat thereof, indorsed with his approval, designating the number and description of the location, the value of the labor and improvements, and the character of the vein exposed : and upon the payment to the proper officer of five dollars per acre, together with the cost of such survey, plat, and notice, and giving satisfactory evidence that said diagram and notice have been posted on the claim during said period of ninety days, the Register of the land office shall transmit to the General Land Office said plat, survey, and description, and a patent shall issue for the same thereupon. But said plat, survey, or description shall in no case cover more than one vein or lode, and no patent shall issue for more than one vein or lode, which shall be expressed in the patent issued.

SEC. 4. *And be it further enacted*, That when such location and entry of a mine shall be upon unsurveyed lands, it shall and may be lawful, after the extension thereto of the public surveys, to adjust the surveys to the limits of the premises according to the location and possession and plat aforesaid ; and the Surveyor-General may, in extending the surveys, vary the same from a rectangular form to suit the circumstances of the country and the local rules, laws, and customs of miners: *Provided*, That no location hereafter made shall exceed two hundred feet in length along the vein for each locator, with an additional claim for discovery to the discoverer of the lode, with the right to follow such vein to any depth, with all its dips, variations, and angles, together with a reasonable quantity of surface for the convenient working of the same, as fixed by local rules : *And provided further*, That no person may make more than one location on the same lode, and not more than three thousand feet shall be taken in any one claim by any association of persons.

SEC. 5. *And be it further enacted*, That as a further condition of sale, in the absence of necessary legislation by Congress, the local Legislature of any State or Territory may provide rules for working mines involving easements, drainage, and other necessary means to their complete development ; and those conditions shall be fully expressed in the patent.

SEC. 6. *And be it further enacted*, That whenever any adverse claimants to any mine located and claimed as aforesaid shall appear before the approval of the survey, as provided in the third section of this act, all proceedings shall be stayed until a final settlement and adjudication in the courts of competent jurisdiction of the rights of possession to such claim, when a patent may issue as in other cases.

SEC. 7. *And be it further enacted*, That the President of the United States be, and is hereby, authorized to establish additional land districts, and to appoint the necessary officers under existing laws, wherever he may deem the same necessary for the public convenience in executing the provisions of this act.

SEC. 8. *And be it further enacted*, That the right of way for the construction of highways over public lands, not reserved for public uses, is hereby granted.

SEC. 9. *And be it further enacted*, That whenever by priority of possession, rights to the use of water for mining, agricultural, manufacturing, or other purposes, have vested and accrued, and the same are recognized and acknowledged by the local customs, laws, and the decisions of courts, the possessors and owners of such vested rights shall be maintained and protected in the same ; and the right of way for the construction of ditches and canals for the purposes aforesaid is hereby acknowledged and confirmed : *Provided, however*, That whenever, after the passage of this act, any person or persons shall, in the construction of any ditch or canal, injure or damage the possession of any settler on the public domain, the party committing such injury or damage shall be liable to the party injured for such injury or damage.

SEC. 10. *And be it further enacted*, That wherever, prior to the passage of this act, upon the lands heretofore designated as mineral lands, which have been excluded from survey and sale, there have been homesteads made by citizens of the United States, or persons who have declared their intention to become citizens, which homesteads have been made, improved, and used for agricultural purposes, and upon which there have been no valuable mines of gold, silver, cinnabar, or copper discovered, and which are properly agricultural lands, the said settlers or owners of such homesteads shall have a right of pre-emption thereto, and shall be entitled to purchase the same at the price of one dollar and twenty-five cents per acre, and in quantity not to exceed one hundred and sixty acres ; or said parties may avail themselves of the provisions of the act of Congress approved May twenty, eighteen hundred and sixty-two, entitled "An act to secure homesteads to actual settlers on the public domain," and acts amendatory thereof.

SEC. 11. *And be it further enacted*, That upon the survey of the lands aforesaid, the Secretary of the Interior may designate and set apart such portions of the said lands as are clearly agricultural lands, which lands shall thereafter be subject to pre-emption and sale as other public lands of the United States, and subject to all the laws and regulations applicable to the same.

Approved July 26, 1866.

CHAPTER XVI.

Geology and Geological History*—Classification of Minerals
found in the Territory†.

GEOLOGY.

THE *Granitic* formation, which is the oldest, formed
by the cooling of the original fiery fluid composing
the globe, may be seen on and beyond the Snowy
Range of the Rocky Mountains in various parts of
Colorado; more abundantly on the western side
of the Range than the eastern.   In masses of true
granite, syenite, or porphyry, it makes its appearance on McClellan Mountain, in the Argentine silver district, where it is seen to have been thrust
through younger formations to the prominent position that it occupies; on the west side of the Boulder
Pass, where massive granitic ranges form the buttresses of the snowy sierra as we descend to the
Middle Park; and on the western side of the Park,
where it forms the grand mountain wall that en-
closes it.

Of *Metamorphic* rocks, gneiss is by far the most
abundant, and most of the gold-bearing veins are

---

* Prepared by Prof. Wm. Denton of Boston.
Prepared by Mr. J. Alden Smith, of Trail Run, Colorado.

found in gneissoid rocks, though they are generally termed "granite" by the miners. Fine exposures may be seen near Black Hawk, the lines of stratification marking the mountain side, as stripes do the body of a zebra.

Resting upon the granite in the Middle Park, on the banks of Grand River, are exposures of conglomerate, probably of *Silurian* age, overlaid by sandstones and limestones, probably of *Devonian* age, and above this the coal measures of the *Carboniferous* formation, the only place in the Territory where true Carboniferous coal is known to exist— coal that will coke.

Near the Sangre de Christo Pass, the granite is overlaid by slates and limestones probably of *Silurian* age, the·limestones containing crinoidal fragments, but too small for the identification of the species. Farther north, the Three Tetons are composed of conglomerates, formed of pebbles, boulders, and large masses of gneiss, granite, mica-schist, and hornblende-schist, with gneissoid rocks, slate, and limestone on their flanks.

Rocks of the *Permean* age have been discovered on the Plains in the eastern part of Colorado, consisting principally of limestones, some of ·which abound with the characteristic fossils of this period.

The *Cretaceous* formation is well represented, especially along the base of the Mountains on the eastern side. The shells of the inoceramus are found in a limestone at Boulder City, baculites of large size in great abundance on the Platte, a few miles from Denver, while the limestones lying be-

tween Colorado City and Pueblo contain the inoceramus, scaphites, baculites, ammonites and other
characteristic cretaceous fossils. These beds extend for a considerable distance to the eastward,
and in wearing down under the action of atmospheric agencies, masses have been left in conical
hills, looking like gigantic ant-hills ; on these, fossils
can be picked up in great abundance. Between
Pueblo and the Sangre de Christo Pass, the teeth,
spines and bones of fishes, principally of the genera
Ptychodus and Lamna, so common in the cretaceous beds of England, are found in remarkable profusion. The neighborhood of Zan Hicklin's ranch
on the Greenhorn River is the richest locality for
fossils of this description that we ever saw.

In Eastern Colorado, coal measures are found of
Cretaceous age, the shale and limestones accompanying them containing the characteristic forms
of this period.

The *Cretaceous* formation is also well represented
in the Middle Park by baculite beds and sandstone
abounding with the scales of fishes.

The following shows the position of these beds
as they occur on Chalk Creek, Middle Park :

FEET.	1	
200	Lava.	Agates and chalcedony.
400	2 White sandstone. Quartzose conglomerate.	Fossil wood in fragments. Some bones of mammals and birds.
400	3 Shaly sandstones.	Scales of cycloidal fishes.
20	4 Blue limestone.	
500	5 Shales, marls. Sandstones.	Fish teeth. Baculites. Conchifers and Tucoids.

Numbers 3, 4, and 5 are probably Cretaceous; the rest Tertiary.

From the disintegration of No. 1 proceed the agates and chalcedonies of the Middle Park. Where No's 1 and 2 are disintegrated, agates and fossil wood lie mixed together on the surface. The slabs of No. 3 are covered with the scales of cycloidal fishes, that is, fishes whose scales resemble those of the salmon and the trout. No. 5 we call Baculite beds, from the great number and large size of the baculites found in them.

The *Tertiary* formation has a remarkable development in Colorado. Its thickness as exposed on the western side of the Rocky Mountains, from the Parahlamoosh Range, which is composed of Tertiary lavas, to the junction of White and Green Rivers, is ten thousand feet. Included in this are coal measures, containing many thin veins of coal, beds of gypsum, thin beds of limestone, and above these, petroleum shales at least a thousand feet in thickness, abounding in fossil leaves and insects, the shales containing them occurring at points sixty miles apart; above them brown sandstones and conglomerates having a thickness of from twelve hundred to fifteen hundred feet and containing silicified wood, turtles, and bones and teeth of large mammals. The following is the order in which they lie in the valley of the White River:

FEET.		
2,000 (?)	**1** Red sandstone. White sandstone.	Seen, but not examined.
1,200	**2** Brown sandstones, alternating with blue shales and beds of conglomerate.	Bones of Mammals, Turtles. Deciduous leaves and insects in the lower shales. Perpendicular veins of petroleum coal.
1,000	**3** Petroleum shales, varying from a cream color to black. One bed, 20 feet thick, resembles cannel coal.	Insects. Leaves of deciduous trees.
800	**4** White or light brown sandstones. White shales, on which are ripple marks. Brown shales and shaly sandstones.	
1,000	**5** Thick white sandstones and brown shales. Thick brown sandstones.	Brown sandstones weathered into cavities.
2,700	**6** *Coal Measures.* Sandstone, limestone, shales, blue, brown and black. Underclays. Beds of coal, or Lignite. Brown sandstones and shales, very soft. Coal in several beds, with underclays. White sandstones, with alternating blue shales.	Limestone contains conchs and small gasteropods. Two wide expansions of White River Valley have been made where the soft shales are.
1,400	**7** Compact red sandstones. White sandstones. Red sandstones, shaly and micaceous. Thin, fetid limestones.	Fragments of shells in the limestone.
300	**8** Yellow, soft sandstone.	
200	**9** Gypsum.	

The thickness of the various beds is merely estimated ; in no case measured.

The upper beds are found near the junction of White and Green Rivers in Utah; the lower ones near the Parahlamoosh Range where they are covered by immense beds of lava; in some places, especially on the eastern side of the Range, alternating with beds of white and very friable sandstone lying in a perfectly horizontal position and rising to a hight on the top of the Range of about 13,000 feet.

The groups 8 and 9 and the lower part of 7 make their appearance in valleys on the eastern side of the Range, the lava having been poured out apparently during the time of the Lower Tertiary coal measures.

Specimens of fossil insects from No. 3 were submitted to Mr. Samuel H. Scudder, Secretary of the Boston Society of Natural History, who has made fossil insects a special study. The following is his description of them:

"This is the fifth discovery of fossil insects in this country, if some tracks and an apparent larva in the Triassic rocks of the Connecticut Valley be correctly referred to insects; but it is the first time that they have been found in the Tertiary beds of America. These were obtained by Professor Denton on a trip of exploration west of the Rocky Mountain Range not far from the junction of White and Green Rivers in Colorado.

"The specimens were brought from two localities called by Professor Denton, Fossil Kanyon and Chagrin Valley, lying about sixty miles apart. The rocks in both cases are the same; above are beds o. brown sandstone, passing occasionally into conglomerate, and thin beds of bluish and cream-colored shale alternating with the sandstones, all dipping to the west at an angle of about 20°. These contain fossil wood of deciduous trees, fragments of large bones, most of which are solid, and turtles, some of which are two feet in length and perfect. Professor Denton considers this sandstone as probably of Miocene age. Beneath these rocks are beds of petroleum shale, a thousand feet in thickness, varying in color from a light cream to inky blackness; these shales are filled with innumerable leaves of deciduous trees, and throughout their extent the remains of insects abound. The specimens brought home are about fifty in number, many of the little slabs containing several different species of insects upon them. The number of species amounts to about fifty also, although a number of specimens are so fragmentary or imperfectly preserved as to be difficult and often impossible of identification.

"The most abundant forms are Diptera, and they comprise indeed two-thirds of the whole number, either in the larval or perfect state; the others are mostly very minute Coleoptera, and besides these are several Homoptera, an ant belonging to the genus Myrmica, a night-flying moth, and a larva apparently allied to the slug-caterpillars or Limacodes.

"The perfect insects among the Diptera are mostly small species of Mycetophilidæ, a family whose larvæ live mostly in fungoid vegetation, and Tipulidæ whose larvæ generally live in stagnant

water ; there are besides some forms not yet determined, of which some are apparently Muscidæ, a
family to which the common house-fly belongs.
The larvæ of Diptera belong to the Muscidæ and
to another family, the latter of which live during
this stage in water only—none of the larvæ, however, belong to the species of which the perfect
insects are represented on these stones. The
Homoptera belong to genera allied to Issus, Gype-
na, Delphax, and some of the Tettigonidæ.

"A comparison of the specimens from the two
localities shows some differences. They both have
Mycetophilidæ, but Fossil Kanyon has a proportionately greater abundance and variety of them. Fossil Kanyon has other flies also in greater number,
though there are some in both ; but Myrmica, the
very minute Diptera, and the minute Coleoptera are
restricted to Fossil Kanyon. On the other hand all
the larvæ, both the Diptera and that which appears
to be a Limacodes, were brought only from Chagrin
Valley.

"Of course the number of specimens is too small
to say that the faunæ of these two localities are distinct, although the same species has not been found
to occur in both, and the strata being 1,000 feet in
thickness, there is opportunity for some difference
in geological age, for new collections may entirely
reverse the present apparent distinction. Neither
is it sufficient to base any satisfactory, that is
at all precise, conclusions concerning their age.
Enough is before us however to enable us to
assert with some confidence that they cannot be

older than the Tertiaries. They do not agree in the
aggregation of species with any of the insect beds
of Europe, or with the insects of the Amber Fauna;
and, since they have been found in Europe in considerable numbers only at rather wide intervals in
the geological record, we should need more facts
than are at our command by the known remains
of fossil insects to establish any synchronism of
deposits between Europe and America. Much
more satisfactory results could probably be reached
by a comparison of the remains of leaves, &c.
Anything more than a very general statement is
therefore at present quite out of the question."

The country in which these are found is a most
remarkable one. From the summit of a high ridge
on the east, a tract of country containing five or
six hundred square miles is distinctly visible. Over
the whole surface is rock, bare rock, cut into ravines,
kanyons, gorges and valleys, leaving in magnificent
relief terrace upon terrace, pyramid beyond pyramid, rising to mountain hights, amphitheatres that
would hold a million spectators, walls, pillars, towers,
castles everywhere. It looks like some ruined city
of the gods, blasted, bare, desolate, but grand "beyond a mortal's telling." Originally an elevated
country, composed of a number of soft beds of
sandstone of varying thickness and softness, underlaid by immense beds of shale, it has been worn
down and cut out by rills, creeks and streams, leaving this strange, weird country to be the wonder of
all generations.

In this region is found a deposit of petroleum

coal, scarcely to be distinguished in any way from the Albertite of New Brunswick. In lustre, fracture, and smell, it appears to be identical, and would yield as much oil as this famous oil-producing coal. It is in a perpendicular vein three feet wide, and was traced from the bottom of Fossil Kanyon, near Curtis Grove, White River, to the summit level of the country, a thousand feet in hight, and for nearly five miles in length, diminishing in width towards the ends of the vein. Its description and analysis is thus given by Dr. Hayes of Boston:

"Black, with high lustre like Albertite, which it resembles physically; specific gravity 1.055 to 1.075. Electric on friction; breaks easily, and contains .33 of one per cent. moisture. It affords 39.67 per cent. of soluble bitumen when treated with coal naphtha, and after combustion of all its parts 1.20 per cent. of ash remains; 100 parts distilled afforded bituminous matter, 77.67; carbon or coke, 20.80; ash left, 1.20; moisture, .33; total, 100.00. It expands to five or six times its volume, and leaves a porous cake, which burns easily."

The vein is in an enormous bed of sandstone, No. 2; and its walls are smooth. Beneath the sandstone are the petroleum shales No. 3, one bed of which, varying from ten to twenty feet in thickness, resembles cannelite, and would, it is thought, yield from fifty to sixty gallons of oil to the ton. This bed was traced for twenty-five miles in one direction, and was seen at points sixty miles apart in another, and it no doubt extends over the entire distance. If so, in that single bed are twenty million million barrels of oil, or a thousand times as much as America has produced since petroleum was discovered in Pennsylvania. There are few beds of coal that can compare with this in the amount of bituminous matter which it contains, or in the great value that it possesses as an article of fuel. The Tertiary beds of Colorado are as rich in fuel and gas-making material, as any coal region with which we are acquainted ; though it is more than probable that the petroleum now in the shales and petroleum coals came originally from the oil-bearing coral beds of some much older formations.

On the eastern or Atlantic side of the Mountains are Tertiary coal measures, containing beds of coal and beds of iron ore of good quality.

At Golden City one bed has been exposed, which owing to upheaval stands nearly vertical, and has a thickness of from ten to twelve feet. About twenty miles north of Denver, on Coal Creek, there are several exposures of thinner beds but still workable. This Tertiary coal is destined to play a very important part in the future history of Colorado. The available wood in the mining regions exhausted, as it soon must be, to these subterranean supplies all parties must come at last. Houses, furnaces, locomotives must depend upon it, and before many years pass its consumption will rise to a million tons annually. These Tertiary coal beds probably extend to the northern boundary of the Territory, which is by no means their limit in that direction.

Above them are beds of sandstone and conglomerate, abounding in fossil palms, firs, and various

17

resinous and gum-bearing trees, together with modern exogens.   Perfect trunks of large size are sometimes found lying on the Plains, where they have been left when the rock that held them was disintegrated.   Between Denver and Golden City many fine specimens may be found; still more on a low range of sand hills about twenty miles south of Denver, and still finer specimens are brought from the South Park.

In the Middle Park, west of the Grand River, is also a coarse sandstone passing into conglomerate and containing silicified wood.   Above it are beds of trap; and where this has disintegrated, chalcedonies and agates are found; principally moss agates, as they are called, but which are really chalcedonies containing oxide of manganese in a dendritic form.   The rock originally holding them was a lava poured out of some long extinct volcano; this was full of vesicles or hollow places produced by gas or vapor, and in process of time these were filled with extremely fine particles of silica, separated from the surrounding rock, forming the ordinary chalcedonies.   In some cases a small quantity of oxide of manganese has been carried in with the silica and this crystallizing in an arborescent or tree-like form has produced the appearance of moss in the chalcedony, and thus have been formed the beautiful moss agates which strew the plains of the Middle Park.

The lava beds of the Plains, as seen near Golden City, Boulder City, and other localities, seem to be the most recent Tertiary deposit of Colorado, and bear witness to the terrible volcanic eruptions, that, at no very distant period, geologically speaking, devastated the country. The hot soda springs at Idaho, where the water has a heat of about 94°, the hot sulphur springs of Middle Park, ranging from 92° to 114°, and the boiling spring of the San Luis Park still bear witness to this stormy time.

The *Drift* period is represented by immense accumulations of boulders and gravel in the valleys of almost every mountain stream, though ice did not produce as much effect during that period, as the hight of the mountains and their latitude would naturally lead us to expect.

HISTORY.

A State as young as Colorado can hardly be expected to have a history, and yet, older than all written history, older than the human race, it has a history stretching through the ages from the fiery beginning of the globe, and indelibly impressed on the rocks that compose it.

The mountainous portion of Colorado is without doubt the oldest; as old, doubtless, as the Silurian period and probably much older; though it must not be supposed that the Mountains were then as high or as broad as at present. The backbone of the Continent was indicated but not fully formed. Mountain chains are gradually elevated, and not "flirted up," as we once heard a gentleman of great pretensions term the process by which the Rocky Mountains were upheaved—that, too, while he was looking at their snowy peaks and rocky buttresses of various geologic ages. Formed as they are by the cooling of the globe and the shrinking of its crust, immense periods of time must have been occupied in lifting these enormous masses to their present hights. The general outline of the Mountains was probably similar to their present outline; but as in the fœtus, the features are marked by lines that give but a hint of what they are to be so the bare, jagged ridges of quartz and granite at that time were mere indications of the lordly Mountains that now tower to heaven—the crest of a mighty Continent.

As early as the Silurian period, the Mountains consisted of separate chains, and inland seas marked the spots where the Parks would eventually be. The ocean occupied the valley of the Rio Grande and passed up to the head of the San Luis Valley, then much wider than now, at the same time laving both eastern and western slopes, and probably communicating with the inland seas between the two ranges. In consequence of this, the Rocky Mountains must have been long, rocky islands, wearing down continually by the flow of a thousand streams, caused by incessant rains ; for with the ocean on every side, and evaporation proceeding more rapidly than now, owing to the thinness of the earth's crust, the rains upon these mountain islands must have been incessant and violent.

The conglomerates in the Middle Park and San Luis Valley, which we attribute to the Silurian age, consist of large pebbles, and sometimes boulders, principally of granite, gneiss, and quartz ; they indicate the force with which water swept down from some old mountain chain, occupying a position at one side of that held by the present Mountains, and carried them into the ocean; their fragments constituting a large portion of their successors. A process of upheaval and degradation must have been carried on simultaneously for many millions of years. Just as in a forest, the individual trees die and fall, and from their dust arise new trees and the forest continues for ages, so has it been with the Rocky Mountains, pulled down by torrents and upheaved by contraction of the earth's crust, and so probably will it continue to be, though in the future the process will necessarily be a slower one.

During the Devonian period, there seems to have been less violence; the conglomerates contain smaller pebbles and the limestones and shales indicate quiescent seas and more abundant life. Tucoidal impressions abound in a water-line of this age.

The Mountains were steadily growing, spreading principally east and west; the Parks were elevated and the water in time drained off, leaving swamps where seas had been, so that in the following Carboniferous period, there sprang up abundant vegetation whose accumulated remains, buried by inflowings of the ocean, formed in time the coal beds of the Middle Park, the only carboniferous coal known in Colorado.

During the Permean and Oolitic periods, we know as yet but little of the history of the mountainous portion of Colorado ; but east of the Mountains, the sea covered the country and limestones of great thickness, abounding with characteristic shells, were deposited.

Of the Cretaceous period we have a full history. The ocean again laved the Mountains on both sides, the ranges being several miles narrower than at present ; for we find rocks formed at the sea-bottom during this time occupying summits two or three thousand feet above the level of the plain. The Parks were again occupied by inland seas, for the elevation of the mountainous portion of Colorado was not by steady uplift ; but uplifts appear to have been followed by subsidences and these many times repeated before the mountain ranges were fully formed. The Middle Park probably communicated with the Western Ocean through the Gore Pass, then a strait like that of Babelmandel, between the Red Sea and the Indian Ocean. In the ocean, then covering three-fourths of Colorado, fishes and shells of many species abounded ; the wonderful profusion of their remains along the base of the Mountains from Colorado City southward to the Spanish Peaks tells loudly of this life swarming in waters that must have been warm and shallow.

The Plains to the south and south-east of Colorado City are strewed for a hundred miles with fossil shells of the Cretaceous period, especially baculites, which by persons unacquainted with their nature, are called fossil fishes.

Near to the Sangre de Christo Pass, thin beds of calciferous or limy sandstone alternate with the limestones and contain immense numbers of bones and teeth of fishes. Weathered slabs may be seen at the foot of the Sierra Mohada or Wet Mountains, on which a hundred perfect teeth might be counted, many of them flat and folded teeth, which formed a pavement for the jaws, enabling their possessors to crush the shells and crustaceas on which they fed.

The sea which occupied the Middle Park and communicated with the great Western Ocean, contained many baculites and some conchifers.

Towards the latter part of the Cretaceous period the Parks seem to have been again elevated, the communication with the exterior ocean cut off, never to be renewed, and brackish lakes, abounding with fish, subsequently becoming fresh water lakes, took the place of the previous interior seas.

During the Tertiary period, a large swamp existed at the foot of the Mountains on the eastern side, occupying the position of Golden City and Denver, and extending for hundreds of miles north and south—north into British America and south into New Mexico. In this swamp a rank vegetation must have flourished for a long period, vegetation of a much more modern character than that of the coal measures, consisting largely of coniferous trees. In time, an immense mass of vegetable matter accumulated, and was covered with clay, sand and pebbles, swept down from the neighboring Mountains ; and thus that remarkable Tertiary coal formation was produced, which may be seen at Golden City and on Coal Creek and other places in the vicinity, with its coal beds, under-clays and iron ores, bearing a great resemblance to the Carboniferous coal measures.

On the western side of the Mountains a similar condition of things seems to have existed, and coal beds were formed resembling those on the eastern side, but changes of level caused the formation of a greater number of coal beds of less thickness.

After the deposition of the coal measures, lakes of fresh or brackish water covered most of the western and central parts of Colorado, as well as the Valley at the foot of the Eastern Range, the higher grounds adorned with palms and other tropical trees, many of them resinous and of strange aspect, while some were of more modern appearance, especially those on the Mountains.

Succeeding the quiet of the Cretaceous and early Tertiary periods, which must have continued for ages, came a stormy time, strongly marked in the rocks of this age. Fire and water united to leave an indelible impress on the land. The Mountains were again elevated, carrying with them the beds made at the sea-bottom during the preceding age. Accompanying this rise must have been earthquakes rending the Mountains and volcanoes pouring out fiery streams. A large part of the Middle Park was a sea of fire, for it was during this time that the traps whose frowning battlements are visible near the hot sulphur springs, and cover so large a portion of the Park, were formed.

During the same period, but previous to this, went of the Western Range, successive beds of lava were poured out over a large area, some under water, until their aggregate thickness amounted to thousands of feet. Largely swept off by denuding agencies, these beds lie exposed on the western side of the Tumbianaw Valley, presenting an enormous wall having a hight of at least three thousand feet above the valley and a length of more than twenty miles. Westward these beds extend for many miles, forming the Parahlamoosh Range. Where are the volcanoes from which the lava that formed these immense beds flowed?

Along the base of the Eastern Range similar streams were poured out, but have been denuded to a still greater extent. A portion of what must have been an immense bed can be seen near Golden City, forming a small *mesa* or table-land known by the name of Table Mountain. The lava here is two hundred and fifty feet thick. Similar beds must have extended over the country between Pike's Peak and the Spanish Peaks, though carried off since that time, leaving one outlying mass in the valley of the Huerfano, which is a striking object for a radius of many miles; looking as it does, like an immense pillar erected in the valley. It has given the name of Huerfano (the Spanish for orphan), to the river that flows past it, the Park in which the river rises, and the valley in which it runs.

Connected with these volcanic disturbances were numerous hot springs, the water of which, containing silica in solution, traversed the ground everywhere, and petrified the wood that was buried

17*

in its vicinity. Hence the beautiful specimens of petrified wood so common in almost every part of Colorado, except the Mountains, and the solid trees silicified to the heart.

During the middle part of the Tertiary period a large lake covered Western Colorado, extending also into Utah. Into it flowed numerous streams carrying fine mud, and at one time immense quantities of petroleum issuing probably from numerous, and powerful springs. The land was covered with trees resembling the oak, maple, willow and other modern trees, and still others that are now extinct. Insects by myriads hovered around the margin of the lake, turtles swam in its waters and aquatic pachyderms, somewhat resembling the tapir, lived in the rivers that supplied it and fed upon the numerous plants on their margins. The water of the lake was probably brackish, it contained but few mollusks, but abounded in turtles having thick, bony shells. The amount of sediment carried into it was so great that beds were formed at the bottom from two to three thousand feet in thickness. This could only have been accomplished by the gradual sinking of the lake bottom, which probably coincided with the elevation of the mountain ranges east and west of it.

The Tertiary period was followed by the Glacial or Drift period. On the Plains Proper there are no evidences of drift action, and it is rare to meet with unequivocal evidences of this even at the foot of the Mountains on the eastern side. But we do not travel far up the mountain gorges before abundant evidences of "glacial action" present themselves. On the Fontaine Qui Bouit, three miles above Colorado City, and at the foot of Pike's Peak, are immense granite boulders, lying near some remarkable soda springs, and a little below them are lateral moraines, principally composed of large boulders, left by some glacier that once passed down a small valley and joined near there a larger one which traversed the valley of the Fontaine Qui Bouit. At the present time the highest peaks of the Rocky Mountains in that latitude lose their snowy covering every year, though but for a short time.

In a small but beautiful park on the South Boulder, and about six miles below the snowy peaks, are beds of boulders from thirty to forty feet high, cut through and exposed on both sides of the river, the bed of which is full of them, and hence its name. On South Clear Creek, a few miles above Empire City, many rocks have been exposed by the workmen in making the new road over the Berthoud Pass. On the surfaces of some of them, glacial striæ are distinctly visible. This is the only place in Colorado east of the Snowy Range where we have seen them ; their general absence is remarkable. The evidences of glacial action increase as we ascend to the Snowy Range. The valleys are no longer bounded by rocks that are rough and craggy, as they are in the lower portions, but they are nearly as rounded and smooth in their outlines as the chalk downs of England, or the glacier-planed hills of Massachusetts.

West of the Middle Park, on the flat summit of

the Parahlamoosh Range, I found rocks planed and plowed into deep furrows, whose direction was due west, and these continuing down the side of the mountain into the valley of the White River, which contains numerous terminal moraines, brought by contributary glaciers proceeding from the high lands on both sides, but principally on the south. These moraines are visible at the mouths of the creeks flowing into White River, for a distance of sixty miles from the top of the Range.

It seems plain, that during the Drift period the Rocky Mountains were not only covered with snow on their higher summits, but the valleys were filled with snow and ice, which never melted, but pressed down the mountain gorges toward the plain; thickest and most glacial in character nearest the Mountains and on the Pacific side; becoming thinner, and occupying but the bottoms of the valleys as the glaciers descended; melting at last into numerous streams laden with debris, which they swept on to the Plains.

Since that time the climate has moderated and the Western Range, possessing at one time the most rigorous climate, has so far changed that pines grow on it 2,000 feet higher than they do on the Eastern Range. The glaciers have disappeared from the valleys, and the snowy patches on the Mountains alone remain to remind us of the immense ice fields of the by-gone times.

METALS AND MINERALS.

Agate—Called by the Greeks and Romans *Achates*, from a river in Sicily, now the Dorillo,

near which it was found. It is one of the forms in
which silica presents itself nearly pure. It is a
variegated chalcedony, the colors being distributed
in spots, clouds, dendritic delineations or concentric
lines. The lines take straight, circular, and zigzag
forms ; when the former it is called *ribbon agate*,
when the latter, *fortification agate*, from its resemblance to the angular outlines of a fortification.
These lines are caused by the edges of the different layers of chalcedony, and the layers are the
successive deposits during the process of its formation. *Moss agate*, or *mocha stone*, is usually
a brownish agate, with dendritic delineations of a
brownish-black color and caused by an oxide of
iron or manganese ; but sometimes the moss is
green, yellow, or red. The green is supposed to
be due to oxide of chrome, and the yellow and red,
to iron. Moss agates are found in the greatest
abundance at different localities in Colorado, but
the best are from the Middle Park. Those found
in the South Park are generally of inferior quality.
When the stone is very pure and transparent, with
moss clearly defined and not too much of it, the
moss agate makes a beautiful gem, and is much
used in jewelry, for brooches, ear-drops, gents'
rings, sleeve-buttons, etc. Very fine gems of this
stone, after being cut, are sold for $5 to $10 each,
but the ordinary stones for 50 cents to $2 each.
Rarely, one is found of exceeding beauty that will
sell for $50, and *very* rarely, as high as $75. The
different varieties of agates are very common in
most all parts of the world, and in the rough state,

possess little or no value, except to collectors. Many of them make fine gems, but the value is generally given them by the work put upon them. Besides being used as gems, they are cut into cups, handles for swords, ladies' parasols, knives and forks, small mortars for chemists' use, and into a variety of ornamental trinkets, the most famous of which is the Mantuan vase, at Brunswick. The colors in the ribbon and fortification agates may be darkened by boiling the stone in oil, and then dropping it into sulphuric acid. A little oil is absorbed by some of the layers, which become blackened or charred by the acid.

Actinolite—Has been observed in some few localities—is quite plenty in Bergen District, near Bear Creek.

Alabaster—In small quantities, of a brownish color, near Mount Vernon. When of pure, snowy whiteness, fine texture, and slightly translucent, alabaster is cut into vases, candle-sticks, statues, and a variety of ornaments. For these purposes it is of considerable value, when very fine. It is so soft as to be easily cut or carved with common cutting implements.

Albite—Occurs sparingly in Banner District, Clear Creek County.

Alum—Has been found native on the Foot-hills, near Mount Vernon.

Soda Alum—Sulphate of soda, is found in abundance in several localities in the South Park, Middle Park, and other places. *Iron alum*, sulphate of iron, can be found as a green, or greenish-white incrustation on piles of tailings, and about old shaft houses all over the country. It is the *copperas* of the drug shops, and is a result of decomposing iron pyrites.

Aluminite—Alum stone, is also found near Mount Vernon.

Amazon Stone—Elk Creek, five miles from the old St. Louis Ranch, with orthoclase, smoky quartz, aventurine (?), micaceous iron and anhydrite—the latter rare. This stone is a green variety of feldspar, and when pure, and of a clear, bluish-green color, makes a very pretty gem, resembling turquoise. It derives its name from having first been observed in the possession of a community of female warriors, on or near the head waters of the river Amazon. Many of them were engraved with the symbols of Aztec worship. The stone is very abundant in some parts of New Mexico.

Amethyst—So named from a Greek word because it was supposed that cups made from it would prevent the liquor they contained from intoxicating. It is a purple, or bluish-violet variety of quartz crystal, often of great beauty. Its color is due to a trace of the oxide of manganese. When large, pure, clear, and finely colored, the amethyst is highly prized as a gem. It should always be set in gold. Amethysts have been found in many different localities in Colorado, and in some places quite abundantly, though generally of a very inferior quality, both for transparency and color, and of no value except to the specimen hunter. Some small ones of a very fine quality are occasionally found

in Nevada. The writer obtained a few there in
the Fall of 1864 that were *very* brilliant, of a delicate color, and when cut, exceedingly beautiful.
Some quite fine ones have been found in York
District, also at Mill City, on Deer Creek, and in
many other places.

Anhydrite—Specimens in the writer's cabinet, of
a very beautiful wine-red color, and very transparent, found near the head of Elk Creek—rare.

Antimony—Occurs as a sulphuret, and probably
in other forms, associated with the sulphurets of
copper, iron, lead, zinc, etc., in many of our gold
and silver mines.

Arsenic—Also occurs occasionally in our mines
the same as antimony. Neither of these metals
has been found in the native state, in the Territory,
within the knowledge of the writer.

Aragonite—Foot-hills, near Golden Gate—fine
specimens.

Asbestus—A small specimen in the cabinet of
the writer, obtained on the Snowy Range, between
the Boulder and Berthoud Passes.

Aventurine Quartz (?) — From Elk Creek, five
miles above the old St. Louis Ranch. This stone
is sometimes used in jewelry under the name of
gold-stone, but the artificial imitations of the stone
are far more beautiful than the genuine aventurine.
The specimens from the above locality in the writer's
collection, show *white* scales, instead of *yellow*, which
is the usual color.

Aventurine Feldspar—Head of Elk Creek, with
Amazon stones.

Baryta—Occurs as a sulphate, (heavy spar,) in many of our gold and silver mines. Specimens in the cabinet of the writer, from the Cooley Lode, Snake River, and from the Sante Fe, Virginia Kanyon.

Beryl—From Bear Creek, below Harrington's saw-mill.

Beryl, Emerald and Aquamarine—Are all one and the same mineral species, and only distinguished from each other by their different shades of green, or by the delicacy of the crystals. The *emerald* includes the rich, deep-green variety, and owes its color to the presence of oxide of chrome. *Beryl* includes the pale, yellowish-green variety, which is colored by oxide of iron. *Aquamarine* includes clear, transparent beryls, of a sea-green, or pale-bluish or bluish-green tint. Both the emeralds and aquamarines make beautiful and valuable gems. An aquamarine in the possession of the writer, obtained in Albany, Maine, in 1862, was pronounced, by the lapidary who cut it, to be fully equal in purity and brilliance to a first-water green diamond. The finest emeralds and aquamarines come from Grenada, where they occur in dolomite. A crystal from this locality, two and a fourth inches long, and two inches in diameter, is in the cabinet of the Duke of Devonshire. It contains numerous flaws, and is therefore but partially fit for jewelry, but is valued at 150 guineas. Another and finer specimen, but about one-fourth less in size, is in the collection of Mr. Hope, of London, and cost £500. No specimens of the emerald or aquamarine varieties have yet been found in Colorado. The largest beryls known were found at Acworth and Grafton, N. H. One from the latter place weighs 2,900 lbs.—is four feet in length, with one diameter of thirty-two inches, and another of twenty-two. Another is estimated to weigh two and a half tons. The writer has often seen them at Albany, Maine, measuring two to three feet in length, and eight to twelve inches in diameter.

Bismuth—Like arsenic and antimony, occurs in many of our mines, but has never, within the knowledge of the writer, been found native.

Ligneous Coal—Found at Golden City, Boulder, and all along the base of the Mountains, the width of the Territory.

Albertine Coal—A large vein, discovered by Prof. Wm. Denton, of Boston, on White River, western portion of the Territory.

Bloodstone, or Heliotrope—Found sparingly in the Middle Park. It is a deep-green variety of jasper, slightly translucent, containing spots of red, which have some resemblance to drops of blood. The red spots are colored with iron. When the stone is very fine, and the spots well defined and distributed, it makes a very pretty gem for seals and rings, and is much used for those purposes. There is a bust of Christ in the royal collection at Paris, cut in this stone, in which the red spots are so managed as to represent drops of blood. *No very fine* specimens have, as yet, been obtained in the Territory.

Brucite—James Creek ; rare.

Cairngorum Stone—Head of Elk Creek, five miles from old St. Louis Ranch. It is a smoky-tinted quartz crystal, and was formerly used by the ancient Scots as a jewel. The lighter shades are sometimes extremely beautiful, and are still used to some extent for seals, tops of claymore hilts, etc.

Calcareous Spar—Near Mt. Vernon, also at Bergen's Ranch, in fine, brownish-white crystals.

Carnelian—White, very fine, from the South Park, and flesh-red, rare, from the Middle Park. The finer varieties are quite extensively worked in India and Germany, beads, bracelets, seals, rings, studs, marbles, chess-men, etc., being made from it. The Japanese cut great numbers into beads of the form of the fruit of the olive. It is a very common stone in many localities in this country, but owing to the expense of cutting, it is not regarded as of any commercial value, except to collectors.

Chalcedony—Very beautiful specimens from the South Park, five miles from the Salt Works ; in the mammillary, botryoidal, and stalactitic form. The finer varieties of this stone, owing to the number and beauty of their shades of color, and the high lustre they have when polished, are much esteemed as ornamental stones, but their great hardness renders them very difficult and expensive to work. Like carnelian, it is quite common in many localities, but very few specimens of extraordinary beauty have ever been found in this country. It is frequently met with, of a flesh-red color, lining cavities in some of our deep mines.

Chrysoprase — Middle Park — rare, An apple-green chalcedony, colored by nickel.

Chlorophane—Argentine Lode, Bergen District.

Chlorite—Trail Creek—foliated and radiated varieties.

Derbyshire Spar—Argentine, Ozark, and Wisconsin Lodes, Bergen District.

Egeran—Near Genesee Ranch, on Bear Creek—fine specimens.

Copper—Native—This species has been found in but few mines in the Territory. The Gregory at Black Hawk, Tennel and Kelley at Trail Run, and a few others are examples. Some very fine cabinet specimens of dendritic, or moss copper, have been taken from the Narragansett mine, on the Gregory Lode.

Copper Pyrites—Sulphuret of Copper—This mineral is one of the most common and best ores for gold. It is what is generally called by the miners, "yellow iron," in contradistinction to common iron pyrites, and it nearly always carries a good per centage of gold. Very fine specimens may be obtained from the Gregory, Bobtail, Briggs, Williams, etc., at Black Hawk, and from the Gunnell, Burroughs, Kansas, etc., about Central City, and from nearly all the *deep* mines in the country.

Erubescite—Is occasionally met with in most of the mines affording the above species, but is not nearly so abundant.

Tetrahedrite — Gray Copper — Silver Fahlerz— Malachite and Liberty Lodes, near Bear Creek.

Red Copper Ore—Malachite Lode, Bear Creek,

four miles south of Genesee Ranch.   *Tenorite*, or *black copper*, from the same mine.

Blue Vitriol—Sulphate of Copper—Spanish Bar.

Malachite—Green Carbonate of Copper—Malachite Lode, Bear Creek, with red copper ore, and copper pyrites.   Earthy variety very abundant, but no finely crystallized specimens have yet been found at that locality.   Some small but very fine specimens of mammillary, crystalline malachite have been found in the Kelley and Champion Lodes, at Trail Run.   It is a very valuable ore of copper; when abundant and pure, it yields, seventy-two per cent copper.   This mineral, in the crystallized form, is susceptible of a very high polish, and is much used for inlaid work, and to a limited extent for jewelry.   It makes beautiful gems, but owing to its softness is not much prized.   Very large masses are sometimes obtained in Siberia and Russia, which are worked into slabs for tables, mantel-pieces, etc., and are of exquisite beauty, owing to the delicate shadings of the radiations and zones of color.   At Versailles there is a room furnished with tables, vases, and other articles of this kind, and similar rooms are to be found in many European palaces.

Azurite—Blue Carbonate Copper—Champion, Kelley, and Tennel Lodes, Trail Run; Running Lode, Black Hawk, etc.

Chryoscolla—Silicate of Copper—Champion and Kelley Lodes, Trail Run, in small, but beautiful botryoidal masses.

Velvet Copper Ore—from the Kellev Lode, Trail Run.

Copper Glance—Liberty, Pocahontas, and other lodes, Bergen District.

Epidote—Trail Creek, crystallized ; also head of Russell Gulch, near Wilson's mill, Bergen District, and other localities.

Feldspar—Fine crystals on Elk Creek, five miles above the old St. Louis Ranch. Also, at the same place, some beautiful and rare pseudomorphs, after specular iron.

Float Stone—Beautiful specimens have been taken from the Mammoth Lode, near Central City.

Flos Ferri—Foot-Hills, near Golden Gate.

Fluor Spar—In large cleavable masses, of various shades of color—white, green, purple, pink, in veins with galena and gray copper ore, in Bergen District, near Bear Creek. Also with silver ores on James Creek. Sparingly in small crystals in a lode opposite Half-Way House, Virginia Kanyon.

Fire-Clay—Golden City, at Bell & Co's brick works ; Middle Park, South Park, Bellemonte Furnace, etc.

Garnet—Precious garnets are found in quantities in the sluice boxes of the gulch miners in the South Park, and also west of the Range about Breckenridge and other places. They are usually quite small, however, and of no value as gems. A few specimens, in the cabinet of the writer, presented by Mrs. Hall, of the South Park, are of a beautiful, deep, wine-red color. Ferruginous garnets occur in great abundance at Trail Creek, in Bergen District on A. F. Post's Ranch, head of Russell Gulch, and many other places, associated with epidote,

white quartz, calc spar, and sometimes copper
pyrites. Some beautiful cabinet specimens in the
collection of the writer, are from the Trail Creek
locality. Dodecahedrons as much as six inches in
diameter have been found at Post's Ranch. Garnet, in its most perfect forms, when cut and polished, makes a very beautiful gem, and resembles in color, lustre and transparency, the Oriental
ruby. It is met with in various colors—red, brown,
black, yellow, white and green. The deep, clear-
red variety is called *precious garnet*, or *almandine*,
and is the variety mostly used in jewelry. The
manganesian garnet, is also of a deep-red color, but
is usually impure and full of fractures. The deep-
brown variety is called *aplome, one* black is called
melanite, and another is called *pyrenaite*—a light
cinnamon-yellow variety, containing 30 to 38 per
cent. of lime, is called *cinnamon stone*, or *essonite*.
Another emerald-green variety is called *ouvarovite*,
and another of a paler color is called *grossularite*.
The best *precious garnets* come from Ceylon and
Greenland — cinnamon stone from Ceylon and
Sweden—ouvarovite from Bissersk, in Russia, and
topazolite from Piedmont. The garnet is the car-
buncle of the ancients—also supposed to have been
the hyacinth. The alabandic carbuncles of Pliny
were so called because they were cut and polished
at Alabanda, hence the name *almandine,* now in
use.

Gold—Crystalline gold has been very rarely
found in the Territory. Some very beautiful arborescent masses were shown us, a short time

since, by Mr. Lowe, of Fairplay, which were washed out of his claims the past season. Judge Costello also showed us a few—larger, but not so fine. Some very beautiful and singular specimens were also taken from the Leavitt Lode, near the Kip & Buell mill the past Summer, but as the writer was not fortunate enough to obtain one, an accurate description cannot be given of them. The gold was in coarse, stringy masses, in some cases only united to the gangue by one or both ends, the wires standing out from the quartz, from half an inch to more than an inch, forming a sort of net-work of angles and circles,—the wires covered with a drusy, silicious coating.

Gypsum—South Park, in a large bed, some ten miles north-west from the Salt Works. Also in fine arrow-head crystals, and fibrous masses near Mount Vernon, and on the Cache-a-la-Poudre.

Graphic Granite—Near Colver's saw-mill, Beaver Creek.

Hornblende—In gneiss, also in nodular masses, at Trail Run, and on Clear Creek, near Idaho.

Hyalite—Middle Park, near the Hot Spring—rare.

Idocrase—Near the Malachite Lode, Bear Creek.

Iron Ores—Iron occurs native, or alloyed with nickel in meteorites, but has never been so found in any mines. Its most abundant ores are its oxides and sulphurets. *Bi-sulphuret*—iron pyrites—occurs in nearly all our mines, either massive or crystallized. Some beautiful cabinet specimens of this mineral, in large cubes, have been taken from the

S. P. Chase, Hill House, Kingston, and other lodes. A specimen in the author's collection, from the Kingston Lode, is associated with brittle silver.

Magnetic Pyrites—Bobtail Hill, near Running Lode.

Specular Iron—Cache-a-la-Poudre, St. Vrain's, Elk Creek, and other localities.

Micaceous Iron—Elk Creek, five miles above old St. Louis Ranch.

Red Hæmatite—Bellemonte Furnace, Boulder, Golden City.

Red Ochre—Bear Creek, below Harrington's mill.

Jaspery Clay Iron—Champion Lode, Trail Run.

Brown Hæmatite—Golden City, Bellemonte Furnace, etc.

Brown Ochre and *Yellow Ochre*—Near the surface, in many of our gold-bearing veins. *Bog Iron Ore*, also found in the same way, though not so common.

Titanic Iron—*Ilmenite*—Quartz Hill, head of Russell Gulch, and numerous other localities. It is this, together with magnetic iron, that forms the black sand, found so plentifully by the gulch miners.

Magnetic Iron—Quartz Hill, Quartz Valley, and other localities.

Lievrite—North Clear Creek, below Black Hawk.

Spathic Iron—*Carbonate of Iron*—Some beautiful cabinet specimens of this mineral have been obtained from the Eureka and Griffith Lodes, Central, and Running Lode, Black Hawk, also from the Freeland, Trail Run.

Blue Iron Earth—Trail Run, Golden Belt Lode.

Washingtonite—Near Dory's Ranch.

Jasper—Is found in abundance in the South and Middle Parks, in many instances forming whole hills in the latter place. It takes various shades of color, as red, brown, yellow, green, black. It admits of a very high polish, and when of fine colors, is a handsome stone for inlaid work, but is rarely used as a gem. The black variety is called Lydian stone, or touchstone, and is used for testing the purity of gold, by marking upon it with the gold under test, and comparing the color of the mark left on it, with that of alloys of known character.

Lead—Galena—Sulphuret of Lead—Occurs in very many of our gold and silver-bearing lodes. Beautifully crystallized cabinet specimens come from the Calhoun Lode, Leavenworth Gulch, also from the Running Lode, Black Hawk, and Gardner, Quartz Hill. Beautiful and rich specimens of the fine, granular variety come from the Whale Lode, Spanish Bar; also, mixed with copper and iron pyrites, from the Freeland, and Holman, Trail Run.

Minium—Oxyd of Lead--Sparingly in the Freeland Lode, Trail Run.

Anglesite—Rarely, in the Freeland Lode. Trail Run.

Caledonite—Abundant in the Freeland Lode, Trail Run, and sparingly in the Running Lode, Black Hawk.

Pyromorphite—In many so-called "lead crevices," near the surface.

Lignite—Coal mines along the base of the Mountains.

Limestone—Mount Vernon, Golden City, Boulder, South Park, Middle Park, etc., in inexhaustible supply.

Meteoric Iron—A large mass discovered by Jas. L. Wilson, of Golden City. It was found in the bed of a deep kanyon, near Bear Creek, four miles south from the Genesee Ranch, on the 13th day of April, 1866. The following is Mr. Wilson's description of this mass: "It is singular in form, 22 inches long, 16 inches wide, and 12 thick. Four of its sides are flat, and two rounded. This form indicates it to be a fragment of a much larger mass. It is magnetic—weight about 600 lbs. The force with which it struck the rocks at the time of its fall, had battered one end, and so shattered it as to enable us to break off a piece that weighed 11 lbs. Its composition appears to be the native metals of nickel, cobalt, iron, and a trace of copper, unequally distributed in the mass. In one part nickel and cobalt are largely in excess of the other metals, while in other parts iron forms the chief ingredient. These metals are aggregated and highly crystallized. A coating of the oxide of iron half an inch thick, has taken the place of the shining black crust observed on ærolites when they first reach the earth. The less oxidizable metals of nickel and cobalt still remain in their metallic state in this coating of iron rust." The mass is now in the collection of Prof. Shepard, of Amherst College, Massachusetts.

Molybdenite—Leavitt Lode, near Kip & Buel mill ; rare.

Mineral Rosin—Langford & Company's coal mine, Boulder.

Manganese—Occurs in many of our mines, especially in dendritic delineations—"forest rock," as it is called by the miners.

Mica—Abundantly distributed throughout the mountains, but rarely in large crystals. A beautiful and very perfect crystal in the collection of the author, from near the Genesee Ranch, on the Mount Vernon and Idaho road, is three and a half inches long, by two wide and one thick.

Onyx—Middle Park, on the west side of Grand River and Willow Creek, associated with jasper, chalcedony, and fortification agates. Onyx is the material used for cameos, the figure being carved out of one layer and standing in relief on another. Very few if any specimens fine enough or of the right kind for this purpose have been found here.

Opal—Semi-Opal—A variety of opal, of a milky white color, and very transparent, is found in a lode of gold-bearing quartz, near Idaho, Clear Creek County. It occurs in thin seams, and in lumps distributed through the crevice. Some small pieces show a very decided opalescence, and a pale bluish shade of color when cut, but do not reflect any play of colors. They are of no value as gems.

Petroleum—Canon City, Bear Creek.

Plasma—South Park, near the Salt Springs.

Porphyry—Some very beautiful specimens may be obtained on the agate patches, in the Middle Park, also in the South Park, and on the Arkansas River, above Cache Creek.

Puddingstone—Middle Park, near the Hot Spring.

Quartz—This very common and abundant mineral is found in all our mines, and from the Foot & Simmons, Gregory, Briggs, Bobtail, and some others about Black Hawk and Central Cities, very beautiful groups of crystals, with cubes of iron pyrites, have been taken. Some very large crystals, from three to six inches in diameter and sometimes partially covered with micaceous specular iron, have been found on the head waters of the north fork of South Platte. Very fine smoky crystals have also been obtained on Elk Creek. Some very beautiful specimens of rock crystal have been found on the divide between the Platte and Arkansas Rivers, near "Dirty Woman's Ranch." *Rose quartz* occurs on Bear Creek, near West's Ranch, and probably in many other places in that vicinity.

Salt—South Park, twenty miles south-east from Fairplay, where there are extensive saline springs, and works already erected, capable of manufacturing 10,000 lbs. per diem.

Sard—*Sardonyx*—Middle Park, also near Golden City, and Mount Vernon. Sardonyx, when fine, is much used in jewelry, for cameos, seal rings, etc. No very fine specimens have been obtained in Colorado.

Satin Spar—Near Mount Vernon, associated with alabaster, and arrow-head crystals of gypsum.

Schreibersite—Specimens in the writer's collection, from the Colorado ærolite.

Serpentine — South Park — observed by Prof. Du Bois.

Silicified Wood—Middle Park, South Park, Cherry Creek, near Denver, Kiowa Creek, and the Plains generally, from Julesburg to Canon City. A large number of stumps of trees, completely silicified, and two to four feet high, and ten to forty inches in diameter, are reported on the Arkansas River; and the writer has seen, on Kiowa Creek, a log completely silicified, twenty inches in diameter, and of undetermined length, as it was in the bank of the stream, with one end protruding a few feet. Many specimens obtained in the South Park, petrified with chalcedony or agate, and very transparent, are exceedingly beautiful when sawed across the grain and polished, they retaining all the texture and grain as perfectly as in the original wood. Some fragments that have evidently been branches or roots, having knots in them, are remarkably beautiful. *Wood opal* occurs sparingly in some localities.

Silver — *Native* — Native silver, containing a small per cent. of gold, has been found in the Fulton Company's mine, on the Crystal Lode, in Virginia Kanyon. It occurs in the form of very fine wires, and in branches, or "snarls" in cavities, about ninety feet below the surface. This is the only mine in Colorado, within the writer's knowledge, in which native silver has been found.

Silver Glance—*Sulphuret of Silver*—Kingston

Lode, Russell District, Herkimer, Georgetown, and in several lodes on Snake River.

Brittle Silver Ore—Sulphuret of Silver and Antimony—Kingston Lode, Russell District.

Ruby Silver—Snake River silver lodes.

Horn Silver—Chloride of Silver—Argentine and Snake River Districts.

Embolite—Chloro-Bromide of Silver—Peru District, Snake River.

Sulphate of Soda—South Park, ten miles northwest of the Salt Works.

Talc—This very common mineral occurs to a greater or less extent in nearly all our mines, and may be detected by its foliated structure, gray or greenish-white color, and *greasy feel*. Beautiful cabinet specimens of indurated talc, of a fine dark green color, very hard, and having crystals of sulphuret of iron disseminated through them, may be obtained at the Ogden Lode, at Montgomery.

Tourmaline—In feldspathic veins, near the Guy House, Guy Hill, black and green.

Zinc—Blende—Sulphuret of Zinc—Occurs more or less in nearly all our gold-bearing veins. It is the miner's *black jack*. Beautiful cabinet specimens are obtained from the Running Lode, Black Hawk, Gunnell, Eureka, Prize and others, near Central City. Also associated with chalcedony, and resembling the moss agate, in the Calhoun.

Smithsonite—Carbonate of Zinc—Occurs in many of our mines. Beautiful cabinet specimens, dotted over with pentagonal dodecahedrons of iron pyrites, occur in the Running Lode, at Black Hawk.

CHAPTER XVII.

OF the Plains in general it may be said that they are characterized by great horizontal expansion and aridity of climate. We shall not linger longer on their eastern and central portions than to note that railways are fast superseding the Tartaric caravans of the past in their trade and travel, and the fact that they may one day be thickly peopled under the revivifying influence of water procured from artesian wells. A considerable change in their distinguishing features is apparent as the Mountains are approached. Where that great barrier rises abruptly from their bosom as a continent from the waste of ocean, it sends out headlands and exhibits reefs and islands which diversify the surface contour, and produce a marked change in the climate, soil, and vegetation. This section has an elevation of 5,000 to 7,000 feet, but is sheltered from the far-sweeping winds of the Plains outside. It catches a share of the mists and rains that moisten the

mountain slope, and receives into its thirsty ex-
panse the more copious tribute of melted snow
from the Range.   It occupies a break in the progress of commercial transportation such as favors
the growth of large cities.

This is what we have termed "The Valley."   It
embraces three-sevenths of the Territory, in round
numbers thirty million acres, of which about one-
sixth can be irrigated, that is to say, cropped.   The
rest is available as pasturage.   Its climate is not
very dissimilar to that of the same latitude in the
Eastern States, except that it is much dryer.   The
mean temperature of Denver and St. Louis is about
the same, but at Denver it is higher at noon and
lower in the morning and evening than at St. Louis,
the average difference of the extremes for the month
of January, 1863, being 25.1° at the former, and only
8.7° at the latter.   The barometrical and thermo-
metrical changes of the two places nearly correspond, only they occur from one to two days sooner
at Denver than at St. Louis, just as they do at St.
Louis one to two days sooner than on the Atlantic
coast.   The scanty meteorological statistics of Denver indicate, also, that the fluctuations of the mean
atmospheric pressure and mean temperature are less
at the base of the Mountains than at St. Louis, giving a calmer atmospheric ocean, fewer and less
severe storms, which conclusion is sustained by experience.   The average annual fall of rain and snow,
counting ten inches of snow as one of rain, in the
Valley, is twenty inches.   Tender plants in the high
mountains are not injured by a degree of cold which

freezes still water half an inch thick. The air is
so clear and pure that the range of vision is almost
infinite. There are points in Colorado where a
well-defined mountain horizon, more than one hundred miles distant, may be seen by the naked eye.
There are all but three hundred and sixty-five days
of sunshine in the year. Clouds are the exception,
storms rare, and fogs never known. Such an atmosphere must be especially tonic. People live
and work 10,000 feet above the sea. The rainy
season of the Mountains—May, June, and July—
favors the Valley with an occasional shower, but
outside of that, rain seldom falls. Frost may be
expected to the end of Spring and by the 15th of
September, giving a season as long as that of New
England and New York.

In the warmer months, under the noon-day sun,
the air of the Valley often becomes oppressively
hot, but toward evening it rises and gives place
to cooler currents from the Range. Here is the
place for those toilers of the brain whose ner-
vous systems are shattered and who are dying for
want of *sleep*. Even a remorseful conscience fails
to banish sleep in this climate, a fact which is commended to the notice of moral and religious teach-
ers. About the middle of October, snows begin to
fall, and to the first of January a snow that will
last two days may be expected every two weeks.
In January the fall of snow is more plentiful, it lies
on longer and is accompanied by severer cold, while
February is usually pleasant and is improved by
the farmers plowing for Spring crops. Thence to

the rainy season, the snows are heavier than in
January but more transient than in November and
December, and melting quickly, or rather being absorbed by the porous soil, and as quickly renewed,
they start or prepare the ground for the new
crop. A snow storm is always succeeded by a cold
night, and that invariably by a bright warm day.
The mercury has been known to mark 32° below
zero at one o'clock in the morning, and 68° above
within twelve hours. It will sink to 10° below, five
or six times in a Winter. Absence of moisture
prevents these cold spells from nipping the flesh.
Men team it all over this region the year round,
always camping out, and seldom suffering incon-
venience. This would be impossible if the indications of the thermometer are to be taken as they
are in the East.

The soil of the Valley rests on calcareous rock,
but the wash from the granite mountains above
negatives the special inference that might be drawn
from that. On the borders of the numerous streams
it is sand, ashes, and decomposed vegetable matter.
On the plateaus between it is sand and gravel, stiff-
ened by a more or less friable clay. Properly supplied with moisture, lowland or upland, it exhibits
a strength rarely equaled by any other soil.

It has been observed by historians that rainless
countries—those in which man can control seed-
time and harvest—are most conducive to the rapid
increase of the race. Such are Egypt, Mexico, and
Peru, the three singular and solitary birthplaces of
civilization. Artificial watering by means of main

canals or *acequias*, and a net-work of smaller ones reaching and fertilizing every acre of the whole face of a country, is called *irrigation*. The Valley is one broad smooth plateau, tipped up just enough by the Mountains to give water a gentle flow over it. It is cut by numerous streams with great fall and carrying abundance of water. Taken from the mouths of the kanyons on a grade of four feet per mile, the chief canals soon achieve the highest ground between the streams, and are thus carried for long distances, supplying all the land below them. Their construction is mostly accomplished with the plow and scraper, each adjoining land-owner contributing his quota of the expense and having a perpetual right to the water at the additional tax for repairs. In this way *acequias* thirty miles long and watering 20,000 acres have been constructed. The Surveyor-General estimates that there were 136 miles of irrigating canal made in 1866, at a cost of $1,000 per mile. The main arteries in operation, each farm arranges its separate system so as to leave no spot unblessed and so that no swift currents shall carry away more than they bring. For the small grains the ground is flooded ; for corn and potatoes the water is run between the rows ; and for fruit trees it is allowed to flow constantly a few feet distant. The attention of one man is required during the operation, which lasts perhaps a month on a large farm and in an average season. All this is extra labor and expense, very true, but it has its advantages. A philosophical farmer of Colorado says of it :

"I have kept an accurate account of the extra expense of irrigation; but when I consider that the soil is made to yield its utmost capacity with uniformity, and that the hands irrigating can always do extra work enough to pay expenses, I am decidedly in favor of systematic irrigation, and never shall own a farm without facilities for irrigating a considerable part of it. To the advantage alluded to may be added, that the soil is constantly being enriched by the sediment of, and the salts and earths held in solution by, the water, which is never allowed to escape from cultivated land, but is kept on till it is absorbed. There need be no injury from the protracted drouths of sections more favored in general by rain."

Considering that the average crop of wheat is twice as large in Colorado as in the States, and that it brings a higher average price in a home market, we think no more need be said in palliation of irrigation. The freight tariff in favor of the Colorado farmer can hardly ever be less than a dollar on a bushel of wheat or corn.

The average crop of wheat is twenty-five bushels per acre,* twice that of Illinois or Ohio. Ten acres of wheat have produced 800 bushels, and of oats more than one thousand. Barley is the favorite crop, however. It makes regular and liberal returns spite of all the pests common to new countries and particular to Colorado. It is rather cold for corn on the Platte waters, but it is a sure crop, yielding thirty bushels per acre, on the waters

---

* Calculation of Surveyor-General John Pierce.

of the Arkansas.   Single fields of 2,000 acres may
be seen in the growing season in south-eastern
Colorado.   Vegetables of all kinds produce enormously, shading all other countries in that respect—
California alone excepted.   Five hundred bushels
of potatoes have been harvested from a single acre.
Cabbage heads weighing thirty pounds, and turnips
half as heavy, are not unusual.   A lady, recently
arrived in Denver, sent her little boy to market for
"a small cabbage."   He returned presently with a
16-pounder, the smallest he could find in town.

At the first annual fair of the Colorado Agricultural Society—September, 1866—there were on
exhibition turnips weighing fifteen pounds which
were grown in the heads of the gulches 1,000 feet
higher than Central City.   There was altogether
one of the finest displays of mammoth vegetables
and roots, of large, ripe, plump grains, and we
might add, of fast roadsters, that ever was seen.
Even those best posted as to the agricultural capacity of the Territory looked on in wonder.   So
long does it take to explode a false idea once firmly
established.   The present generation were taught
in school that next to Sahara "The Great American
Desert" was the largest and worst in the world.
The old emigration to California and Oregon sent
back only confirmation of this teaching.   Ten years
ago, that desperate man who was forced to risk a
trip across the Plains, bade farewell to the scenes
of childhood, regarding the chances of life and death
in the "desert" as about equal.   The enormous returns of California and then of Mormon farming

were slow of circulation and slower of credence. The first Pike's Peakers were so impressed with the "desert" idea that their safe arrival in the Mountains no less astonished than challenged their profound gratitude. They were not buried by the snow the first Winter, and this so increased their bewilderment that they failed of noticing the heavy burden of grass on the streams and the fine condition of stock in the Spring. So that late in 1859 the finding of two accidental but perfect heads of wheat in a garden at Denver was regarded as an important public event, marking an era in the history of things. Possibly there might be an oasis in this "desert." The feeble attempts at farming on the best bits of moist ground in 1860 were so successful that those personally cognizant of them were driven entirely from the "desert" theory. Next year the business considerably enlarged. *Acequias* were dug and most of the low land brought under cultivation. Two years later, that is to say, five years after the finding of gold, it was discovered that the uplands, by the aid of irrigation, would produce as bountifully as the river bottoms, when the "desert" theory was finally dismissed in Colorado, and farming took its rightful place, as the second if not the first great industry of the new State. In the year 1866, 50,000 acres, as near as could be determined, were under cultivation, and the grain crop was estimated by competent authority at 1,500,000 bushels, a surplus over the consumption of a people numbering at the outside 50,000. This surplus was chiefly wheat. At the end of the year wheat was worth $1.80 per bushel in Denver; corn, $2.80; buckwheat flour, $17 to $20; Spring wheat flour, $8 to $10; corn meal, $6 to $8.

The native fruits of Colorado are a small, worthless *thorn-apple;* a large, pleasant *plum*, trees rather shy bearers; small, black, acid *gooseberry* in abundance, not of much value; *cherry*, called "choke," really a pleasant fruit, size of large wild cherry, black, heart-shaped, free from insects, quite as good as the Morello, bushes large and prolific; *currants*, black, yellow, and red, black the best, a large, pleasant, acid fruit, superior to many cultivated varieties, bushes large, hardy, and good bearers, furnishing fruit for six weeks; *raspberry*, good size, red, juicy, fine flavor, makes a choice wine, bush twenty inches high, very prolific and continues in bearing for six weeks; the *strawberry* and *whortleberry*, the former ripening in altitudes where it freezes every night of the year according to Fahrenheit, abundant in some parts of the Foot-hills, just beginning to be cultivated, sold in 1866 at $3 a quart; the whortleberry not found much below but plenty at an elevation of 9,000 feet. It is said that wild grapes grow in the southern portion of the Territory, and a small variety of the common red cherry in some of the parks and kanyons of the Foot-hills. Apples, peaches, grapes, and pears are raised by the Mexicans in the San Luis Park, and something in that direction has been accomplished on the Arkansas. On the Platte, seedling plums, peaches, and apples made a most thrifty growth the past season, and about $20,000 worth of pear, apple, and peach trees, raspberry and blackberry bushes, grape and strawberry vines, were set out in the Fall. Fruit growing is yet in its veriest infancy. It took the settlers three years to learn that they could farm at all, and two more to discover the importance of the interest, and the Territory is but eight years old. From the full success of fruit culture in Utah, in about the same altitude and latitude, there is reason to hope everything from it here.

The greatest pest of the Colorado farmer is the locusts, which swarm occasionally as when the Lord plagued Egypt, consuming every green thing. Some years they are the only full crop that is raised. Little is known of their habits, one side of their astonishing appetite. This would seem to indicate a tape-worm in the stomach, and sure enough a story of something of the kind is seriously told. They are not permanent residents of the Territory, but pay it visits, not particularly like those of angels. They have no especial "calling" season, they make themselves at home, whether it be Spring, Summer, or Fall, sometimes staying, most unfashionably, through all three. They lay their eggs in the ground in the Fall, and *wherever* they happen to do that, the young crops of the next year will be eaten as fast as they grow by the wee locusts. When they have grown wings they fly away, to the great joy of their compulsory hosts. The fact that they will not deposit their eggs in moist ground points out the remedy. Irrigation at the period of deposit will keep them from making an incubating bed of the cultivated land, and a judicious arrangement of canals and use of water during the early Summer will keep the little wingless pests off. As the country is more widely cultivated they will probably cease to be a serious evil. Such is the case in Utah.

We come at last to the most important resource of the Valley—its broad, pastoral acres, numbering 25,000,000.* Its native grasses are many and rich, the buffalo and bunch varieties being equal to oats in the sheaf. Starting with the sap-snows, they attain their growth by the end of the rainy season, and then ripen into hay, standing. On this stuff large herds have made four hundred pounds weight per head in a Summer. With a fresh range for Winter, they come into market in the Spring better beef than the seven-months-stall-fed stock of Iowa and Illinois. Oxen, worked till in single file they hardly cast a shadow, run on this grass a few weeks and become beef. But the best illustration of the pastoral capacity of the Plains is their own countless aboriginal cattle. They live through the Winter and through all the Winters to a most tough old age, and there are a good many of them although few to what they were.

Between the years 1826 and 1836, according to Fremont, they roamed from Independence to the Fishing Falls of the Columbia River, fancy free.

---

*Artesian wells are turning the Desert of Sahara into a garden of fertility; so they would "The Great American Desert," in so far as there is any such thing.

In the year 1824 they filled the Green and Bear River valleys, descending on the Colorado to the mouth of White River, and ranging thence northward beyond Lewis's Fork of the Columbia, the Meridian of Fort Hall limiting them on the west. In 1836 they began to diminish very fast throughout this section, and in 1840 they had abandoned all the waters of the Pacific north of Lewis's Fork. Five years later, the "Buffalo Wallow" had contracted to what was designated as "The Great American Desert" on the old atlases. A curious desert indeed, sustaining nearly as many of these huge quadrupeds as could stand upon it. Now, the buffalo are confined to the Smoky Hill and Republican Forks of the Kaw, rarely straggling on to either the Platte or Arkansas, within two hundred miles of the state line of Missouri, or the base of the Mountains. It is doubtful if there exist as many to-day as used to be slain in a season. The chief business of the old trading posts was in their skins. The number of robes annually traded for by the American, Hudson's Bay, and other fur companies, was ninety thousand, and this tells not half the story of their destruction. It will be seen that the buffalo had passed away before the discovery of gold and silver in the Rocky Mountains. It is not certain that they were much fewer in 1866 than in 1856. But with railways running through and settlers occupying their last limited range, they must soon utterly disappear unless all slaughter of them in mere wantonness shall in some way be prevented. There is little sport in hunting, or rather in killing, buffalo. You ride stealthily on to a great herd, and while they are taking alarm and getting under motion, you knock over two or three. It is something like killing snow-corraled deer with a hatchet, more of cruelty than sport.

Well, the existence of buffalo proves the fine pastoral quality of the Plains, the best of which is the Valley of Colorado. When the buffalo of forty years ago shall have been replaced by domestic cattle, and the Indians, antelope and wolves by horses and sheep, the idea of a "great American desert" will doubtless be finally dismissed by the whole world, as it should be. Stock not only thrive in Winter without feeding, they are driven to the Eastern market in the Spring, and constantly improve. With a route five hundred miles wide they do better to move ten miles a day than to remain in one place. The raising of stock has not become much of a business yet, because it has been cheaper to buy and make beef of the train oxen. These usually arrive out in June pretty thin, and rather than drive them back with no load, their owners sell them low. Last Summer five thousand head of this stock were bought at Denver by Iowa farmers to drive home and feed during the Winter. Early frosts cut the corn in the north-west, the price doubled in a few days, and that badly frosted this speculation. Cattle bred on the Plains mature younger than elsewhere. Fall calves are not checked in their growth by the Winter as in the East, and they commonly become mothers at eighteen months of age, a precocity which argues a healthy and rapid development. It is estimated by those in the business that there are one hundred thousand head of horses and cattle in the Territory, and there are large flocks of sheep in the southern portion. These sheep were never shorn until 1866, and but few were then, from the lightness of the fleece, the coarseness of the wool, and the distance to market. The Mexican sheep is small and hardy, economical in its use of wool, wearing merely a little hempen stuff on its back. No pains was ever taken in breeding, and the article can barely be called a sheep, either in quality of mutton or wool, or in fecundity. The first cross of an improved breed increases the size, doubles the yield of wool, and restores prolific power, indicating that as a basis for extensive sheep-breeding, the native stock, if we may so call them, cannot be excelled. The only drawback to the business is the wolf, and he is fast disappearing. The conditions of climate and soil could not be more favorable. It is high and dry, there is little snow or severe cold, the grasses are short, sweet, and rich. Only second to its adaptability to sheep, are its advantages as a dairy country. Butter and cheese, unsurpassed in quality and of home production, are proportionally as cheap as in the East. The first cost of cows is high, from $60 to $100, but their keeping amounts to very little. On the whole we believe we are safe in affirming that there is no such country for stock as this.

Of the game and wild beasts native to the valley, the Indian is the most prominent, useless, pernicious, and costly to hunt. Indians and railways do not well agree, and as the country bears more of the latter it will less of the former. With an able and honest administration of their affairs in Colorado, no serious trouble need be apprehended in the future. Next to the Indian come the grizzly, cinnamon and black bear; and after them the cougar or mountain lion, the big white, or buffalo wolf, the shaggy brown, the black, the gray or prairie wolf, and the *coyote*, wachunka-monet, or medicine-wolf of the Indians; the buffalo, noticed before; the elk, black and white-tailed deer; the antelope and mountain sheep; lynx, wild-cat, badger; four varieties of the hare; the silver gray, the cross, the red, and the swift foxes; mink, pine marten, and beaver, and the prairie dog. The latter resemble the fox-squirrel, their flesh is tender and palatable, and their oil very superior in quality. They live together in subterranean villages, seem to have a communal system of government and things, whether founded on Divine right or the consent of the governed, has not been discovered. They locate their towns without regard to the vicinity of water, sometimes in places where none is to be seen and subject neither to rain nor dew. It is gravely doubted by some writers whether they make the same use of that fluid as other animals—the drunkard excepted. The large prairie wolf used to be a characteristic feature of the Plains, but like its fellows, the buffalo and Indian, is fast passing away.

Of game birds there are the wild turkey, mountain grouse, sage hen, prairie chicken, ducks, geese, swans, ptarmigan, &c. The sage hen is only found

west of the Range which is true also of its favorite
food, the sage bush. The ptarmigan exists only in
the frosty breath of the Range, being white when
the snows mostly fly and turning partially brown
when they melt and run off.

Of timber the principal varieties are pine, hem-
lock, spruce, cedar, fir, cotton-wood, box-elder,
quaking-aspen. There is a little scrubby oak, and
willow and alder-bushes on every brook. Nearly
one half the Territory is more or less timbered, the
trees generally thin on the ground and small.

CHAPTER XVIII.

Recapitulation — Mills and Mining Machinery — Production of Gold — State Organization — General Statistics — Newspapers — Railways on the Plains — Population, Society.

THE steady progress in material and social development of all the gold-producing States and Territories is sufficient evidence that on the whole, mining for the precious metals pays. This, too, in spite of the heavy drawbacks incident to starting anew—to creating and establishing the industries of civilization in the isolated wildernesses. In the body of this volume there are notices of the mines and works of 165 companies, firms, and individuals, now operating in Colorado. Most if not all of them have valuable mine property, which must prove, in the general advance of the country, a valuable investment. The present condition of this property is superior to what it ever was before. In the old mines shafts have been straightened, enlarged, and timbered, pumps put in, steam machinery and mills erected. Shafts and galleries have been excavated, by means of which ores can be produced to the best advantage. Costly experimenting with the refractory pyrites has been carried on, and much of value learned.   In opening the newer lodes, the experience of the past is brought in play ; work is planned and executed as it should be from the start. This preparatory work is still in progress, and the production of gold is not a fair indication of what is doing.

There are ninety-five stamp-mills in the Territory, containing 1,700 stamps, varying in weight from 500 to 900 lbs. each.   Nearly all these are in good repair and might be started within a month if desirable.   There are forty-one mills designed for the Keith, Dodge, Mason, Bertola, Crosby & Thompson, and processes other than stamps, of equal average capacity with the stamp-mills, and many of them fine, substantial structures.   There are twelve large mills in an unfinished state.   There are twelve mine-pumps, varying in size from four to nine inches, in operation, and six more under way.   There are forty steam hoisting rigs on mines, besides the great number in which the same engines drive a mill and do the hoisting, and besides innumerable horse-whims and hand-windlasses.   There are miles upon miles of shafts, levels, adits, tunnels, winzes, inclines, etc., excavated and in shape to be used.   Forty mills are now running, realizing from twenty to thirty thousand dollars' worth of gold per week.

With regard to the production of bullion, chiefly gold, by the Territory up to June 30, 1866, official Mint returns furnish the following :

19

Deposited at the Mint of the United States, Phila-
delphia, - - - - - - - - $5,641,886 91
Deposited at the Branch Mint, San Francisco, - 60,152 00
"   "   "   New Orleans, - 3,437 20
"   "   "   Dalonegha, Ga., - 35,345 84
"   "   "   Denver, Col., - 957,917 25
"   "   Assay Office, New York, - - 5,702,635 00

Total, - - - - - - - $12,401,374 20

Deposited at the Mint and Branches of the United
States and the Assay Office of New York, in
1859, - - - - - - - - $4,171 70
In 1860, - - - - - - - - 599,846 30
" 1861, - - - - - - - - - 2,091,197 17
" 1862, - - - - - - - - - 2,035,416 50
" 1863, - - - - - - - - - 2,893,336 87
" 1864, - - - - - - - - 2,136,684 69
" 1865, - - - - - - - - - 1,622,249 45
" 1866, - - - - - - - - 1,018,471 52

Total, - - - - - - - $12,401,374 20

"A careful examination of the gold mines in the
United States," says Gen. E. M. Barnum, of Idaho,
"and of statistics showing its final destination,
gives decided evidence that, by as near an approxi-
mation as practicable, the amount of deposits at
the mint and branches of the United States, embraces only one-third of the total product of the
mines." In support of this proposition, Gen. Barnum states that for the twelve fiscal years ending
June 30, 1866, the average annual deposits at the San
Francisco Branch Mint amounted to $17,000,000;
and that three times that sum very closely approxi-
mates the total annual yield of California during
that period, according to the best authority. Bullion
was first taxed under the Act of June 30, 1864, the
impost being one-half of one per cent. ad valorem.

By the Act of March 3, 1865, the tax was increased to three-fourths of one per cent. Its collection is required of the assayers in all cases, and the assay must be stamped on all bullion melted. The official statement of the aggregate receipts from this tax shows the bullion crop of the United States to have been for 1865, $73,560,937, and for 1866, $81,389,541. Now, the total amount deposited at the Mint and branches during the year 1865 was $27,982,849.09, and during the year 1866, $31,911,719.24, but a little more, in each case, than one-third the total yield. It is likely that enough bullion escapes the tax to make the rule perfectly good. Accepting it as such, therefore, we have $37,204,122.60, as the bullion yield of Colorado to June 30, 1866, which is probably not far from the truth.

The silver mines of Snake and Clear Creeks are growing in importance as they are developed, and must soon become a rich and unfailing source of revenue. Smelting for argentiferous and galenous ores, has been introduced, and the making of regulus for the cupriferous and auriferous pyrites. The enlargement of the latter, both in capacity and scope, may be said to be already under way. The opening of the mineral lands to pre-emption by the Government must have a beneficial influence, giving, as it does, absolute security to mining titles. The law is given in Chapter XV. of this work. Its details may require alteration from time to time, but it extends the principle that has obtained in the disposal of the arable to that of the mineral public lands, which is enough to begin with.   It is a concession to the settlers by the Government that can never be taken back.

Near the close of the Thirty-eighth Congress, a bill was enacted in response to a petition of the Colorado Legislature, enabling the Territory to organize a State government and enter the Union. Under its provisions a convention met in Denver, July 4, 1864, and framed a constitution.   Owing somewhat to bad management of the enterprise, but more to its evident prematurity, it was rejected by the people on the second Tuesday of October following.   Next Spring the civil war suddenly ceased, returning a million men and enormous transportation to the field of productive industry, the Indian war on the Plains had died out, the new mining companies and several new methods of treating ores seemed to have got well under way, gold had fallen to 130, agriculture had been fairly established, railways were building across the Plains—the aspect of affairs was very different from that of the year previous.   After brief agitation, all parties joined in another attempt to organize a State of the Union.   A convention met in Denver in August and framed a constitution, which was adopted by a majority of 155 on a light popular vote.   Suffice it that a State was fully organized, that application for admission into the Union was made at each session of the Thirty-ninth Congress, granted, and vetoed by President Johnson.   Whatever the final fate of this attempt at Statehood, the effort must go on until it is successful.   The popu-

lation of the Territory is compact, self-reliant, well
organized, socially and politically, enterprising, and
ambitious, and spirited as it can be ; the interests
of the Territory are in good degree national, it occupies a commanding position as regards the Rocky
Mountains, it is going ahead in everything, it is in
the nature of things for it to become one of the
family of States. With a Government title to the
mines, bringing them under control of the State
with its laws and courts, mining and all that depends on it will assume as permanent a character
as can be desired. In 1865 the taxable property
amounted to about nine millions ; in 1866, to about
eleven millions. The mines, belonging to Government, have never been taxed, and do not appear in
this valuation, which they would more than double.
In 1865, 140,000 acres of farming land were taken
up ; in 1866, 251,000 ; in the first month of the
current year, 23,000. The internal revenue tax
for 1865 was $130,000 ; 1866, $141,000. The in-
come tax return was about $40,000 for each year,
and the licenses taken out, exceeded in amount
those of many of the States. There were 250
buildings erected in Denver last year, at a cost of
$500,000. The First National Bank of Denver
drew Eastern exchange, from May 10, 1865, to
November 1, 1866, to the amount of $11,822,000.
The postal receipts for last year footed up $33,000,
a larger figure than in many of the States. It
would have been much larger but for that invidious
law which compels the Territories to pay letter
postage on everything carried by mail within their

borders.   Congress ought to undo this mean discrimination against the Territories.

The existence of sufficient arable land and the inauguration of a system of farming commensurate with the home demand for sustenance, has been fully noticed.   Also the establishment of iron manufacture.   In the altered sandstone which is tilted up on edge along the base of the Mountains, occur thick cellular bands, and also bands of bituminous shale, which are no doubt the storehouses of petroleum.   From Canon City northward one hundred miles, surface indications of its presence below are abundant.   A full set of machinery for boring wells and refining the product arrived at Canon City in 1866, and steps have been taken to thoroughly prospect for oil, sections near and at Golden City. No doubt is entertained of the capacity of the Territory to supply itself with petroleum.   Bands of limestone which burn easily and make a strong quicklime, are associated with the petroleum rocks, and crop out plentifully near Golden City.   Within the Foot-hills a short distance, on Bear Creek, occurs a cluster of copper veins, among which there is one of great extent and richness, called the "Commercial Lode."   It is vertical, cutting the dip and strike of the strata at a considerable angle, has been traced continuously four thousand feet, and after being concealed for a mile and a half by alluvium, outcrops again for a number of rods.   The gangue is quartzose, invaded by fluorspar at a depth of fifty feet ; the ores, green malachite, silicate, red oxide, and yellow sulphuret ; and a trial shaft fifty-five feet in depth shows a uniform thickness of vein of eighteen feet. This lode and its outlyers is but five miles from the coal mine of Wheeler & Company, and in its immediate vicinity, all the materials necessarily used in the reduction of the ore to metal exist in plenty. The Mountains and Parks present many saline springs ; one in the South Park has been improved, and is equal to the production of ten thousand pounds of salt per diem, and, by increasing the size of the evaporating surface, any higher quantity for which there may be a demand. There are twenty saw-mills and as many flour-mills in the Territory, two tanneries, and there are parties engaged in the establishment of paper and glass manufactories.

Denver has for many years supported two newspapers, each daily and weekly. Up to the great flood of May, 1864, these were " The Rocky Mountain News," and " The Rocky Mountain Herald and Commonwealth." On that occasion the former, having been founded on the sand, was washed away, and the proprietors proceeded to further fulfill the Scriptures by realizing Pharaoh's dream of the lean kine ; for, stripped of all they had in the world, they bought and swallowed " The Commonwealth," and were then leaner than before. Having the whole lot to themselves for about a year, however, they picked up fast and got fat again. Then was started " The Denver Gazette," daily and weekly, a Democratic print, F. J. Stanton, editor and proprietor, which has since gradually gained ground, and correspondingly improved in tone and appearance. In January of the current year, a third daily and weekly journal, the former called "The Denver Daily," the latter, "The Christian Radical," was started in Denver by Luther M. Kouns and Daniel Schindler. The first is independent, the second religious. There are two journals, each daily and weekly, published in Central City. "The Miners' Register," Republican in politics, was founded by Alfred Thompson, David C. Collier, and Hugh Glenn, in the Spring of 1862. Subsequently Thompson and Glenn sold out and a Mr. Wells became associated with Collier in its ownership. In the Fall of 1865 Wells was bought out by Frank Hall, so that the editors and proprietors are Collier and Hall. "The Colorado Times" has a more varied history. It is a combination of two newspaper establishments one or other of which had been run for a time in Denver once, in Golden City twice, in Canon City and Black Hawk each once, before the end of 1863. In the Fall of that year it failed for the severalth time. Through the agency of Lee, Judd & Lee, the writer and Frank Hall started it afresh November 30, 1863, as "The Colorado Mining Journal," daily and weekly, at Black Hawk. Three years later to a day it passed into the hands of an association called "The Times Publishing Company," who changed its politics from Republican to Democratic, its name from "Journal" to "Times," and removed it to Central City. Henry Garbanati and O. J. Goldrick are the editors. In December, 1866, Capt. George West established "The Weekly Colorado Transcript"

at Golden City, independent in politics. During
the Legislative sessions, which are supposed to be
held at Golden City, the Territorial Capital, though
they most always are not, it is published as a daily.
A small weekly paper called " The Boulder News,
or Progress " is published at Valmont, in Boulder
County.   A monthly, called "The Sunday School
Casket," and edited by the Rev. B. T. Vincent, is
published in Denver.   It is not the least patronized
and successful of these journalistic enterprises.
None of them has a large circulation, but their
prices for work are high enough to give them a
good living.

The construction of a railway along the Platte
Route during the Summer of 1866, at the rate of
twenty miles a week, has reduced freights to Colorado fifty per cent. of their previous average.
Three hundred and five miles of track west from
Omaha were laid last year, accepted by the Government Commissioners, who report it thoroughly
constructed and equipped with all the necessary
turn-outs, buildings, rolling stock, etc., of a first-
class road ; and 224 miles more, carrying it to the
base of the Black Hills, are contracted for and
under process of construction since March 20, at
the rate of two miles per day.   It is generally considered settled that the road will leave the South
Platte at the north-east corner of Colorado, and
go up Lodge-Pole, a tributary stream, to the Black
Hills, which it will enter 112 miles north of Denver ;
but it is not yet built, and it is so incontestably in
the interest of the Company to make Denver a

19*

point on it, thus securing the trade of Colorado and New Mexico against all after comers, that it is impossible to believe in the stupid folly of not doing so until one sees it. If they do run straight west, however, a branch will soon be built via Denver, Golden City, and the Clear Creek Kanyon, to Central City, Empire, and Georgetown.* Meanwhile, Wells, Fargo & Co.'s overland stages will connect with the cars at Julesburg, mouth of Lodge-Pole, 180 miles from Denver, only thirty-six hours' ride on the best managed stage-line in the world. Through competing fast-freight lines the cost of wagoning over this space, on a hard level road, will be but a trifle in excess of the usual railway tariff.

The Union Pacific Railway, Eastern Division, is also fast approaching Colorado. The track is already laid to Salina, confluence of the Saline and Smoky Hill Forks of the Kansas, nearly two hundred miles west from Kansas City or Leavenworth, and but about four hundred from Denver. It is hoped and expected that half the intervening distance to Denver will be overcome the present season. As soon as grass grows parties will be sent by this Company to survey the mountain passes thoroughly, they hoping to find a way through instead of having to turn them at either end. Stage, express, and fast-freight lines, con-

---

* A company called "The Central Colorado Pacific," is already organized for this purpose, the bonds of which it is believed will be guaranteed by the Pacific Company, thus enabling construction to commence very soon.

nect with this road at its constantly advancing terminus, running to Denver, Salt Lake, and Santa Fe. Some idea of the westward movement of merchandise, may be obtained from the Quartermaster General's report to the Secretary of War for the year ending June 30, 1866, which exhibits the transportation on account of Government, and the rates paid per hundred pounds per hundred miles. The rates from the Missouri River to northern Colorado, Nebraska, Dakota, Idaho, and Utah were $1.45 ; to southern Colorado, Kansas, and New Mexico, $1.38, with an addition from Fort Union in New Mexico to posts in that Territory, in Arizona, and western Texas of $1.79 per hundred pounds per hundred miles. The total number of pounds transported was 81,489,321 or 40,774 6-10 tons, at a cost of $3,314,495.

For the current year proposals have been invited for carrying to these posts, on Government account, fifty million pounds. The books of the railways will soon give us full statistics of the Plains trade, exclusive of that via the Missouri, Columbia, and Colorado Rivers, and the California Division of the Pacific Railway,* something which we have noth-

---

*This railway is completed to Cisco Station, 93 miles east of Sacramento, (elevation above the sea, 5,911 feet,) and within about 12 of the summit of the Sierra Nevada, the intervening distance graded, elevation of summit, 7,050 feet. The heaviest grade eastward from the summit is 90 feet to the mile, the average, 40. From the base of the Sierra Nevada to that of the Rocky Mountains is almost a natural grade. The cost thus far is $9,000,000. Chinamen are employed as laborers, at $30 a month, fifty per cent. cheaper than white labor. The road is to be completed to Virginia

ing yet but the wildest guesses at ; nor, had we anything near correct, would it be of much use, because the railways ought presently to double and quadruple the figures. Once finished to the base of the Mountains, it cannot be long until these railways will have penetrated, either themselves or by branches, into the heart of the best mining counties which constitute the Great Mineral Belt. Half a dozen streams offer facilities for this—Boulder, Clear Creek, and the South Platte can be followed up on a water grade of not more than one hundred feet per mile into Boulder, Gilpin, Clear Creek, and Park, the great mining counties.

The price of labor, provisions and supplies has fallen off thirty to fifty per cent. of its range of 1864–'65. The effect is seen in the increasing activity in mining, and the larger production of gold from week to week. In the three best months of 1866, it was about $200,000 a month. This increase is not likely to be seriously checked again by an advance in prices, because everything is

---

City, 156 miles east from Sacramento, this year, and to Salt Lake City, 429 miles further, in two more years. The following are overland distances :

	MILES.
From Omaha, via Union Pacific Railroad and branch, to Denver,	630
From San Francisco, via Omaha, to St. Louis,	2,311
From San Francisco, via Omaha, to Chicago,	2,392
From San Francisco, via St. Louis, to New York,	3,385
From San Francisco, via Chicago, to New York,	3,291
From San Francisco, via St. Joseph, St. Louis, and Cincinnati, to Washington,	3,210
From San Francisco, via Chicago and Harrisburg, to Washington,	3,233

tending to bring them to a reasonable level and keep them so by removing the causes of their former ruinous fluctuations. Railways will make the Mississippi the base of supplies so far as the miner is concerned. A swarm of locusts, a freshet, hail-storm, hurricane, or severe frost, an attack on some defenceless wagon by lawless Indians, will not greatly effect such a base of supplies. And if the farmers of Colorado cannot successfully compete with those of Iowa and Missouri, which they would hate to acknowledge, they can abandon farming and go to mining. For there is ground enough— the hay-stack is big enough and the needles sufficiently numerous to outlast the eyes of many generations. Not that nearly all of its area has not already been flown over; it is because it has been flown over and not lighted upon that it is still unknown. Only the most accessible and easily made available spots are occupied, and they are to the grand whole as Rhode Island and Delaware to the family of States. It would seem to be impossible, indeed, to exaggerate on the subject of the mineral region of Colorado. It is all but limitless in surface area and enjoys a climate to which, at the same altitudes, no other part of the world can begin to approximate; is abundantly supplied with water, timber, and fuel; is accompanied by a noble dower of arable and pastoral lands sequestered within its rugged bosom and forming an apron to the eastward containing thirty millions of acres; is centrally located as regards the western half of the Continent; is nearer than any other to the grain

producing Mississippi Valley; abounds in grand
and picturesque scenery; in thermal springs, wild
fruit, game, and fish; is easily accessible throughout its varied extent, and is blessed with the purest
atmosphere, the bluest of skies, and the brightest
and most constant of suns.

For the six years that annual elections have been
held, the popular vote has averaged 7,000. Counting five persons for each voter would give a population of 35,000, exclusive of 6,000 or 7,000 Indians.
William Hepworth Dixon says, in his very accurate
"New America," that there are twenty men to one
woman in Colorado. It may have been so or half
so in Jefferson. When Colorado was organized in
June, 1861, a census was taken, which showed a
preponderance of the stronger sex of about four to
one. Since that there has been no authoritative
census, but at the Territorial Sunday School Convention of June, 1866, representing neither the
Mexican nor the mass of the rural population which
together constitute three-fifths of the whole, between 1,500 and 2,000 scholars were reported.
Where, in a population of 35,000, there are 4,000
or 5,000 school children, there can be no terrific
disparity in number of the sexes. Still there is a
great lack of women in the mines. There are too
many young men vegetating in shabby hotels and
loose-jointed cabins like cellar onions in Winter,
growing gray between the memories of the past
and the hopes of the future, wasting the present.
This is not well for the health, morals, and general
welfare of the community. Not that, as a class,

they lead dissolute lives. In one of his Colorado letters, Mr. Bowles says: "Most agreeable of all our experiences here are the intelligent, active, earnest, right-minded and right-hearted young men and women we meet ; people, many of whom have been here for years, but, instead of losing anything of those social graces that Eastern towns and cities are wont to think themselves superior in, have not only kept even pace in these, but gained a higher play for all their faculties, and ripened with opportunity and incentive, and necessary self-reliance, into more of manhood and womanhood." But the fact remains that love, chastened and consecrated by marriage, is so prime a necessity of our many-sided human nature, that it cannot be generally ignored for any considerable period with impunity. But what is to be done? Shall we have another cargo of Yankee girls assembled to serve as a Summer's theme for the coarse wit of the Continent? It is clear that the Colorado men are not going to make a raid on the Eastern as the Romans on the Sabine women. Opportunity does not serve. Neither can Eastern women be expected to go through the scattered settlements of the West hunting mates.

But a middle course might be adopted. That is to say, the young men of the West might make individual forays on Eastern women without getting worse than a Sabine war on their hands, and now that the East is annexed to the West by railways, every Western woman might have her female relatives with her a good part of the time. Thus might the sexes become more evenly distributed. Women would not be starving on two cents a day in the East while two *dollars* were vainly awaiting them in the West. It would be possible, after a while, to keep female waiters at a Western hotel, at *some* rate. And best of all, less of that painful and outrageous thing would be seen—the fruit before the flower—girls keeping young company at fifteen, married at sixteen, and weighed down with the cares of maternity at seventeen, which is not uncommon in Colorado.

Nor is the society of the Rocky Mountains behind that of the East in the graces and charities, nor yet much in the frivolities. Mr. Bowles says: "Never was progress in wealth, in social and political organization, in the refinements of American home life, more rapid and more marked than in the brief history thus far of Colorado." Property and life are as secure in Colorado as anywhere. There are churches, schools, and charities, lyceums, libraries, institutes, and lectures, concerts, fairs, theatricals, donations, calico, dinner, and card parties, billiards, fast horses, and "going East" in the line of social enjoyments. No social talent need rust for want of use. The shops furnish the latest Eastern fashionable beauty or abomination, the periodical literature, new books and music and news of the day, while the markets are as good as any, except in the fruit line. Aged people, confirmed invalids, cripples, beggars, helpless, idiots, and insane, are almost unknown. Perhaps the incident most peculiar to the country is the large attendance at the last rite to some comparative stranger suddenly cut down, unprepared, by death. Every woman in the community seems to imagine herself the mother or sister of the deceased, and these are the most human scenes of the whole world. The expense is provided for, no one knows how. In the same way cases of destitution from sickness are relieved.

From its position and character as metropolis, Denver is frequently honored by distinguished visitors, public officers and men of affairs, scientific and literary men and artists, and it always entertains them with spirit. Its resident population is bright and energetic, eager in their pursuit of business and pleasure, their style and fashion, by some mysterious means, full up with the East. Perfect roads radiate from Denver in every direction, and no other town of its size can turn out so many good roadsters. Not to have a fast nag is not to be "fast" in the mildest sense of the term. Gambling used to be a licensed vocation, parading its attractive temples on the Broadway of the town, but within a year it has been compelled to hide itself. When the great *acequia* which is to give grass, flowers, fruit, and shade, shall be in operation, Denver will be one of the pleasantest of residences. Rambles in the Mountains, riding, hunting, bathing, fishing, berrying, camping out, living on *air*, puts new cheeks on old bones and paints them the richest brown.

Finally, there is a nameless, indefinable charm in the constitution of Rocky Mountain society.

Whether it come of the incongruity of its original materials, drawn from every part of the Union, from much travel, from attrition of many and widely-differing ideas and consequent enlargement of view, from out-door life and resulting health and vigor, from the exciting nature of business, from contempt for postage stamps and pennies, from that isolation, which, while it has compelled people to open their hearts to each other, has forced the same style of living on rich and poor alike,— whether from any or all these, or from the fact that beneath that sky of Heaven with its far horizons, in presence of those colossal hills, and overlooking the dry beds of nameless oceans, the soul expands, and, freed in good part from the restraint and guidance of custom, creed, and law, and thrown upon its native mettle, rarely fails of finding in its deeper springs a stronger incentive to noble endeavor, so that GREAT is the adjective ever on the tongues of the people, and to *be* great, ever in their thought, we know not. Certain it is that those who have lived there long enough to become at all acclimated are loath to leave and anxious to return.